CONTENTS

C000183951

ADVICE & REFERENCE
How to use this book   5
Guide to watermarks   7
A-Z of philatelic terms   9
Useful contacts   271

MARKET PRICES
Queen Victoria issues (1840-1901)   23
King Edward VII issues (1901-1911)   36
King George V issues (1911-1936)   38
King Edward VIII issues (1936)   43
King George VI issues (1937-51)   45
Queen Elizabeth II pre-decimal (1952-1970)   48
Queen Elizabeth II Machins (1967-2012)   64
Queen Elizabeth II decimal (1971-2012)   88

Regional definitives (1948-71)   194
Country definitives (1958-2012)   196
Stitched booklets (1904-1976)   208
Folded booklets (1976-2000)   214
Retail booklets (1987-2012)   222
Christmas booklets (1978-2012)   230
Greetings booklets (1989-1998)   233
Prestige stamp books (1969-2012)   234
Officials (1882-1904)   242
Postage dues (1914-94)   244
Vending machine stamps (1984-2012)   248
Smilers sheets (2000-2012)   250
Commemorative sheets (2008-2012)   254
Presentation packs (1960-2012)   256
Yearbooks & year packs (1967-2012)   266

ABOUT THIS BOOK

The objective of this guide is to give collectors the accurate market values of Great Britain stamps, as sold by most dealers, as opposed to the inflated prices quoted by some catalogues. The publisher of British Stamp Market Values is not a dealer and is not affiliated to any dealer.

This guide is produced by *Stamp Magazine* www.stampmagazine.co.uk

Editor
Guy Thomas
Consultant Editor
Richard West
Art Director
Alexandra Bourdelon
Advertisement Manager
Jay Jones

Sales Executive
Sophie North
Advertisement Production
George Kesta
Publisher
MyHobbyStore Ltd, Hadlow
House, 9 High Street, Green
Street Green, Kent BR6 6BG.

Copyright MyHobbyStore Ltd.
Published in 2011
ISBN 978-1-907063-19-0

PROTECTIVE SHIELD

**In a market filled with many pitfalls, it's good to know
who you can rely on.**
Members of the Philatelic Traders' Society agree to abide by a strict code of ethics,
which ensures that you can deal with them in total confidence.
Established over 60 years, the PTS is the premier British dealer organisation with
over 400 members, all respected throughout the philatelic community.
For more information on the society and its members, which also organises the world
famous, **twice yearly Stampex national stamp exhibitions** held in London, go to
www.philatelic-traders-society.co.uk

The Business Design Centre, 52 Upper Street, Islington, London N1 0QH
SPRING 2013 - 20th to 23rd February ● **AUTUMN 2013** - 18th to 21st September

The Philatelic Traders' Society Limited, P.O. Box 139, Brighton, Sussex, BN41 9DH
Tel: +44 (0)1273 594110 Fax: +44 (0)1273 595379 E: info@philatelic-traders-society.co.uk

HOW TO USE THIS BOOK

The prices we quote and the abbreviations we use

This guide offers independent and accurate price information about all GB stamps issued from 1840 to date.

It quotes not the inflated prices that some dealers and catalogue publishers might hope to achieve, but accurate market prices to help you pinpoint the exact worth of your collection.

The publisher of *British Stamp Market Values* is not affiliated to any dealer.

ABBREVIATIONS

The following abbreviations are used:

Des: designer
Perf: perforation
Wmk: watermark

GENERAL NOTES

☐ Unused prices assume stamps are se-tenant where applicable, but used prices do not.
☐ Used prices quoted are for fine examples with full perforations or reasonable margins as applicable, and with either a light Duplex cancellation (pre-1880) or a clear steel datestamp (post-1880).
☐ When a dash (–) appears in a price column it means that the stamp doesn't exist in that particular state, or that it is impracticable to price it.
☐ As modern GB special stamps are usually sold only in sets, the price for a full set may be given instead of individual prices.

EXPERTS WE CONSULTED OVER PRICING

RUSHSTAMPS

PO Box 1, Lyndhurst, Hampshire SO43 7PP
Rushstamps, run by Allan Grant, deals primarily in Great Britain. It publishes a bulging catalogue offering a wide range of material, which is available upon request.

BB STAMPS

PO Box 6277, Overton, Basingstoke, Hampshire RG25 3RN
Run by Brian Bayford, BB Stamps deals in GB stamps from Queen Victoria to Wildings.

MARK BLOXHAM

PO Box 204, Morpeth NE61 9AA
Mark Bloxham is a specialist in classic British stamps at the top end of the market.

PACKS & CARDS

Oaklands House, Reading Road North, Fleet, Hampshire GU51 4AB
Packs & Cards specialises in presentation packs and PHQ cards, selling by mail order, from its website and via eBay. It also supplies unusual items such as Post Office posters.

DON STADDON

Stamp Magazine contributor
Don Staddon is one of the leading authorities on Machin definitives.

IAN HARVEY

Member of the RPSL Expert Committee
Ian Harvey is a leading specialist collector of booklets from Edward VII to Elizabeth II.

A F Brock & Co. Ltd

AUCTIONEERS, VALUERS & BUYERS est. 1969

WE BUY & SELL STAMPS

- ❀ Regular Sales held in Cheshire / North West of England
- ❀ Public Auctions with Live Internet Bidding inc. Audio
- ❀ Call 0161 456 5050 for a Complimentary Catalogue
- ❀ Free Online Catalogues with Multiple Images
- ❀ Absentee Bidding & Telephone Bidding Available
- ❀ Public Viewing Days & Private Viewing by Appointment
- ❀ In-house Postal Service - *insured & tracked mail posted worldwide*

Sale Dates, Catalogues, Images, Info. & Prices Realised on:

www.afbrock.co.uk

Sales include: Stamps, Postal History, Coins, Medals & Militaria, Banknotes, Cigarette Cards, Early Postcards & other Collectables

Email info@afbrock.co.uk to request Auction Alerts

SELLING YOUR STAMPS, COINS, OR MEDALS?

Sell by Auction *or choose a* **Cash Payment**	**FREE VALUATIONS & Auction Estimates** by Appointment	**AUCTION SERVICE** - Low Commission - No Unsold Fees - Free Images - Print & Online Catalogues - Prompt Payment

Home Visits for Quality Collections of Significant Value

Send Email with Images for a quick Estimate

Auction Prices Realised on www.afbrock.co.uk

We also provide Insurance & Probate Valuations & Short Term Pawn Loans up to £5000

269 London Road, Hazel Grove, Stockport, Cheshire, SK7 4PL

0161 456 5050   info@afbrock.co.uk

GUIDE TO WATERMARKS

Identify the watermarks referred to in the price listings

Small crown	Large crown	Half penny	V R
Emblems	Small garter	Medium garter	Large garter
Spray of rose	Maltese cross	Large anchor	Small anchor
Orb	Imperial crown	Simple royal cypher GVR	Multiple royal cypher GVR
Single crown and script GVR	Multiple crowns and block GVR	Large crown and script GVR	Multiple crowns and E8R
Multiple crowns and GVIR	Single crown and GVIR	Tudor crown and E2R	St Edward's crown and E2R
Multiple St Edward's crown	Loops		

Watermarked paper was used to print most British stamps from 1840 until the later 1960s, as a security measure to make forgery difficult

Quite Exceptional Offers
Just compare and save at Rushstamps

GERMAN EDWARD VII TRIALS

Produced in 1913 in Blue with no watermark. Imperf single at just **£120.00**

Marg Block (4) £500.00

(Ask for further details)

WOULD YOU PAY £15 FOR THIS STAMP?

Ask for the latest list of Commemoratives, including Complete Year Units at the very best prices

COMPARE AND SAVE!

Mint, Used, FDC's and Presentation Packs

1000 MINT GREAT BRITAIN!

All issued before 1971 in singles, blocks and multiples to include Commorratives Definitives and Regionals. The face value alone is over £30.

SPECIAL OFFER...................... **£25.00**

DO YOU COLLECT GB ERRORS/VARIETIES

Ask for photocopies *(please state your interests)* Pre-decimal or decimal

2010 LONDON 'SPECIAL' OPD MINIATURE SHEET

Max 2 per order

On Sale for 8 days only ....**only £4.95**

1929 £1 PUC OFFICIAL ROYAL MAIL REPRINT

ONLY **£5.00**
BLOCK OF 4 IN SPECIAL PACK **£15.00**

STARTER COLLECTION OF QUEEN VICTORIA AND EDWARD VII USED OFFICIALS

10 stamps * **AT ONLY** **£6.95**

*Ask for full details of contents which will really surprise you.

2000 £1 CORONATION MINIATURE SHEET

On Official Royal mail card with Westminster Abbey cancellation

SG MS2147 (CAT.£21) **£2.95**

1897 DIAMOND JUBILEE 'PHANTOMS

½d., 1d. 2d and 3d.
Normally £11 Only **£3.50**

WORLDWIDE KILOWARE

A really good assortment accumulated from various sources, mainly on paper, including some older material, plenty of smaller countries and higher and unusual values

Lots of sorting! Per ½ Kilo (approx. 2,500 stamps) .... **£22.00** (UK post paid)

CAN YOU REFUSE THIS OFFER? Send us £2 (coins, stamps, P.O or cheque) and we will forward our latest 144 page G.B. RushExpress, together with a special **"Mystery Free Gift"** and a **"£5 Credit Note"** to be used against your first order over £10! Too good to miss! Mention CBS please. You will not be disappointed.

YES - WE ALSO BUY - GB also

British Commonwealth & Foreign. Top prices – Prompt Payment. Send for offer or write with details. Complimentary Courier Collection Service available for faraway / bulky lots.

CHANNEL ISLANDS AND IOM SOUVENIR FDC'S

100 Different Souvenir FDC's, Superb Selection............ **£25.00**

FDC EXTRA SPECIAL

100 different G.B. commemoratives, definitives & regional souvenir first day covers. To good to miss.
ONLY **£24.00**
150 different **£39.00**

G.B. HI-VAL COLLECTION

All Used, 1883 2/6 to 1993 £10 Britannia 42 different stamps * Normally cat over £1000 'One of our best sellers'.
ONLY **£89.00**

SMILERS SHEETLETS

Compare and Save Special 50% Discount Offer Compare and Save! Ask for listing.

MACHIN 1999 20p. Imperforated Pair Error SG Y1681a Unmounted mint Contact us for a very special price to tempt you

BUMPER G.B. ONLY, FOREIGN BRITISH COMMONWEALTH OR WORLDWIDE ONLY BONUS MIXED LOTS

A real pot-pourri – a wonderful selection on album pages, stock leaves, packets, loose etc. with little duplication – great value. Satisfaction or refund
Lots at .... **£25, £50 and £100**
(Please state which required)

We accept Mastercard and Visa credit/debit cards.
UK orders post paid

CHINA WANTED

Visit our website at **www.rushstamps.co.uk**

RUSHSTAMPS (RETAIL) LTD.
P.O BOX ONE, LYNDHURST, HAMPSHIRE, ENGLAND SO43 7PP
TEL: (023) 8028 2044,   FAX: (023) 8028 2981

E-mail: enquiries@rushstamps.co.uk

A TO Z OF PHILATELIC TERMINOLOGY

Here's an easy-to-understand alphabetical guide to stamp collecting jargon, from simple concepts to complex printing processes

AEROGRAMME
A specially printed, ready stamped letter sheet on lightweight paper, which is intended for air mail use. It is also known as an air letter.

AIR MAIL
Any item of post sent to its destination by air.

ALBINO
A colourless impression that is usually produced in embossing.

ALPHABET LETTERS
The lettering printed in the corners of stamps from 1840-1887 to make forgery difficult. Each stamp in a sheet had a unique combination of letters, with those in the top row lettered AA, AB, AC, and so on, and those in the second row BA, BB, BC and so on. Originally these letters appeared in the lower corners only, but later they appeared in the top corners too, in reverse order.

ARROWS
The margins of many sheets of stamps feature arrows, intended to help post office clerks to divide the sheets into sections.

BACKSTAMP
A postmark on the back of an envelope, usually applied in transit or on arrival.

BANTAM
A stamp printed in a smaller than standard size.

BISECT
A stamp cut in half (normally diagonally) to create two stamps, each of half the usual value, to meet a postal rate in times of shortage.

BLIND PERFORATION
Perforation in which the stamp paper is merely dented because the perforating machine has blunt teeth.

BLOCK
Four or more stamps still joined together.

BOOKLET
A small book containing one or more panes of stamps, usually commonly used definitives, either stitched in or stuck within a card cover.

ALPHABET LETTERS: on a block of four of the 1870 ½d rose-red

CACHET

A postal mark, other than the cancellation, applied to a cover or card. This is often unofficial in nature, with a commemorative purpose.

CANCELLATION

A postmark applied to a stamp on an envelope or card, to prevent its re-use.

CANCELLED TO ORDER (CTO)

Postmarked in bulk, usually for sale to collectors on first day covers rather than for actual posting.

CHALK-SURFACED PAPER

Paper with a security coating to prevent a cancellation being cleaned off so that a stamp can be re-used.

CHANGELING

A stamp whose colour has altered through immersion in water or exposure to sunlight.

CHARITY STAMPS

Stamps issued to support a charity, usually sold with a surcharge above their postal face value.

COILS

Stamps issued in reels (usually for sale from vending machines), which can therefore be collected in strips.

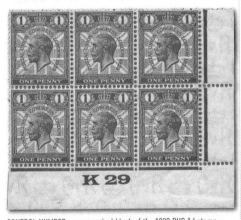

CONTROL NUMBER: on a marginal block of the 1929 PUC 1d stamp, which also shows a Jubilee line running under the bottom perforation

COLOUR TRIALS

Proofs produced in various colours prior to the issue of a stamp, to determine the most suitable colour for it.

COMB PERFORATION

Perforation applied to three sides of a stamp at a single stroke, with the fourth side being perforated by the following stroke. This technique is aimed at providing perforations which meet perfectly at the corners.

COMPOUND PERFORATION

Perforation which has different gauges on different sides of a stamp.

CONTROL NUMBERS

Letters and numerals printed in the sheet margins of British stamps from 1881-1947 for accounting purposes. A letter indicates which part of the year the stamps were printed, and the number represents the last two digits of the year.

CORNER BLOCK

Four or more stamps from the corner of the sheet still joined together, with margins.

COVER

Envelope or wrapper with stamps affixed or pre-printed.

CYLINDER BLOCK

Four or more stamps still joined together, with the cylinder numbers showing in the margin.

CYLINDER NUMBERS

Numerals printed in the sheet margin, for security reasons, denoting the cylinder from which it was printed. There is usually one number for each colour in which the stamp is printed.

DEFINITIVES

Stamps produced to remain in general use over a period of years.

DIE

The piece of soft steel onto which the design of recess (intaglio) printed stamps is engraved.

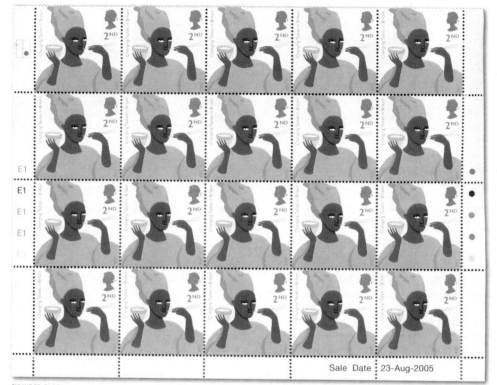

CYLINDER BLOCK: of the 2005 Changing tastes in Britain 2nd class stamp, with cylinder numbers in the left margin and traffic lights in the right

DIE PROOF
A proof impression taken from the die to check that it is satisfactory.

DOCTOR BLADE VARIETY
A streak of ink appearing across a sheet of photogravure stamps, after a build-up of dust forces the doctor blade (which wipes off excess ink) away from the cylinder for a moment.

DUMB CANCELLATION
Postmark with no inscription or identifying mark, for example applied to naval mail in wartime for security reasons.

DUTY PLATE
Plate used to print the 'duty' (value) on stamps in conjunction with the key plate, where stamps share a common design.

EMBOSSING
A portion of a stamp design that has a relief or raised impression. This is achieved by placing the paper between male (relief) and female (recess) dies during the printing process.

ERROR
Stamp deviating from the normal in some respect, for example with missing, shifted or inverted colours or perforations, caused by problems at the printing stage..

ESSAY
Preliminary design for a stamp, which might or might not subsequently be issued.

FAKE
A genuine stamp that has been tampered with in some way in an attempt to make it more

ERROR: a strip of the 1964 Botanical Congress 1s 3d value on which some stamps are missing yellow

valuable, usually by forging an overprint or removing a cancellation.

FISCAL

Stamp originally intended for fiscal or revenue purposes, although possibly subsequently authorised for postal use.

FIRST DAY COVER (FDC)

Souvenir envelope bearing stamps postmarked on their first day of issue. In modern times, envelopes are designed specifically to match a set of stamps, and pictorial handstamps are available to suit the theme, both from Royal Mail and from private providers.

FLAW

A defect in printing, resulting in a constant

blemish on the same stamp in every sheet.

FRANK

A mark or label that indicates that mail is transmitted free of postage. This is widely used by government departments and armed forces.

GRAPHITE LINES

Black lines incorporated into the back of some stamps between 1957 and 1959, which could be recognised by experimental electronic sorting machines.

GUM

The adhesive on the back of a stamp. On early issues this was a natural product, gum arabic, which has a shiny appearance. On later issues it was a synthetic product, polyvinyl alcohol (PVA),

FIRST DAY COVER: for the 2008 Houses of Lancaster & York set

which is colourless but usually given a yellow tinge by printers; with dextrin added, this is known as PVAD, and has a bluish tinge.

GUTTER
The white central margin separating two panes of stamps on sheets printed by Harrison & Sons' Jumelle printing press. The machine was capable of printing in several colours and perforating in one operation, but this layout of sheets was necessary because the circumference of the printing and perforating cylinders differed.

GUTTER PAIR
Two stamps from adjoining panes, with a gutter in the middle.

IMPERFORATE
Stamps printed on sheets without perforations, and needing to be cut apart with scissors. Early Victorian stamps were imperforate, before perforating them became a practical necessity. Stamps imperforate on one or more adjoining sides could be from booklets; those imperforate on opposite sides will be from coils.

IMPRIMATUR
The first sheet of stamps off the printing press, marked to indicate that it has been approved. All imprimatur sheets should have been retained by the Post Office (now Royal Mail), but some have 'escaped' into the hands of collectors.

IMPRINT
Inscription in a sheet margin giving the printer's name or logo, the date of printing and sometimes other details.

INTAGLIO PRINTING
A printing process, also known as 'recess', which requires the design of the stamp to be engraved into the printing cylinder. When the ink is applied, it fills the recesses and any excess ink is wiped away. On contact with the paper, the design is transferred as the ink leaves the recesses. Intaglio stamps can be identified from the way the ink parts of the design feel raised when you run a finger over them.

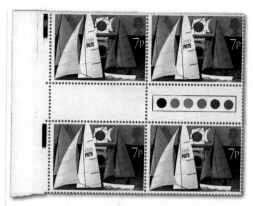

GUTTER BLOCK: of the 1975 Sailing set, with traffic lights

INVERT
A stamp with part of the design upside-down in relation to the rest.

IVORY HEAD
An outline of the portrait of Queen Victoria which can be seen on the backs of certain stamps printed on blued paper.

JUBILEE LINE
A line of printer's rule reinforcing the edge of the printing plate, appearing as a bar of colour at the foot of the sheet. It is so-named because it first appeared on the 'Jubilee' issue of 1887.

KEY PLATE
A plate that provides the main part of a stamp design (usually the sovereign's head and border) where two separate printings are required, for example in a two-colour stamp. The key plate is used in conjunction with different duty plates, so the same basic design can be reproduced with different values.

KILOWARE
Any mixture of stamps sold by weight. Originally the term applied to those sold in sealed one-kilogramme bags of stamps on paper.

LINE PERFORATION
A form of perforation in which the horizontal and vertical perforations are applied by separate

MALTESE CROSS: in red ink on an 1840 Penny Black

processes. This frequently results in ragged edges at the corners of stamps.

LITHOGRAPHIC PRINTING

A printing process in which the design appears as a number of dots, as in photogravure printing, but with the dots differing in size. The larger the dot, the deeper the colour. A lithographed stamp can be differentiated from a photogravure stamp by examining any lettering, which will appear solid.

LOCAL

A stamp (or more correctly a 'label') whose validity is restricted to a limited local area, and which cannot be used on national or international mail. It might pay for carriage from offshore islands to the mainland before entering the national postal system, but onward postage must be paid using the requisite national stamps.

MACHIN

British stamp design featuring a profile of Queen Elizabeth II's head, in use for all low-value and some high-value definitive since 1967. The name comes from the designer of the profile, Arnold Machin.

MALTESE CROSS

The cancellation used for the first British stamps, from 1840 to 1844. The name comes from its shape.

METER MARK

A mark applied by a meter to indicate pre-payment of postage. This usually consists of an indicium (country name and value), a date and a slogan advertising a firm or organisation.

MINIATURE SHEET

A small sheet containing a single stamp or a small group of stamps, often with broad decorative margins. Some modern stamps are issued only in a miniature sheet and in no other format.

MINT

Unused stamp with its full, original gum intact. Collectors generally prefer 'unmounted mint', with the gum undisturbed by any mounting.

OBLITERATION

Original term for the cancellation of stamps to prevent their re-use.

OFFICIAL

A stamp produced solely for the use of government departments.

OVERPRINT

An additional printing applied to a stamp after the original printing, to convert it to some other purpose, denote a surcharge or commemorate a current event.

PANE

Originally this term meant a portion of a sheet divided by gutters, but it is now also applied to a block of stamps issued in a booklet.

PERFIN

An abbreviation for 'perforated initial'. Some stamps have been perforated with the initials of firms or government departments as a security measure, to prevent pilferage or improper use.

PERFORATION

Tiny circles of paper punched out by machine between stamps on a sheet, to make it easier to separate them. Different printings and varieties can sometimes be identified by a difference in the style or number of their perforations.

PHOSPHOR BANDS

Almost invisible stripes of phosphor coating applied to the face of modern stamps to facilitate electronic sorting.

PHOTOGRAVURE PRINTING

A printing process, also known as 'gravure', in which the printing cylinder consists of a large number of very small cells, each containing ink, with the depth of the cell determining how dark the colour will look. The printed stamp appears as a series of minute dots of equal size.

PLATE

Flat or curved piece of metal from which stamps are printed.

PLATE NUMBERS

The cylinder numbers of recess (intaglio) printed stamps are often referrred to as 'plate numbers'. With many Queen Victoria stamps, these were incorporated into the design of the stamp.

POSTAGE DUE

Label denoting the amount of the outstanding postage fee to be recovered from the addressee, on unpaid or underpaid mail. This is sometimes called a 'to pay' label.

OVERPRINT: for the Morocco Agencies, on a King George V 5s

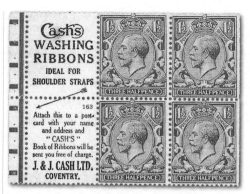

PANE: of four 1½d definitive stamps and advertisement labels, produced for a King George V booklet of the 1920s

POSTAGE PAID IMPRESSION (PPI)

Mark printed or handstruck on bulk postings denoting prepayment of postage.

POSTAL STATIONERY

Envelope or postcard that is sold ready-stamped to the required basic postal rate, usually as part of its design.

PRESENTATION PACK

A set of stamps mounted within a black card and contained in a folder which gives background details of the issue. The first proper example was made available with the Shakespeare Festival issue of 1964, although the 1960 prepackagings of certain definitives are now regarded as presentation packs by collectors.

PRESS SHEET

Printed sheet of miniature sheets, which is sold to collectors in its entirety rather than being cut up into separate items.

PRESTIGE STAMP BOOK

A large stitched booklet containing several panes of stamps, usually a mixture of definitives and commemoratives, along with background information.

PROVISIONAL

A stamp temporarily overprinted or surcharged to meet a shortage of regular issues.

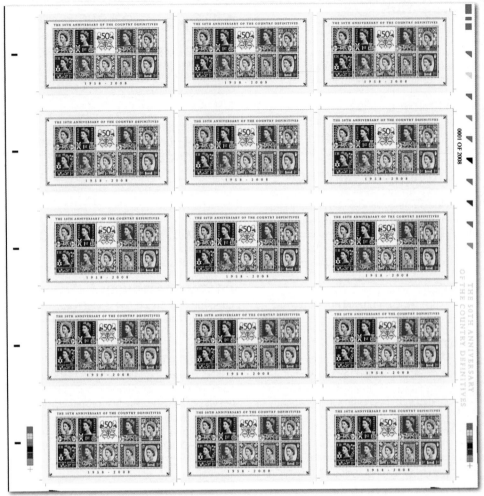

PRESS SHEET: of 15 of the 50th Anniversary of the Country Definitives miniature sheet, issued in 2008

RE-ENTRY
Part of an intaglio printing plate which is re-engraved by the transfer roller. This can usually be detected by a slight doubling of the lines.

REGIONAL
Definitive issued in deference to a specific region of the UK, and depicting appropriate regional symbols, but valid for postage throughout the nation. More recent examples for England, Wales, Scotland and Northern Ireland are known as 'country' definitives.

REPRINT
A stamp printed from the original plate, but long after the issue has ceased. This is usually distinguishable from the original by a difference on colour, paper or watermark.

RETOUCH
A repair to a letterpress (surface printing) plate or photogravure cylinder to correct a flaw.

SE-TENANT: strip of three different 9d designs from the 1969 British Ships set

ROULETTE
A form of separation effected using serrated instruments to produce cuts in the paper.

SELF-ADHESIVE
A stamp that is attached to a backing paper and, when peeled off, has sticky adhesive on the back that is sufficient to stick it to an envelope with no wetting agent required.

SE-TENANT
The term applied to two or more stamps of different designs printed side by side on a sheet.

SMARTSTAMPS
A modern service whereby small businesses can order their own special postal barcodes online, to save them going to post offices to buy stamps. Businesses can include their logo in the design.

SMILERS
A modern service whereby an individual can buy sheets of stamps with se-tenant customised labels bearing an image of his choice. Where these are supplied with labels chosen by Royal Mail, they are known as Smilers generic sheets.

SPECIAL STAMPS
Limited-lifespan stamps issued in addition to the standard definitives, often to commemorate a particular event or anniversary.

SPECIMEN
Overprint on a stamp printed for record or publicity purposes, signifying that it has no postal validity.

STAMP CARD
A postcard (also known as a PHQ card) issued by Royal Mail bearing an enlarged image of a stamp.

SURCHARGE
An overprint that alters the face value of a stamp, either upward or downward.

SURFACE PRINTING
A printing process, also known as 'typography' or 'letterpress', in which the design to be printed stands proud of the surface of the cylinder. The ink is applied only to the raised parts, so only the design is printed on contact with the paper.

TÊTE-BÊCHE
French term denoting se-tenant stamps which are upside-down in relation to each other.

TRAFFIC LIGHTS
The solid circles of colour which appear in the margins of many sheets of stamps, as a check to prove that all colours have been printed.

TRAINING LABEL
A stamp found with thick black bars across it, having been used at a Post Office training school. The bars render the stamp invalid for postage.

THEMATIC
A form of philately which involves collecting philatelic material surrounding a chosen theme.

UNDERPRINT
A motif printed on the gummed side of a stamp, usually from a booklet, to indicate that it has been sold at a discount off face value. Typically, this is the letter 'D' or a star pattern.

USED
A stamp that has performed its postal function

STAMP CARD: reproducing the enlarged image of a 1999 stamp in the Millennium series

and has had a cancellation applied. Collectors will prefer a neat and clear cancellation, which can easily be read and doesn't obscure too much of the stamp design.

VARIETY

Any stamp which varies from the norm, in shade, paper, perforation, watermark, and so on. A variety differs from an error in that it usually applies to small corrections that are made deliberately, and affect every sheet printed.

UNDERPRINT: denoting that these stamps from a 1980s Christmas booklet were sold at a discounted rate

VENDING MACHINE LABEL

Stamp of 1984-85 (also widely known by collectors as a Frama label), whose denomination was printed by a machine on insertion of a suitable value in coins.

VIGNETTE

The central pictorial portion of a stamp design, printed in a different colour from the frame.

WATERMARK

A translucent impression used as a security device in stamp printing paper, usually visible only when held up to the light.

WILDING

British definitive stamp featuring a bust of Queen Elizabeth II, in use from 1952-1967. The name comes from that of the photographer, Dorothy Wilding. □

OUR WEEKLY AUCTIONS ARE BURSTING WITH STAMPS!

Whether you're looking for Commonwealth classics, bulging box lots, specialized foreign or unusual postal history - Sandafayre has it all! We have been the #1 choice for collectors wanting great stamps and great service for over 30 years! Join thousands of satisfied collectors around the world already taking part in our auctions from the comfort of their own home!

NEW EASY TO USE WEBSITE

MORE STAMPS | MORE IMAGES | MORE CHOICE

Sandafayre
STAMP AUCTIONS

- **Fantastic Weekly Auctions - catalogues or online**
  - Thousands of lots from £15 to £15,000!
- **100% Satisfaction Guaranteed - or your money back!**

www.sandafayre.com

Please send me my **FREE** introductory Sandafayre catalogues

Name:

Address:

Postcode:

Enter details below if you would like to be added to the **Collectors Register**
My interests:

E-mail:

(BMV)

SANDAFAYRE, PARKGATE, KNUTSFORD, WA16 8DX, UK.

SHOWGARD

THE FINEST STAMP MOUNT MONEY CAN BUY!
Twin parallel welds keep your stamps securely in position

SHOWGARD MOUNTS - ORDER FORM

Mount Size (in millimetres)		Price	Quantity		Value
Cut to size - GB stamp packs of 30			Black	Clear	
36 x 36	GB Square Issues	2.45			
37 x 35	Horizontal oblong Commems	2.45			
35 x 37	Vertical oblong Commems	2.45			
Cut to size - GB stamp packs of 45			Black	Clear	
21 x 24	Definitives (low values) Regionals	2.45			
41 x 24	Commems to '70 (horizontal)	2.45			
30 x 41	Commems from '67 (vertical); Defins (Machin high values from '77)	2.45			
41 x 30	Commems from '67 (horizontal)	2.45			
24 x 41	Commems to '70 (vertical)	2.45			
44 x 27.5	GB Castle high values 1955-1963	2.45			
30 x 35	Defins (Machin high values)	2.45			
Strips - 210mm long per packet of 22			Black	Clear	
21	GB Postage Dues "information tech."	5.35			
24	Low value Defins; Regional Commems to 1970	5.35			
26	Isle of Man; Guernsey; Australia	5.35			
27.5	Festival & Castle high values	5.35			
29	Channel Islands (various)	5.35			
30	Commems from '67 (horizontal)	5.35			
31	Channel Islands (various)	5.35			
33	Foreign issues (various)	5.35			
Strips - 210mm long per packet of 15			Black	Clear	
36	GB Machin high values	5.35			
39	Foreign issues (various)	5.35			
41	GB Commems (vertical); Defins (Machin high values from '77)	5.35			
44	Foreign issues (various)	5.35			
48	Blocks of 4 - GB Booklet Panes	5.35			
55	Blocks of 4 (various)	5.35			
Blocks - per packet of 10			Black	Clear	
60 x 210	Blocks of GB Commems	6.40			
66 x 210	Large Blocks, etc.	6.40			
70 x 210	Machin high values; Blocks of 4	6.40			
76 x 264	GB gutter strips; Gutter Blocks	6.80			
91 x 264	GB Post Office Miniature Sheets	7.55			
Blocks - per packet of 7			Black	Clear	
100 x 243	Miniature Sheets & Cylinder Blocks	6.00			
Blocks - large size - per packet of 10			Black	Clear	
148 x 105	Blocks; Covers; GPO Postcards	6.40			
160 x 120	Blocks: Miniature Sheets; etc.	6.40			
190 x 115	Blocks; Covers	6.40			
Blocks - large size - per packet of 5			Black	Clear	
210 x 170	Blocks; Miniature Sheets; etc.	6.40			
Mixed Strips	Strips - 21mm to 55mm (pack of 20)				
			SUB-TOTAL £		
POST & PACKING	Order value less than £20.00 - £1.50 (UK ONLY)		Add P & P		
	Order value over £20.00 - POST FREE (UK ONLY)				
	(includes VAT @ 20%) ORDER TOTAL £				

OTHER SIZES AVAILABLE - PLEASE REQUEST FULL LIST OR SEND FOR FREE SAMPLE PACK

I wish to pay by: ☐ cheque (payable to BARRINGTON SMITH) ☐ debit card ☐ credit card

Card number: ☐☐☐☐ ☐☐☐☐ ☐☐☐☐ ☐☐☐☐

Issue No. (switch):
Start date:
Expiry date:
Security code (last 3 numbers on back):

Signature:

Name:
Address:

Postcode: Telephone:

Post to: **BARRINGTON SMITH**
Cross Street, Oadby, Leicester, LE2 4DD
Telephone: 0116 2719181   Fax: 0116 2712114   Stamp Mag

GREAT BRITAIN ON AND OFF PAPER MIXTURES

Our GB mixtures are our best sellers thanks mainly to some great charity sources providing us with very modern and clean material.

SPECIAL OFFER: Buy 1lb GB Commems, 1lb GB H.V Defins, 2 lbs GB Regionals & 18 kgs GB Defins for £110.00. List price £125.00.

GB COMMEMS NO XMAS. Wide ranging on paper mix includes h.v's & modern. ½ lb £15.00, 1 lb £29.00.

GB HIGH VALUE DEFINS. On paper, many from registered mail so good cancellations, a clean mix. Includes modern security issues which will become very rare with all the labels used on mail. ½ lb £14.00, 1 lb £27.00.

GB REGIONALS. (On paper). A wealth of variety from all four regions, find those elusive band/perf varieties very cheaply. Over 7000 – 8000 stamps/ 2lbs   1 lb £10.00, 2 lbs £19.00.

GREAT BRITAIN DEFINITIVES. An 18 kg sack of On paper which is bound to contain much post-mark interest, possibly Regionals, High Values, much Phosphor, paper and perf varieties. Sorted and delivered only by charitable institutions. (Delivered to your door, post paid inland). Only £50.00.

GB MULTIPLES ISSUES. Try to keep up with the recent multiple issues. Increasing variety, right up to the latest issues including 2012 GB Fashion, A-Z UK, Comics, Britons of Distinction, World Wildlife, Olympics, Mammals, Cats & Dogs, Royal Society, Albums etc. Try and complete those difficult sets. ½ lb £36.00, 1 lb £70.00.

GB SPECIAL CHARITY MIX. A well balanced on paper Charity mix covering Defins, Commems, H.Value Commems, H.Value Defins, Pre-decimal, Wildings & Pre QEII. Covers all periods. 1 lb £12.00, 2 lbs £22.00.

GB GOLD SELF ADHESIVE SECURITY LABELS. Prices on auction sites have gone crazy. There are many different types to collect.½ lb £18.00, 1 lb £35.00.

GREAT BRITAIN OFF PAPER MIXTURES

GREAT BRITAIN Off paper mixture. The tedious washing of this modern mix has been done for you already. There are over 500 basic machins to collect. One of each in good nick can cost over £500.00. We can't guarantee all in there but you'll have great fun sorting, includes commems, h.v commems & defins, worth the price on their own. Guaranteed totally unpicked. At least 10,000 stamps / 1 lb.   1 lb £16.50, 2 lbs £30.00.

GREAT BRITAIN OFF PAPER COMMEMS NO XMAS. Previously included Xmas, we can now supply without so the rarer Commems only. Wealth of variety from KGVI to 2011, includes some high values. Approx 5000 stamps to 1 lb weight. ¼ lb £22.00, ½ lb £42.00, 1 lb £80.00.

We are always interested in buying back spare on or off paper mixtures you may have.
We can now take Paypal Payments through courtphilatelics@aol.com.
EBAY Sales: Check out our offers on rudd3325. Many items listed are not in our usual list.

WE ACCEPT: CHEQUES, POSTAL ORDERS, PAYPAL, ALL MAJOR CREDIT CARDS - advise expiry date and security code.
We always offer a full refund.
UK customers pay no postage (overseas add: £2 / ¼ lb, £3 / ½ lb and £4.50 / 1lb. There are no credit card charges and no VAT payable

COURT PHILATELICS

Dept GBSM, P.O Box 6198, Leighton Buzzard, Beds LU7 9XT.   TEL: 01296 662420.   E-Mail: courtphilatelics@aol.com

---

GB POSTAGE

FOR SALE FROM 85% FACEVALUE

Reduce the cost of your mailings. Values
supplied in 100's @ 90%, £50 mixed bags at 85% of face value.

Weekly lists of stock values available by fax.

No charge for mailing costs, but minimum order required £200

JOHN CURTIN LIMITED
International Stamp Dealer
P.O. Box 31,
Sunbury - on - Thames,
Middlesex, TW16 6HD
Tel: 01932 785635 (24 hrs)
Fax: 01932 770523
e-mail: jcbuying@btinternet.com

STAMP POSTAL AUCTIONS

held every few months with good selection of GB, Commonwealth and World, also Cigarette Cards. Suit both collectors and dealers. Keen estimates and no buyer premiums.

Free catalogue from:

**G Sharples, 32 Carr Gate,
Thornton Cleveleys, Lancashire, FY5 1LB**

Tel: 01253 825464
email: sharples601@btinternet.com
You won't regret it!

Alliance AUCTIONS

Incorporating Pottergate and Express Stamp Auctions
founded in 1966

We especially are seeking to buy,

both for auction or private treaty,

particularly decent GB

& Commonwealth,

covers & postcards,

philatelic literature,

coins & banknotes,

medals and militaria.

So, if ever you'd like

us to look over your collection

please contact us at Latchmore Bank

and we'll arrange everything to suit you.

There's absolutely no obligation

and any assessment

is free.

AND **IF YOU'RE BUYING...**

WE HAVE REGULAR AUCTIONS

ON THE FIRST TUESDAY OF

EVERY MONTH

IN COMFORTABLE SURROUNDINGS

AT THE BURY LODGE HOTEL

LONDON STANSTED AIRPORT

VIEWING FROM 12 noon until 7:15pm

AND BUYING FROM 7:30pm

priority catalogue requests,

please telephone: 01279 758854 or, if you prefer

email us at info@allianceauctions.com

or write to us at Dept.CP.,

Latchmore Bank Farmhouse,

Latchmore Bank,

nr. Bishop's Stortford, Hertfordshire CM22 7PJ

and you can visit us anytime at

www.allianceauctions.com

where you can download a catalogue

and bid too if you're unable to make it to a sale.

John Auld john@allianceauctions.com

TRUSTED FOR OVER FORTY YEARS

INTERNATIONAL PRIVATE or PUBLIC VALUATIONS, ASSESSMENTS, CONSULTATIONS, SALES and AUCTIONS

NORTHERN STAMPS

From Penny Blacks to Presentation Packs!

A large selection of GB material always available at reasonable prices!

Large stock of smilers available

Please email us with your wants lists!

www.northernstamps.com

email@ mark@northernstamps.co.uk
ebay ID@ uknorthernstamps
Tel 0191 413 1431

K & C Philatelics

Keith and Christine Wood
Specialist Dealers since 1977

Great Britain Queen Victoria (1840 - 1901)
Quality Stamps, Covers and Prestamp Material

PO Box 5003, Danbury CM3 4JU
Tel: 01245 223120 Fax/ Ans: 01245 224608

www.kcphilatelics.co.uk

M&C Stamps

GB, Commonwealth and World Stamps, with a
GB New Issue Service available and Accessories
for all collectors. Visit us in our premises at:
Shop 1.12 Antiques Centre,
High Orchard Street,
Gloucester GL1 5SH
Tel: 01452 506 361
Fax: 01452 307 161

We are open:
Monday, Thursday, Friday, Saturday 10:00 – 5:00pm
Sunday 11:00 - 5:00pm

◆ Lighthouse ®

For all your collecting needs

- Hingeless albums
- Stock books
- Binders
- Hawid mounts
- Magnifiers
- UV lamps
- FDC albums
- Accessories

THE DUNCANNON PARTNERSHIP · 4 Beaufort Road
REIGATE · SURREY · RH2 9DJ · Telephone 0 17 37/24 42 22 · Fax 0 17 37/22 47 43
Buy online at www.duncannon.co.uk

QUEEN VICTORIA

For this reign prices are given for lightly mounted unused (left) and fine used (right). The exception is for the 1840-1841 issues, where fine used prices are subdivided into stamps with four margins (centre) and three margins (right).

Take care when buying unmounted mint because there are known cases of regumming.

LINE-ENGRAVED ISSUES

1d black

■ 1840, May 6. Penny Black

Engraved by Charles and Frederick Heath. Printed in recess by Perkins, Bacon. Wmk: Small crowns. Imperforate. Letters in lower corners only.

1d black	£11,000	£250	78.00
1d intense black	£15,000	£275	90.00
1d grey black	£14,000	£275	90.00
Plate 1a	£14,000	£300	90.00
Plate 1b	£11,000	£225	80.00
Plate 2	£11,000	£225	80.00
Plate 3	£14,000	£250	85.00
Plate 4	£11,000	£225	80.00
Plate 5	£11,000	£225	80.00
Plate 6	£11,000	£225	80.00
Plate 7	£12,000	£275	90.00
Plate 8	£14,000	£300	95.00
Plate 9	£14,000	£350	£125
Plate 10	£24,000	£600	£175
Plate 11	£16,000	£3,500	£750
Wmk inverted	£28,000	£1,400	£295
Bleute paper	£15,000	£375	95.00
Red Maltese cross cancellation	-	£250	90.00
Black Maltese cross cancellation	-	£225	78.00
Blue Maltese cross cancellation	-	£8,000	£2,000
Magenta Maltese cross cancellation	-	£1,950	£400
Ruby Maltese cross cancellation	-	£750	£225
Violet Maltese cross cancellation	-	£12,000	£3,000
Number in cross (1-12)	-	£10,000	£3,000
Penny Post cancellation only	-	£2,600	£600
Town datestamp only	-	£2,750	£600
1844 cancellation	-	£1,000	£175

2d blue

■ 1840, May 8. Twopenny Blue

Engraved by Charles and Frederick Heath. Printed in recess by Perkins, Bacon. Wmk: Small crowns. Imperforate. Letters in lower corners only.

2d blue	£30,000	£500	£140
2d deep full blue	£36,000	£600	£170
2d pale blue	£36,000	£550	£150
Plate 1	£30,000	£500	£140
Plate 2	£40,000	£600	£170
Wmk Inverted	£50,000	£5,000	£2,500
Red Maltese cross cancel (Plate 1)	-	£550	£150
Red Maltese cross cancel (Plate 2)	-	£1,000	£225
Black Maltese cross cancellation	-	£500	£140
Blue Maltese cross cancellations	-	£6,000	£1,250
Magenta Maltese cross cancellation	-	£4,000	£850
Ruby Maltese cross cancellation	-	£2,000	£500
Number in cross (1-12)	-	£9,000	£3,000
Penny Post cancellation only	-	£5,000	£1,200
Town datestamp only	-	£3,750	£800
1844 cancellation	-	£1,250	£250

1d red

■ 1841, February 10. Penny Red

Engraved by Charles and Frederick Heath. Printed in recess by Perkins, Bacon. Wmk: Small crowns. Imperforate. Letters in lower corners only.

Id red brown	£275	9.00	3.00
Id deep red brown	£550	15.00	4.00
Id orange brown	£1,200	£120	12.00
Id lake red	£3,500	£550	£100
Plate 1b	£18,000	£225	40.00
Plate 2	£18,000	£175	25.00
Plate 5	£5,000	£150	20.00
Plate 8	£8,000	90.00	20.00
Plate 9	£4,000	90.00	20.00
Plate 10	£2,000	90.00	20.00
Plate 11	£4,000	75.00	15.00
Wmk inverted	£4,000	£250	75.00
Lavender paper	£1,000	£150	40.00
Red Maltese cross cancellation	-	£3,850	£875
Black Maltese cross cancellation	-	40.00	6.00
Blue Maltese cross cancellation	-	£375	75.00
Green Maltese cross cancellation	-	£8,000	£1,000
Violet Maltese cross cancellation	-	£9,000	£1,500
Number in cross (1-12)	-	95.00	22.50
Penny Post cancellation only	-	£700	£125
Black town datestamp only	-	£300	95.00
Blue town datestamp only	-	£1,200	£275
Green town datestamp only	-	£2,750	£650
Black 1844 cancellation	-	9.00	3.00
Blue 1844 cancellation	-	£100	25.00
Green 1844 cancellation	-	£1,250	£250
Red 1844 cancellation	-	£12,000	£3,000
Violet 1844 cancellation	-	£2,500	£600
B blank error	-	£40,000	£18,000

Wmk inverted	£7,500	£400	£125
Black Maltese cross cancellation	-	£150	22.50
Blue Maltese cross cancellation	-	£3,000	£400
Number in cross (1-12)	-	£250	60.00
Black town datestamp only	-	£1,000	£275
Blue town datestamp only	-	£4,000	£700
Black 1844 cancellation	-	50.00	12.00
Blue 1844 cancellation	-	£475	£100
Green 1844 cancellation	-	£2,750	£750
Red 1844 cancellation	-	£17,500	£3,500

■ 1854
Designs as above. Perf: 16.

Id red-brown (February 1854)		£195	12.00
2d blue (March 1, 1854)		£2,100	60.00

■ 1855
Designs as above. Perf: 14.

Id red-brown (January 1855)		£450	45.00
2d blue (March 4, 1855)		£7,000	£160

■ 1855
Designs as above. Wmk: Large crown. Perf: 16.

Id red-brown (May 15, 1855)		£700	65.00
2d blue (July 20, 1855)		£9,000	£230

■ 1855
Designs as above. Perf: 14.

Id red-brown (August 18, 1855)		£160	8.00
2d blue (July 20, 1855)		£1,600	30.00

2d blue

■ 1841, March 13. Twopenny Blue
Engraved by Charles and Frederick Heath. Printed in recess by Perkins, Bacon. Wmk: Small crowns. Imperforate. Letters in lower corners only. Horizontal white lines added to design.

2d blue	£3,000	50.00	12.00
2d pale blue	£3,200	55.00	12.00
2d deep full blue	£4,000	70.00	15.00
2d violet (lavender paper)	£18,000	£950	£175
Plate 3	£3,000	60.00	12.00
Plate 4	£3,500	50.00	12.00

1d rose-red

2d blue

■ 1858-1879
Designs as above. Wmk: Large Crowns. Perf: 14. Letters in all four corners. Plate number included in design.

Id rose-red (April 1, 1864)

Plate 71	22.00	2.00
Plate 72	27.00	2.50
Plate 73	24.00	2.00
Plate 74	25.00	1.50
Plate 76	25.00	1.50
Plate 77	-	-
Plate 78	45.00	1.50
Plate 79	22.00	1.50
Plate 80	30.00	1.50
Plate 81	35.00	1.50

Plate 82	85.00	2.75	Plate 144	75.00	16.00
Plate 83	£110	6.00	Plate 145	23.00	1.75
Plate 84	40.00	1.60	Plate 146	25.00	4.50
Plate 85	27.00	1.60	Plate 147	30.00	2.00
Plate 86	35.00	2.75	Plate 148	25.00	2.00
Plate 87	22.00	1.50	Plate 149	25.00	4.50
Plate 88	£170	7.00	Plate 150	12.00	1.50
Plate 89	25.00	1.50	Plate 151	40.00	7.50
Plate 90	25.00	1.50	Plate 152	40.00	4.00
Plate 91	35.00	4.50	Plate 153	90.00	7.00
Plate 92	21.00	1.50	Plate 154	30.00	1.50
Plate 93	30.00	1.50	Plate 155	30.00	1.75
Plate 94	28.00	4.00	Plate 156	35.00	1.50
Plate 95	25.00	1.50	Plate 157	30.00	1.50
Plate 96	28.00	1.50	Plate 158	23.00	1.50
Plate 97	25.00	2.50	Plate 159	23.00	1.50
Plate 98	30.00	4.50	Plate 160	23.00	1.50
Plate 99	35.00	4.00	Plate 161	40.00	5.00
Plate 100	40.00	1.50	Plate 162	30.00	5.00
Plate 101	40.00	7.50	Plate 163	30.00	2.00
Plate 102	28.00	1.50	Plate 164	30.00	2.00
Plate 103	30.00	2.75	Plate 165	35.00	1.50
Plate 104	80.00	4.00	Plate 166	35.00	4.50
Plate 105	95.00	5.50	Plate 167	35.00	1.50
Plate 106	35.00	1.50	Plate 168	30.00	6.00
Plate 107	40.00	5.00	Plate 169	30.00	6.00
Plate 108	60.00	1.75	Plate 170	21.00	1.50
Plate 109	65.00	2.50	Plate 171	12.00	1.50
Plate 110	40.00	7.50	Plate 172	23.00	1.50
Plate 111	36.00	1.75	Plate 173	48.00	6.50
Plate 112	50.00	1.70	Plate 174	23.00	1.50
Plate 113	30.00	9.00	Plate 175	40.00	2.50
Plate 114	£240	9.00	Plate 176	40.00	1.75
Plate 115	85.00	1.75	Plate 177	32.00	1.50
Plate 116	60.00	7.50	Plate 178	40.00	2.50
Plate 117	28.00	1.50	Plate 179	30.00	1.75
Plate 118	30.00	1.50	Plate 180	40.00	4.00
Plate 119	28.00	1.50	Plate 181	36.00	1.50
Plate 120	12.00	1.50	Plate 182	75.00	4.00
Plate 121	25.00	8.00	Plate 183	35.00	2.00
Plate 122	12.00	1.50	Plate 184	23.00	1.75
Plate 123	25.00	1.50	Plate 185	30.00	2.00
Plate 124	22.00	1.50	Plate 186	35.00	1.75
Plate 125	25.00	1.50	Plate 187	30.00	1.50
Plate 127	35.00	1.75	Plate 188	50.00	7.50
Plate 129	25.00	6.50	Plate 189	50.00	5.50
Plate 130	35.00	1.75	Plate 190	30.00	4.50
Plate 131	45.00	12.00	Plate 191	23.00	5.50
Plate 132	£140	18.00	Plate 192	30.00	1.50
Plate 133	£105	7.50	Plate 193	23.00	1.50
Plate 134	12.00	1.50	Plate 194	30.00	6.50
Plate 135	70.00	22.00	Plate 195	30.00	6.50
Plate 136	65.00	17.00	Plate 196	30.00	4.00
Plate 137	22.00	1.75	Plate 197	35.00	7.00
Plate 138	14.00	1.50	Plate 198	32.00	4.50
Plate 139	40.00	12.50	Plate 199	35.00	4.50
Plate 140	14.00	1.50	Plate 200	40.00	2.00
Plate 141	£100	7.00	Plate 201	23.00	4.00
Plate 142	50.00	22.00	Plate 202	40.00	6.50
Plate 143	40.00	12.00	Plate 203	23.00	13.00

			½d rose-red (October 1, 1870)		
Plate 204	35.00	1.75	Plate 1	£180	50.00
Plate 205	35.00	2.25	Plate 3	£120	25.00
Plate 206	35.00	7.00	Plate 4	£100	18.00
Plate 207	40.00	7.00	Plate 5	75.00	10.00
Plate 208	35.00	12.50	Plate 6	80.00	10.00
Plate 209	30.00	8.00	Plate 8	£225	60.00
Plate 210	45.00	10.00	Plate 9	£5,000	£600
Plate 211	50.00	18.00	Plate 10	85.00	10.00
Plate 212	40.00	10.00	Plate 11	80.00	10.00
Plate 213	40.00	10.00	Plate 12	80.00	10.00
Plate 214	45.00	15.00	Plate 13	80.00	10.00
Plate 215	45.00	15.00	Plate 14	80.00	10.00
Plate 216	50.00	15.00	Plate 15	£115	24.00
Plate 217	50.00	6.00	Plate 19	£140	28.00
Plate 218	45.00	7.00	Plate 20	£200	50.00
Plate 219	80.00	58.00	**1½d** rose-red (October 1, 1870)		
Plate 220	32.00	6.00	Plate 1	£450	48.00
Plate 221	50.00	15.00	Plate 3	£275	32.00
Plate 222	60.00	30.00			
Plate 223	75.00	50.00			
Plate 224	£110	45.00			
Plate 225	£2,900	£650			
2d blue (July 1858)					
Plate 7	£1,200	40.00			
Plate 8	£1,200	25.00			
Plate 9	£250	8.00			
Plate 12	£1,800	£100			
Plate 13	£260	15.00			
Plate 14	£340	16.00			
Plate 15	£320	16.00			

EMBOSSED ISSUES

6d lilac

10d brown

½d rose-red

1/- green

1½d rose-red

■ 1870-1879

Printed in recess by Perkins, Bacon. Wmk: Half Penny extending over three stamps (½d) or Large Crowns (1½d). Perf: 14. Letters in all four corners. Plate number included in design, except plate 1 of the 1½d value.

■ 1847-1854. High values

Die engraved at the Royal Mint by William Wyon. Printed using the embossed process at Somerset House. Wmk: VR (6d), or unwatermarked (10d, 1/-). Imperforate.

6d lilac (March 1, 1854)	£14,000	£525
10d brown (November 6, 1848)	£8,000	£775
1/- green (September 11, 1847)	£16,000	£550

(* The above are priced cut square; examples cut to shape are worth considerably less.)

 **WHAT ALWAYS TRAVELS FIRST CLASS?**

OUR NEW FULL COLOUR GB LIST
with over 1,000 individual items
ALL ILLUSTRATED

 For your **FREE COPY** contact

ERIC PAUL LTD
PO BOX 44, MARPLE
CHESHIRE SK6 7EE

Tel: 0161-427 2101   Fax: 0161-427 6386
E-mail: info@ericpaul.co.uk   Web site: www.ericpaul.co.uk
Members: PTS   M&DPTA   GBPS   ADPS

SURFACE-PRINTED ISSUES

Most issues from 1862-64 to 1880-83 have the plate number incorporated into their design. Many can be found with wing margins, where the vertical gutters between panes were perforated by way of a single row of holes down the centre.

4d carmine

■ 1855-1857
Surface-printed by De La Rue. Perf: 14. No corner letters.
4d carmine (Wmk: Small Garter)

(July 31, 1855)	£8,000	£275
4d carmine (Wmk: Medium Garter)		
(February 25, 1856)	£9,000	£325
4d carmine (Wmk: Large Garter)		
(January 1857)	£1,400	55.00

6d lilac

1/- green

■ 1856
Surface-printed by De La Rue. Wmk: Emblems. Perf: 14. No corner letters

6d lilac (October 21, 1856)	£775	68.00
1/- green (November 1, 1856)	£2,200	£160

3d carmine   4d red

6d lilac   9d bistre

1/- green

■ 1862-1864
Surface-printed by De La Rue. Wmk: Large Garter (4d), Emblems (3d, 6d, 9d, 1/-). Perf: 14. Small corner letters.

3d carmine (May 1, 1862)	£1,800	£225
4d red (January 15, 1862)	£875	55.00
6d lilac (December 1, 1862)	£1,600	50.00
9d bistre (January 15, 1862)	£4,000	£280
1/- green (December 1, 1862)	£2,200	£150

3d carmine

4d vermilion

6d lilac (without hyphen)

2/- blue

6d lilac (with hyphen)

9d bistre

■ 1867-1880

Surface-printed by De La Rue. Perf: 14. Wmk: Spray of Rose.
Designs as above except 6d and 2/-.

3d red (July 12, 1867)

Plate 4	£1,100	£125
Plate 5	£375	35.00
Plate 6	£400	35.00
Plate 7	£500	35.00
Plate 8	£400	35.00
Plate 9	£400	35.00
Plate 10	£550	75.00

6d lilac (June 21, 1867)

Plate 6, with hyphen	£400	55.00
Plate 8, without hyphen	£400	55.00
Plate 9, without hyphen	£400	55.00
Plate 10, without hyphen	-	£29,000

9d bistre (October 3, 1867)

Plate 4	£1,300	£200

10d brown (July 1, 1867)

Plate 1	£1,900	£225
Plate 2	£40,000	£12,000

1/- green (July 13, 1867)

Plate 4	£675	40.00
Plate 5	£500	25.00
Plate 6	£700	25.00
Plate 7	£750	45.00

2/- blue (July 1, 1867)

Plate 1	£2,100	£140

2/- brown (February 27, 1880)

Plate 1	£26,000	£3,000

10d brown

1/- green

■ 1865-1867

Surface-printed by De La Rue. Wmk: Larger Garter (4d) or
Emblems (3d, 6d, 9d, 10d, 1/-). Perf: 14. Large corner letters.

3d carmine (March 1, 1865)

Plate 4	£1,000	£125

4d vermilion (July 4, 1865)

Plate 7	£500	65.00
Plate 8	£400	40.00
Plate 9	£400	40.00
Plate 10	£475	85.00
Plate 11	£400	40.00
Plate 12	£400	40.00
Plate 13	£400	40.00
Plate 14	£440	60.00

6d lilac (April 1, 1865)

Plate 5	£650	55.00
Plate 6	£2,200	£100

9d bistre (December 1, 1865)

Plate 4	£4,000	£360

10d brown (November 11, 1867)

Plate 1	-	£35,000

1/- green (February 1, 1865)

Plate 4	£2,000	£125

(* Mint examples of the 9d exist from a perforated imprimatur
sheet of plate 5.)

6d grey

■ 1872-1873

Surface-printed by De La Rue. Perf: 14. Wmk: Spray of Rose.

6d brown (April 12, 1872)

Plate 11	£450	35.00
Plate 12	£2,400	£160

6d grey (April 24, 1873)

Plate 12	£1,100	£130

5/- red   10/- grey-green

£1 brown

£5 orange

2½d mauve   3d red

4d green   6d buff

8d orange   1/- green

3d on 3d lilac   6d on 6d lilac

■ 1867-1883. High values
Surface-printed by De La Rue.

A) Wmk: Maltese Cross. Perf: 15.
5/- red (July 1, 1867)

Plate 1	£3,850	£450
Plate 2	£5,000	£550
10/- grey-green (September 26, 1878)		
Plate 1	£50,000	£2,200
£1 brown (September 26, 1878)		
Plate 1	£75,000	£3,500

B) Wmk: Large Anchor. Perf: 14.
5/- red (November 25, 1882)

Plate 4	£26,000	£1,950
10/- grey-green (February, 1883)		
Plate 1	£120,000	£4,000
£1 brown (December, 1882)		
Plate 1	£130,000	£6,500
£5 orange (March 21, 1882)		
Plate 1	£13,000	£4,500

■ 1873-1883
Surface-printed by De La Rue. Perf: 14.

A) Wmk: Small Anchor.
2½d mauve (July 1, 1875)

Plate 1	£385	55.00
Plate 2	£385	55.00
Plate 3	£600	80.00

B) Wmk: Orb.
2½d mauve (May 16, 1876)

Plate 3	£750	75.00
Plate 4	£350	35.00
Plate 5	£350	35.00

Plate 6	£350	35.00
Plate 7	£350	35.00
Plate 8	£350	35.00
Plate 9	£350	35.00
Plate 10	£375	40.00
Plate 11	£350	35.00
Plate 12	£350	35.00
Plate 13	£350	35.00
Plate 14	£350	35.00
Plate 15	£350	35.00
Plate 16	£350	35.00
Plate 17	£1,050	£190
2½d blue (February 5, 1880)		
Plate 17	£325	40.00
Plate 18	£350	22.50
Plate 19	£325	22.50
Plate 20	£350	22.50

C) Wmk: Spray of Rose.
3d red (July 5, 1873)

Plate 11	£300	30.00
Plate 12	£325	30.00
Plate 14	£375	30.00
Plate 15	£300	30.00
Plate 16	£300	30.00
Plate 17	£325	30.00
Plate 18	£325	30.00
Plate 19	£300	30.00
Plate 20	£300	55.00
6d buff (March 15, 1873)		
Plate 13	-	£18,000
6d grey (March 31, 1874)		
Plate 13	£300	40.00
Plate 14	£300	40.00
Plate 15	£300	40.00
Plate 16	£300	40.00
Plate 17	£525	90.00
1/- green (September 1, 1873)		
Plate 8	£500	80.00
Plate 9	£500	80.00
Plate 10	£500	90.00
Plate 11	£500	80.00
Plate 12	£475	65.00
Plate 13	£475	65.00
Plate 14	-	£28,000
1/- brown (October 14, 1880)		
Plate 13	£2,400	£400

D) Wmk: Large Garter.
4d vermilion (March 1, 1876)

Plate 15	£1,400	£300
Plate 16	-	£24,000
4d green (March 12, 1877)		
Plate 15	£825	£180
Plate 16	£775	£170
Plate 17	-	£14,000
4d brown (August 15, 1880)		
Plate 17	£1,250	£325
8d orange (September 11, 1876)		
Plate 1	£900	£175

E) Wmk: Imperial Crown.
2½d blue (March 23, 1881)

Plate 21	£350	18.00
Plate 22	£325	18.00
Plate 23	£325	14.00
3d red (February 1881)		
Plate 20	£500	90.00
Plate 21	£380	55.00
3d (in red) **on 3d** lilac (January 1, 1883)		
Plate 21	£400	80.00
4d brown (December 9, 1880)		
Plate 17	£300	38.00
Plate 18	£300	38.00
6d grey (January 1, 1881)		
Plate 17	£350	45.00
Plate 18	£310	45.00
6d (in red) **on 6d** lilac (January 1, 1883)		
Plate 18	£425	80.00
1/- brown (May 29, 1881)		
Plate 13	£525	90.00
Plate 14	£425	90.00

½d green

1d Venetian red

1½d Venetian red

2d red

5d indigo

■ **1880-1881**
Surface-printed by De La Rue. Perf: 14. Wmk: Imperial Crown.

½d green (October 14, 1880)	35.00	6.00
1d Venetian red (January 1, 1880)	18.00	3.00
1½d Venetian red (October 14, 1880)	£140	30.00
2d red (December 8, 1880)	£180	60.00
5d indigo (March 15, 1881)	£600	65.00

1d lilac

■ 1881-1901
Surface-printed by De La Rue. Perf: 14. Wmk: Imperial Crown.

A) Die I. 14 white dots in each corner.
1d lilac (July 12, 1881)   £150   15.00

B)Die II. 16 white dots in each corner.
1d lilac (December 12, 1881)   1.75   0.75

2/6 lilac

5/- red

10/- blue

£1 green

■ 1883-1891. High values
Surface-printed by De La Rue. Perf: 14.

A) Wmk: Large Anchor.
2/6 lilac (July 2, 1883)   £350   70.00
5/- red (April 1, 1884)   £700   £110
10/- blue (April 1, 1884)   £1,800   £275

B) Wmk: Imperial Crown.
£1 brown (April 1, 1884)   £30,000   £2,500
£1 green (January 27, 1891)   £6,000   £700

C) Wmk: Orbs.
£1 brown (February 1, 1888)   £60,000   £3,800

½d blue   1½d lilac and 5d green

3d lilac and 1/- green   4d green

6d green and 2d lilac   9d green and 2½d lilac

■ 1883-84. 'Lilac & Green' series
Surface-printed by De La Rue. Perf: 14. Wmk: Imperial Crown
(sideways on 2d, 2½d, 6d, 9d).
½d blue (April 1, 1884)   14.00   3.50
1½d lilac (April 1, 1884)   80.00   23.00
2d lilac (April 1, 1884)   £140   40.00
2½d lilac (April 1, 1884)   57.50   5.00
3d lilac (April 1, 1884)   £135   38.00
4d green (April 1, 1884)   £325   £100
5d green (April 1, 1884)   £325   £100
6d green (April 1, 1884)   £300   £110
9d green (August 1, 1883)   £725   £300
1/- green (April 1, 1884)   £775   £150

SELLING YOUR COLLECTION?

The latest valuations. Old fashioned values.

Building a stamp collection can take years, so the decision to sell is not taken lightly.

Which is why it makes good sense to entrust the sale to someone who understands your feelings and your needs.

Tony Lester is a fellow philatelist and provides a service based on the old fashioned values of care, friendliness, consideration and total sensitivity, whether buying or selling.

However, when it comes to the 'bottom line' - you will be hard pressed to find someone offering a better valuation or a quicker response.

All you need to do now is to decide how you would like us to deal with your collection. We offer two choices.

1 PURCHASE

From modest collections of just a few hundred pounds up to collections in excess of £100,000, we can and do deal with all - and provide immediate payment.

2 AUCTION

We run regular auctions throughout the year, each attracting wide interest both nationally and internationally and covering a wide range including stamps, postal history, postcards and cigarette cards. Our commission charges are attractively low.

Free catalogue available on request.

We offer a free 'visiting' service to view and value suitable lots, alternatively we can arrange collection, or you can forward any material by registered post for our written valuation by return. All with no obligation.

We regret that we do not handle 'SCHOOLBOY COLLECTIONS' as they are typically worth less than £10 even if over a hundred years old.

TONY LESTER *Auctions*

For a friendly and personal service just call **01926 634 809** and speak directly to me or to Robin Taylor.

Tony Lester Auctions Limited, The Sidings, Birdingbury Road, Marton, Nr. Rugby CV23 9RX. Email: tonylester@btconnect.com
Web: www.tonylester.co.uk

We are long standing members of the Philatelic Traders' Society, complying with its strict code of ethics. We have been established for over 30 years, with a reputation for honesty and fair dealing.

½d orange

1½d purple and green

6d purple on red

9d violet and blue

2d green and red

2½d purple on blue

10d purple and red

1/- green

3d purple on yellow

4d green and brown

■ 1887-92. 'Jubilee' series

Surface-printed by De La Rue. Perf: 14. Wmk: Imperial Crown.

A) Wmk upright.

½d orange (January 1, 1887)	1.20	0.50
½d green (April 17, 1900)	1.40	0.60
1½d purple and green (January 1, 1887)	10.00	2.00
2d green and red (January 1, 1887)	18.00	8.00
2½d purple, blue paper (January 1, 1887)	14.00	0.75
3d purple, yellow paper (January 1, 1887)	18.00	1.50
4d green and brown (January 1, 1887)	22.00	7.00
4½d green and red (September 15, 1892)	7.00	25.00
5d purple and blue (January 1, 1887)	26.00	5.00
6d purple, red paper (January 1, 1887)	20.00	5.00
9d violet and blue (January 1, 1887)	45.00	25.00
10d purple and red (January 1, 1887)	40.00	24.00
1/- green (January 1, 1887)	£150	40.00
1/- green and red (July 11, 1900)	45.00	70.00
Set	£400	£200

B) Wmk inverted.

½d orange	60.00	60.00
½d green	60.00	60.00
1½d purple and green	£1,400	£400
2d green and red	£1,400	£400
2½d purple, blue paper	£3,500	£1,100
4d green and brown	£1,400	£500
5d purple and blue	£15,000	£1,000
6d purple, red paper	£8,000	£1,200
9d violet and blue	£7,000	£1,800
10d purple and red	£8,000	£2,500
1/- green	£1,600	£800
1/- green and red	£1,700	£900

4½d green and red

5d purple and blue

The best magazine for GB collectors
www.stampmagazine.co.uk

STAMP

Leading Buyers
and
Recognised Valuers

Est. **40** *Years*

Serious professional buyers of all things philatelic

Corbitts would welcome the opportunity to discuss the
sale of your collection by your preferred method.

PUBLIC AUCTION ⚜ OUTRIGHT PURCHASE ⚜ PRIVATE TREATY

We need all types of Philatelic material from general ranges and accumulations
to specialised studies, good singles and covers. We buy it all.

So if you are considering selling part or all of your collection - I urge you to
call now and discuss the many advantages of selling through Corbitts.

For a friendly and personal service, call Freephone **0800 525804**
and ask for David McMonagle or Richard Vincent.

Mosley Street, Newcastle upon Tyne, NE1 1YE
Tel: 0191 232 7268 Fax: 0191 261 4130
Email: info@corbitts.com Website: www.corbitts.com

**PLEASE CONTACT US FOR
A COMPLIMENTARY CATALOGUE**

Members of: Philatelic Traders Society • American Stamp Dealers Association • American Philatelic Society

KING EDWARD VII

For this reign most stamps are priced in three columns: unmounted mint (left), mounted mint (centre) and fine used (right). But booklet panes are priced for mounted mint only.

De La Rue printings are generally cleaner, with good centring and neat perforations. Harrison and Somerset House printings are coarser, with poor centring and ragged perfs. A vast range of shades exists, the details of these being beyond the scope of this publication.

6d purple

7d grey

9d purple and blue

10d purple and red

½d yellow-green

1d scarlet

1½d purple and green

2d green and red

1/- green and red

2/6 lilac

2½d blue

3d purple on yellow

5/- red

10/- blue

4d orange

5d purple and blue

£1 green

■ 1902-10

Surface-printed by De La Rue. Wmk: Imperial Crown (½d to 1/-), Large Anchor (2/6, 5/-, 10/-), Three Imperial Crowns (£1). Perf: 14.

½d blue-green (Jan 1, 1902)	2.00	1.00	0.70
½d yellow-green (Jan 1, 1902)	2.00	1.00	0.70
Wmk inverted	20.00	12.00	12.00
1d scarlet (Jan 1, 1902)	1.75	1.00	0.50
Wmk inverted	7.00	5.00	6.00
1½d purple and green (Jan 1, 1902)	60.00	30.00	10.00
on chalky paper	60.00	30.00	10.00
2d green and red (Mar 25, 1902)	70.00	30.00	10.00
on chalky paper	60.00	28.00	12.00
2½d blue (Jan 1, 1902)	25.00	12.00	3.00
3d purple on yellow (Jan 1, 1902)	70.00	30.00	7.00
on chalky paper	60.00	30.00	10.00
4d green and brown (Jan 1, 1902)	95.00	40.00	18.00
on chalky paper	65.00	30.00	15.00
4d orange (Nov 1, 1909)	32.00	15.00	10.00
5d purple and blue (May 14, 1902)	90.00	40.00	15.00
on chalky paper	85.00	45.00	15.00
Wmk inverted	£5,500	£4,000	£3,000
6d purple (Jan 1, 1902)	60.00	28.00	14.00
on chalky paper	60.00	30.00	14.00
7d grey (May 4, 1910)	10.00	7.00	16.00
9d purple and blue (Jan 1, 1902)	£170	70.00	40.00
on chalky paper	£155	60.00	40.00
10d purple and red (Jul 3, 1902)	£210	60.00	40.00
on chalky paper	£175	55.00	40.00
1/- green and red (Mar 24, 1902)	£165	60.00	20.00
on chalky paper	£165	60.00	24.00
2/6 lilac (Apr 5, 1902)	£450	£200	75.00
on chalky paper	£450	£300	90.00
Wmk inverted	£6,500	£4,000	£2,500
5/- red (Apr 5, 1902)	£700	£280	£120
10/- blue (Apr 5, 1902)	£1,800	£525	£350
£1 green (Jun 16, 1902)	£2,800	£1,200	£600

Booklet panes	Wmk Upright	Inverted
Pane of five ½d with label showing St Andrew's Cross	£500	£500
Pane of six ½d	55.00	90.00
Pane of six 1d	40.00	70.00

■ 1910

Surface-printed by De La Rue. Wmk: Imperial Crown. Perf: 14. Prepared for use but not issued. One example is known used.

2d Tyrian plum	£80,000	-

■ 1911-13

Designs as 1902-10 series.

A) Surface-printed by Harrison. Wmk: Imperial Crown. Perf: 14.

½d yellow-green (May 3, 1911)	3.50	2.00	1.30
Wmk inverted	60.00	40.00	40.00
1d red (May 3, 1911)	10.00	6.00	8.00
Wmk inverted	60.00	40.00	40.00
2½d blue (Jul 10, 1911)	£100	45.00	18.00
Wmk inverted	£1,800	£1,000	£1,000
3d purple (Sep 12, 1911)			
on yellow paper	£140	80.00	£140
4d orange (Jul 13, 1911)	£130	60.00	45.00

Booklet panes	Wmk Upright	Inverted
Pane of five ½d with label showing St Andrew's Cross	£1,100	£1,100
Pane of six ½d	80.00	£110
Pane of six 1d	70.00	90.00

B) Surface-printed by Somerset House. Wmk: Imperial Crown (½d to 1/-), Large Anchor (2/6, 5/-, 10/-), or Three Imperial Crowns (£1). Perf: 14.

1½d purple and green (Jul 13, 1911)	50.00	25.00	12.00
2d green and red (Mar 11, 1912)	46.00	24.00	11.00
5d purple and blue (Aug 7, 1911)	50.00	28.00	11.00
6d purple (Oct 31, 1911)	50.00	26.00	14.00
chalky paper	50.00	28.00	60.00
7d grey (Aug 1, 1912)	20.00	12.00	15.00
9d purple and blue (Jul 24, 1911)	£105	65.00	40.00
10d purple and red (Oct 9, 1911)	£140	75.00	45.00
1/- green and red (Jul 17, 1911)	£115	58.00	25.00
Wmk inverted	£250	£150	-
2/6 purple (Sep 27, 1911)	£450	£190	85.00
5/- red (Feb 29, 1912)	£700	£280	£120
10/- blue (Jan 14, 1912)	£1,800	£600	£400
£1 green (Sep 3, 1911)	£2,800	£1,200	£700

C) Surface-printed by Harrison. Wmk: Imperial Crown. Perf: 15x14.

½d green (Oct 30, 1911)	50.00	30.00	30.00
1d red (Oct 5, 1911)	32.00	16.00	8.50
2½d blue (Oct 14, 1911)	45.00	21.00	7.00
3d purple on yellow (Sep 22, 1911)	55.00	30.00	13.00
4d orange (Nov 22, 1911)	48.00	26.00	10.00

2d Tyrian plum

The best magazine for GB collectors

STAMP MAGAZINE

Jubilee celebrations

KING GEORGE V

For this reign the stamps are priced in three columns: unmounted mint (left), mounted unused (centre) and fine used (right). Stamps are found in a wide range of shades, details of which are beyond the scope of this guide.

½d green

■ 1911-1912

Des: Bertram Mackennal and G.W. Eve. Portrait based on photograph by Downey. Die engraved by J.A.C. Harrison. Printed in typography by Harrison. Perf: 15x14.

A) Wmk: Imperial Crown.

½d green (Jun 22, 1911)	7.50	3.50	2.00
Wmk inverted	15.00	7.50	3.50
1d red (Jun 22, 1911)	6.50	3.00	1.50
Wmk inverted	12.50	7.00	3.00

(* These stamps also exist with Wmk sideways and printed in error with perf: 14.)

Booklet panes	Wmk Upright	Inverted
Pane of six ½d	80.00	£120
Pane of six 1d	75.00	£110

B) Wmk: Simple Royal Cypher. Issued August 1912 in booklets.

½d green	70.00	30.00	28.00
Wmk inverted	70.00	30.00	28.00
1d green	35.00	16.00	18.00
Wmk inverted	35.00	16.00	18.00

Booklet panes	Wmk Upright	Inverted
Pane of six ½d	£500	£500
Pane of six 1d	£250	£240

■ 1912

As above except that the King's hair is lighter on the ½d and the lion is shaded on the 1d.

A) Wmk: Imperial Crown

½d green (Jan 1, 1912)	8.50	4.50	1.00
Wmk inverted	£1,200	£800	£450
1d red (Jan 1, 1912)	5.00	2.00	0.80
Wmk inverted	£450	£350	£250

B) Wmk: Simple Royal Cypher.

½d green (Aug 1912)	8.00	4.00	1.25
Wmk inverted	£225	£140	60.00
1d red (Aug 1912)	7.00	3.50	1.00
Wmk inverted	22.00	14.00	12.00

C) Wmk: Multiple Royal Cypher.

½d green (Oct 1912)	12.00	7.00	9.00
Wmk inverted	15.00	12.00	12.50
Wmk sideways	-	-	£3,250
1d red (Oct 1912)	15.00	9.00	4.50
Wmk inverted	20.00	15.00	16.00
Wmk sideways	£220	£150	£160

1d red

■ 1912-1924

Designed and engraved as before. Printed in typography by Harrison (all values except 6d) and at Somerset House (½d, 1d, 1½d, 2d, 2½d, 3d, 4d, 5d, 6d, 7d, 8d, 9d, 10d, 1/-)

A) Wmk: Simple Royal Cypher.
i) Wmk upright

½d green (Jan 1913)	1.00	0.40	0.40
Wmk inverted	4.00	2.25	1.10
1d red (Oct 1919)	1.00	0.40	0.40
Wmk inverted	4.00	2.25	0.90
1½d brown (Oct 1912)	3.50	2.00	0.80
Wmk inverted	8.00	4.00	1.60
2d orange (Aug 1912)	3.50	1.75	0.60
Wmk inverted	20.00	10.00	8.50
2½d blue (Oct 1912)	16.00	8.00	2.25
Wmk inverted	£110	75.00	75.00
3d violet (Oct 1912)	8.00	3.75	1.00
Wmk inverted	£160	95.00	95.00
4d green (Jan 1913)	16.00	7.00	1.50
Wmk inverted	40.00	25.00	25.00
5d brown (Jun 1913)	20.00	8.00	4.00
Wmk inverted	£1,100	£700	£700
6d purple (Aug 1913)			
chalky paper	18.00	8.00	2.00
Wmk inverted	85.00	50.00	50.00
7d green (Aug 1913)	28.00	11.00	7.50
Wmk inverted	80.00	50.00	50.00
8d black (Aug 1913)			
yellow paper	42.00	20.00	11.00
Wmk inverted	£180	£110	£110
9d black (Jun 1913)	20.00	10.00	3.75
Wmk inverted	£200	£125	£125
9d green (Sep 1922)	£200	75.00	24.00

Wmk inverted	£1,200	£800	£750
10d blue (Aug 1913)	32.00	15.00	18.00
Wmk inverted	£3,500	£2,500	£1,400
1/- brown (Aug 1913)	28.00	13.00	1.80
Wmk inverted	£300	£250	£200

Booklet panes	Wmk Upright	Inverted
Pane of six ½d	35.00	45.00
Pane of six 1d	35.00	45.00
Pane of six 1½d	60.00	75.00
Pane of four 1½d with two advert labels	£750	£750
Pane of six 2d	80.00	£130

B) Wmk: Multiple Royal Cypher.

½d green (Aug 1913)	£160	£100	95.00
Wmk inverted	£500	£350	£350
1d red (Aug 1913)	£350	£225	£180
Wmk inverted	£800	£600	£600

■ 1924-1926

As above, but printed by typography by Waterlow (all values except 6d), Harrison (all values) or Somerset House (1½d, 6d), Wmk: Multiple Crown and block GVR.

½d green (Feb 1924)	0.60	0.30	0.20
Wmk inverted	5.00	2.50	1.00
Wmk sideways	11.00	5.50	4.50
1d red (Feb 1924)	0.85	0.35	0.20
Wmk inverted	5.00	2.50	1.25
Wmk sideways	26.00	15.00	16.00
1½d brown (Feb 1924)	0.90	0.40	0.20
Wmk inverted	2.50	1.25	1.00
Wmk sideways	14.00	7.00	4.50
2d orange (Sept1924)	2.00	0.85	0.70
Wmk inverted	60.00	40.00	40.00
Wmk sideways	£175	60.00	65.00
2½d blue (Oct 1924)	7.50	4.00	1.10
Wmk inverted	125.00	70.00	50.00
3d violet (Oct 1924)	11.00	5.00	1.00
Wmk inverted	125.00	70.00	50.00
4d green (Nov 1924)	18.00	7.00	1.40
Wmk inverted	£200	£110	75.00
5d brown (Nov 1924)	30.00	12.00	2.00
Wmk inverted	£140	95.00	80.00
6d purple (Sep 1924)	3.80	1.50	0.50
chalky paper	15.00	9.00	1.75
ordinary paper, Wmk inverted	£120	70.00	60.00
chalky paper, Wmk inverted	80.00	60.00	40.00
9d green (Dec 1924)	20.00	7.00	2.50
Wmk inverted	£120	75.00	70.00
10d blue (Nov 1923)	65.00	28.00	22.00
Wmk inverted	£3,500	£2,200	£1,600
1/- brown (Oct 1924)	35.00	16.00	1.40
Wmk inverted	£550	£400	£260

Booklet panes	Wmk Upright	Inverted
Pane of six ½d	35.00	45.00
Pane of six 1d	35.00	45.00
Pane of six 1½d	60.00	75.00
Pane of four 1½d with two advert labels	£125	£125
(* A wide range of advertising labels exists)		

1/- brown

■ 1934-1936

As above but printed in photogravure by Harrison. Designs differ in the shading behind the portrait. Wmk: Multiple Crown and block GVR, Perf: 15 x 14.

½d green (Nov 19, 1934)	0.25	0.10	0.15
Wmk inverted	15.00	7.00	3.00
Wmk sideways	9.00	6.00	3.00
1d red (Sep 24, 1934)	0.25	0.20	0.15
Wmk inverted	15.00	7.00	2.50
Wmk sideways	22.00	11.00	14.00
1½d brown (Aug 20, 1934)	0.20	0.15	0.10
Wmk inverted	2.50	1.25	0.60
Wmk sideways	10.00	6.00	2.50
2d orange (Jan 21, 1935)	0.60	0.35	0.40
Wmk sideways	£175	70.00	65.00
2½d blue (Mar 18, 1935)	1.40	0.90	0.75
3d violet (Mar 18, 1935)	1.80	1.00	0.75
4d green (Dec 2, 1935)	2.50	1.40	0.75
5d brown (Feb 17, 1936)	9.00	5.00	2.50
9d deep green (Dec 2, 1935)	16.00	7.00	2.25
10d blue (Feb 24, 1936)	25.00	11.00	9.00
1/- brown (Feb 24, 1936)	32.00	12.00	0.75

Booklet panes	Wmk Upright	Inverted
Pane of six ½d	60.00	£100
Pane of six 1d	60.00	£150
Pane of six 1½d	20.00	25.00
Pane of four 1½d with two advert labels	75.00	75.00

2/6 brown

■ 1913-1934. High values. 'Seahorses'

Des: Bertram Mackennal. Dies engraved by J.A.C. Harrison. Wmk: Simple Royal Cypher. Perf: 11x12

A) Printed in recess by Waterlow. Released in July 1913.

2/6 brown	£500	£175	£100

5/- red	£1,000	£325	£175
10/- blue	£1,900	£700	£300
£1 green	£4,000	£2,250	£110

B) Printed in recess by De La Rue. Released in December 1915.

2/6 brown	£500	£200	£100
5/- red	£900	£280	£190
10/- blue	£3,500	£2,000	£600

C) Printed in recess by Bradbury, Wilkinson. Released in December 1918.

2/6 brown	£225	75.00	32.00
5/- red	£325	£150	45.00
10/- blue	£600	£300	£100

(* To distinguish between the above, note that the De La Rue printings have a yellow gum, while the Waterlow design is about 22mm high and that of Bradbury, Wilkinson 23mm high.)

D) Printed in recess by Waterlow by die re-engraved so that the background to the portrait consists of horizontal and diagonal lines. Released in October 1934.

2/6 brown	£130	60.00	12.00
5/- red	£350	£120	45.00
10/- blue	£500	£300	50.00

1d, 1½d
(inscribed '1924'
and later '1925')

■ 1924-1925. British Empire Exhibition

Des: H. Nelson. Printed in recess by Waterlow. Wmk: Multiple Crown and block GVR. Perf: 14.

Set (1924)	18.00	8.00	8.00
Set (1925)	45.00	30.00	30.00
First day cover (1924)	-	-	£375
First day cover (1925)	-	-	£1,600

£1

■ 1929, May 10. Postal Union Congress

Des: J. Farleigh (½d, 2½d), E. Linzell (1d, 1½d), H. Nelson (£1). Printed in typography by Waterlow (½d to 2½d) or in recess by Bradbury, Wilkinson (£1). Wmk: Multiple Crown and block GRV (½d to 2½d), Large Crown and script GVR (£1). Perf: 15x14 (½d to 2½d), 12 (£1).

½d green	1.50	0.50	0.45
Wmk inverted	20.00	11.00	8.00
Wmk sideways	70.00	25.00	25.00
1d red	2.50	1.50	1.00
Wmk inverted	25.00	13.00	14.00
Wmk sideways	90.00	60.00	60.00
1½d brown	2.00	1.25	0.80
Wmk inverted	12.00	6.00	4.50
Wmk sideways	65.00	20.00	20.00
2½d blue	16.00	7.00	5.00
Wmk inverted	£3,500	£2,000	£900
Set	20.00	9.00	6.75
First day cover	-	-	£450
£1 black	£1,000	£550	£550
First day cover	-	-	£8,500

Booklet panes		Wmk Upright	Inverted
Pane of six ½d		40.00	£120
Pane of six 1d		45.00	£200
Pane of six 1½d		30.00	90.00
Pane of four 1½d with two advert labels		£250	£280

2½d

■ 1935, May 7. Silver Jubilee

Des: B. Freedman. Printed in photogravure by Harrison. Wmk: Multiple Crown and block GVR. Perf: 15x14

½d green	0.80	0.40	0.30
Wmk inverted	11.00	6.00	6.00
1d red	1.40	0.70	0.70
Wmk inverted	11.00	6.00	6.00
1½d brown	1.25	0.50	0.40
Wmk inverted	2.00	1.00	0.90
2½d blue	3.00	2.00	4.00
2½d Prussian blue	£16,000	£13,000	£14,000
Set (excluding Prussian blue)	6.00	3.25	4.75
First day cover	-	-	80.00
Pictorial cover	-	-	£800

Booklet panes		Wmk Upright	Inverted
Pane of four ½d		30.00	60.00
Pane of four 1d		30.00	60.00
Pane of four 1½d		15.00	20.00

Selling Your Stamps?

Because 95% of the stamps we sell are sold to collectors - we can afford to pay that bit more than other dealers........and with 4 different selling systems from Mixtures to Approvals to Auction.........

......WE BUY EVERYTHING!

Please contact our head buyer Andrew McGavin on 01451 861111
email: info@upastampauctions.co.uk

or Write to us at:
Universal Philatelic Auctions, 4 The Old Coalyard, West End, Northleach, Glos, GL54 3HE. Tel: 01451 861111
(Please make sure to include your telephone number).

TO SEE WHAT WE SELL...

...Request your catalogue now...

If you collect GB, British Empire, Foreign or Thematics, you need these 3 real price auction catalogues worth £10.00 each - posted to you each quarter. OVER 40,000 LOTS Real Price Guide.

PLEASE MAIL ME YOUR FIRST FREE AUCTION CATALOGUE – WORTH £10.00
NAME..
ADDRESS...
....
Tel:.. Postcode................................... **BSMV**
Post to: Universal Philatelic Auctions, 4 The Old Coalyard, West End, Northleach, Glos. GL54 3HE

For **FREE** 'Stamp Tips of The Trade'
visit our website...

www.upastampauctions.co.uk

We put Real Value on
Providing Excellent Service

We take pride in our
unrivalled reputation
for providing insurance
broking and risk management
solutions to collectors and
dealers of Coins and Medals.

We have a wide
range of
flexible insurance
plans available
and one of them is
sure to provide the
coverage that you
need.

H.W. Wood Limited
Building 18, Gateway 1000,
Arlington Business Park,
Stevenage, Hertfordshire
SG1 2FP
Telephone: **01438 742033**
Email: **collectibles@hwint.com**

www.hwint.com
H.W. Wood Limited is authorised and regulated by the
Financial Services Authority
CMA 2011

PRINZ PUBLICATIONS (UK) LTD
UNIT 3A HAYLE IND. PARK, HAYLE,
CORNWALL, TR27 5JR
Telephone: 01736 751910
Email: info@prinz.co.uk

STAMP ALBUMS & ACCESSORIES

**World-wide
mail order
service
Shop online at
www.prinz.co.uk**

PRESENTATION PACKS

British Presentation Packs • Commemorative
Definitive • Regional • POM • Year Packs and Books
German and Japanese Language Packs
PHQ Cards • Miniature (Mini) Sheets

FREE 32 PAGE COLOUR LIST

Oaklands House (BSM), Reading Road North, Fleet
Hampshire, GU51 4AB, UK
Email: info@packsandcards.com
Tel: 01252 360530 Fax: 01252 620519

 PACKS & CARDS

www.PacksAndCards.com

KING EDWARD VIII

For this reign stamps are priced in two columns: unmounted mint (left) and fine used (right). The exception is booklet panes, which are priced only for unmounted mint with good perforations.

½d green

■ 1936. Accession

Des: H. Brown, adapted by Harrison. Portrait by H. Cecil. Printed in photogravure by Harrison. Wmk: Multiple Crown and E8R. Perf: 15x14.

½d green (September, 1, 1936)	0.10	0.10
Wmk inverted	6.00	2.50
1d red (September 14, 1936)	0.20	0.20
Wmk inverted	5.00	2.25
1½d brown (September 1, 1936)	0.20	0.10
Wmk inverted	0.75	0.80
2½d blue (September 1, 1936)	0.20	0.30
Set	0.50	0.50

Booklet panes	Wmk Upright	Inverted
Pane of six ½d	15.00	42.00
Pane of six 1d	15.00	42.00
Pane of two 1½d	10.00	10.00
Pane of four 1½d with two advert labels	55.00	55.00
Pane of six 1½d	8.00	14.00

G **B**

Classic Great Britain

RETAIL LISTS & POSTAL AUCTIONS PRODUCED MONTHLY
CATALOGUE SENT FREE ON REQUEST
1000's OF ITEMS TO VIEW AND BUY ON OUR WEBSITE

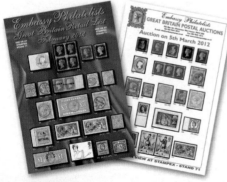

Rare GB bought and sold daily

• REGULAR RETAIL LISTS SENT FREE.
• POSTAL AUCTIONS 3 TIMES A YEAT.
• BASIC ITEMS - MAJOR RARITIES HANDLED ALL THE TIME, LET US KNOW WHAT YOU ARE AFTER

PTS *Embassy Philatelists* **Est. 30 Years**

P.O. BOX 161, CHICHESTER, W.SUSSEX PO19 3SU
Tel: 02392 412 512   *Fax:* 02392 512513
Email: info@embassystamps.co.uk
www.embassystamps.co.uk

BUYING

From single items to major collections, for a fast professional transaction call us today.

Fine Stamps and Postal History

Visit our website to view hundreds of fine GB items:
www.andrewglajer.co.uk

Full colour brochure sent free upon request

Andrew G Lajer Ltd
sales@andrewglajer.co.uk / T: 01189 344151
The Old Post Office, Davis Way,Hurst, Berkshire, RG10 0TR

KING GEORGE VI

For this reign, prices are priced in two columns: unmounted mint (left) and fine used (right). The exception is booklet panes, which are priced only for unmounted mint with good perforations.

1½d

■ 1937, May 13. Coronation
Des: E. Dulac. Printed in photogravure by Harrison. Wmk: Multiple Crown and GVIR. Perf: 15x14

1½d	0.25	0.15
First day cover		3.00
Pictorial cover		20.00

½d, 1d, 1½d, 2d, 2½d, 3d

4d, 5d, 6d

7d, 8d, 9d, 10d, 11d, 1/-

■ 1937-47. Definitives
Des: E. Dulac and E. Gill (½d to 6d), E. Dulac (7d to 1/-). Printed in photogravure by Harrison. Wmk: Multiple Crown and GVIR. Perf: 15x14

A) Original colours

½d green (May 10, 1937)	0.15	0.10
Wmk inverted	7.00	0.50
Wmk sideways	0.25	0.30
1d red (May10, 1937)	0.15	0.10
Wmk inverted	30.00	2.50
Wmk sideways	15.00	5.00
1½d red-brown (July 30, 1937)	0.15	0.15
Wmk inverted	9.00	1.00
Wmk sideways	1.00	0.50
2d orange (January 31, 1938)	0.50	0.35
Wmk inverted	36.00	2.50
Wmk sideways	36.00	20.00
2½d blue (May 10, 1937)	0.25	1.00
Wmk inverted	32.00	3.00
Wmk sideways	50.00	25.00
3d violet (January 31, 1938)	1.50	0.60
4d green (November 21, 1938)	1.75	0.20
5d brown (November 21, 1938)	2.00	0.30
6d purple (January 30, 1939)	1.00	0.15
7d emerald (February 27, 1939)	3.50	0.50
8d carmine (February 27, 1939)	5.00	0.50
9d deep green (May 1, 1939)	4.00	0.50
10d blue (May 1, 1939)	3.00	0.50
11d brown-purple (December 29, 1947)	1.75	1.00
1/- brown (May 1, 1939)	4.00	0.15
Set	24.00	4.00

Booklet panes	Wmk Upright	Inverted
Pane of two **½d**	10.00	10.00
Pane of six **½d**	15.00	25.00
Pane of two **1d**	10.00	50.00
Pane of six **1d**	15.00	£150
Pane of two **1½d**	5.00	10.00
Pane of four **1½d** with two advert labels (*)	£110	£110
Pane of six **1½d**	20.00	25.00
Pane of six **2d**	50.00	£200
Pane of six **2½d**	50.00	£195
		Wmk Sideways
Pane of four **½d**		45.00
Pane of four **1d**		70.00

(* 15 different combinations of advertising labels exist. Prices quoted are for the cheapest; scarcer panes can fetch up to twice as much)

B) As above, but with paler colours

½d pale green (September 1, 1941)	0.15	0.10
Wmk inverted	3.00	0.40
1d pale red (August 11, 1941)	0.20	0.10
Wmk sideways	3.00	3.00
1½d pale red-brown (September 28, 1942)	0.50	0.35
2d pale orange (October 6, 1941)	0.50	0.25
Wmk inverted	3.00	0.40
Wmk sideways	10.00	8.00
2½d pale blue (July 21, 1941)	0.15	0.10

Wmk inverted	1.00	0.50
Wmk sideways	7.00	6.00
3d pale violet (November 3, 1941)	1.00	0.25
Set	1.50	1.00

Booklet panes	Wmk Upright	Inverted
Pane of two ½**d**	9.00	-
Pane of six ½**d**	10.00	25.00
Pane of two **1d**	9.00	-
Pane of two **1½d**	9.00	-
Pane of six **2d**	7.50	30.00
Pane of six **2½d** pale blue	4.00	15.00

C) As above, but with colours changed

½**d** orange (May 3, 1951)	0.10	0.20
Wmk inverted	0.20	0.30
1d blue (May 3, 1951)	0.10	0.10
Wmk inverted	2.25	1.00
Wmk sideways	0.20	0.40
1½d green (May 3, 1951)	0.25	0.20
Wmk inverted	2.75	2.00
Wmk sideways	1.25	1.50
2d red-brown (May 3, 1951)	0.25	0.25
Wmk inverted	4.00	3.50
Wmk sideways	0.75	0.75
2½d red (May 3, 1951)	0.15	0.15
Wmk inverted	1.00	0.50
Wmk sideways	0.60	0.85
4d blue (October 2, 1950)	1.00	0.65
Set	1.50	1.10

Booklet panes	Wmk Upright	Inverted
Pane of two ½**d**	9.00	-
Pane of four ½**d**	7.00	9.00
Pane of six ½**d**	5.00	6.00
Pane of two **1d**	9.00	-
Pane of three **1d** with three labels reading 'MINIMUM INLAND PRINTED PAPER RATE 1½d'	25.00	25.00
Pane of three **1d** with three labels reading 'SHORTHAND IN ONE WEEK'	35.00	35.00
Pane of four **1d**	6.00	7.00
Pane of six **1d**	5.00	20.00
Pane of two **1½d**	5.00	-
Pane of four **1½d**	6.00	14.00
Pane of six **1½d**	8.50	22.00
Pane of six **2d**	17.00	60.00
Pane of six **2½d**	3.50	6.50

2/6, 5/-

10/-, £1

■ 1939-1948. High Values

Des: E. Dulac (2/6, 5/-), G. R. Bellew (10/-, £1). Printed in recess by Waterlow. Wmk: Single Crown and GVIR. Perf: 14

2/6 brown (September 4, 1939)	70.00	5.00
2/6 green (March 9, 1942)	9.00	0.50
5/- red (August 21, 1939)	18.00	1.25
10/- dark blue (October 30, 1939)	£220	17.00
10/- ultramarine (November 30, 1942)	30.00	3.50
£1 brown (October 1, 1948)	18.00	12.00
Set	£280	40.00

½d green, 1d red, 1½d brown, 2d orange, 2½d blue, 3d violet

■ 1940, May 6. Centenary of the First Adhesive Postage Stamps

Des: H. L. Palmer. Printed in photogravure by Harrison. Wmk: Multiple Crown and GVIR. Perf: 14½ x 14

Set	4.00	3.50
First day cover		7.50
Pictorial cover		35.00

Farming, homes, industry, transport (2½d)
Dove of peace (3d)

■ 1946, June 11. Victory

Des: H. L. Palmer (2½d), Reynolds Stone (3d). Printed in photogravure by Harrison. Wmk: Multiple Crown and GVIR. Perf: 15x14

Set	0.20	0.25
First day cover		9.00
Pictorial cover		45.00

2½d

£1

1948, April 26. Royal Silver Wedding

Des: G.T. Knipe and Joan Hassall (from photographs by Dorothy Wilding Studios). Printed in photogravure by Harrison. Wmk: Multiple Crown and GVIR. Perf: 15x14 (2½d), 14 x 15 (£1).

Set	27.00	25.00
First day cover		50.00
Pictorial cover		£400

1948, May 10. Liberation of the Channel Islands

Although this set was placed on sale at eight post offices in Great Britain, it is listed under Regional Issues

Globe surrounded by a Laurel Wreath (2½d)
Globe with Olympic Rings (3d)
Olympic Rings (6d)
Victory and Olympic Rings (1/-)

1948, July 29. Olympic Games

Des: P. Metcalfe, A. Games, S. Scott and E. Dulac. Printed in photogravure by Harrison. Wmk: Multiple Crown and GVIR. Perf: 15x14

Set	7.00	1.20
First day cover		8.00
Pictorial cover		35.00

Two Hemispheres (2½d)
UPU Monument (3d)
Globe and Compass (6d)
Globe and Posthorn (1/-)

1949, October 10. 75th Anniversary of the Universal Postal Union

Des: Mary Adshed (2½d), P. Metcalfe (3d). H. Fleury (6d), G. R. Bellew (1/-). Printed in photogravure by Harrison. Wmk: Multiple Crown and GVIR. Perf: 15x14.

Set	1.50	1.25
First day cover		9.50
Pictorial cover		47.00

H.M.S. Victory (2/6)
White Cliffs of Dover (5/-)
St. George and the Dragon (10/-)
Royal Coat of Arms (£1)

1951, May 3. High Values

Des: Mary Adshead (2/6, 5/-), P. Metcalfe (10/-, £1). Printed in recess by Waterlow. Wmk: Single Crown and GVIR. Perf: 11x12.

Set	65.00	15.00

2½d red,
4d blue

1951, May 3. Festival of Britain

Des: E. Dulac (2½d), A. Games (4d). Printed in photogravure by Harrison. Wmk: Multiple Crown and GVIR. Perf: 15x14.

Set	0.35	0.40
First day cover		3.00
Pictorial cover		17.00

QUEEN ELIZABETH II PRE-DECIMALS

In this section, prices are priced in two columns: **unmounted mint (left) and fine used (right). The exception is booklet panes, which are priced only for unmounted mint with good perforations.**

Except where otherwise stated, all the stamps have the same technical details: **Printed in photogravure by Harrison. Perf: 15x14 (definitives), 15x14 (special issues with a horizontal design) or 14x15 (special issues with a vertical design).**

½d, 1d, 1½d, 2d

2½d, 3d

4d, 4½d

5d, 6d, 7d

8d, 9d, 10d, 11d

1/-, 1/6

1/3

■ 1952-1967. Wilding definitives

Des: Miss E. Marx (½d, 1d, 1½d, 2d). M.C. Farrar-Bell (2½d, 3d, 4d, 4½d), G. Knipe (5d, 6d, 7d), Miss M. Adshead (8d, 9d, 10d, 11d), E. Dulac (1/-, 1/3, 1/6): portrait by Dorothy Wilding Studios.
On the 2½d value the top line of the diadem was initially broken (Type I), but this was later corrected (Type II).

A) Wmk: Multiple Tudor Crown and E2R.

½d orange (August 31, 1953)	0.10	0.10
Wmk inverted	0.15	0.40
1d blue (August 31, 1953)	0.15	0.10
Wmk inverted	4.50	2.50
1½d green (December 5, 1952)	0.10	0.10
Wmk inverted	0.35	0.30
Wmk sideways	0.35	0.30
2d deep brown (August 31, 1953)	0.20	0.15
Wmk inverted	20.00	12.00
Wmk sideways	0.75	0.50
2½d carmine (type 1) (December 5, 1952)	0.15	0.10
Wmk inverted (type 2)	0.40	0.30
Wmk sideways (type 1)	3.50	4.00
3d violet (January 18, 1954)	1.00	0.20
4d blue (November 2, 1953)	1.00	0.70
5d brown (July 6, 1953)	4.00	2.50
6d purple (January 18, 1954)	3.00	0.75
7d pale green (January 18, 1954)	8.00	2.00
8d magenta (July 6, 1953)	5.00	0.75
9d myrtle-green (February 8, 1954)	14.00	1.50
10d blue (February 8, 1954)	12.00	1.50
11d brown-red (February 8, 1954)	30.00	10.00
1/- bistre (July 6, 1953)	1.00	0.50
1/3 deep green (November 2, 1953)	3.00	1.50
1/6 grey-blue (November 2, 1953)	12.00	1.25
Set	70.00	20.00
Wmk inverted	18.00	14.00
Wmk sideways	4.50	4.50
First day cover		£140
Pictorial cover		£600

Booklet panes	*Wmk Upright*	*Inverted*
Pane of two ½d	2.00	-
Pane of four ½d	4.00	4.00
Pane of six ½d	2.00	4.00
Pane of two **1d**	2.00	-
Pane of four **1d**	3.00	25.00
Pane of three **1d** with three labels reading: MINIMUM INLAND PRINTED PAPER RATE **1½d**	£300	£300
Pane of three **1d** with three labels reading: PLEASE POST EARLY IN THE DAY	40.00	40.00
Pane of three **1d** with three labels reading: PACK YOUR PARCELS SECURELY/ ADDRESS YOUR LETTERS CORRECTLY/ POST EARLY IN THE DAY	40.00	40.00
Pane of six **1d**	8.00	30.00
Pane of two **1½d**	2.00	-
Pane of four **1½d**	4.00	4.00
Pane of six **1½d**	2.00	4.00
Pane of six **2d**	27.00	£160
Pane of six **2½d**	3.50	3.50

B) As before but Wmk: St. Edward's Crown and E2R.

½d orange (August 1955)	0.15	0.10
Wmk inverted	0.20	0.20
1d blue (September 19, 1955)	0.20	0.10
Wmk inverted	0.50	0.50

1½d green (August 1955)	0.15	0.10
Wmk inverted	0.30	0.20
Wmk sideways	0.20	0.25
2d deep brown (September 6, 1955)	0.25	0.30
Wmk inverted	7.00	5.00
Wmk sideways	0.50	0.50
2d brown (October 17, 1956)	0.25	0.10
Wmk inverted	5.00	4.00
Wmk sideways	5.00	3.00
2½d carmine (type 1) (September 28, 1955)	0.25	0.15
Wmk inverted	0.75	1.00
Wmk sideways	0.75	1.00
2½d carmine (type 2) (September 1955)	0.30	0.60
Wmk inverted	0.30	0.30
3d violet (July 17, 1956)	0.25	0.20
Wmk inverted	1.75	1.50
Wmk sideways	12.00	7.50
4d blue (November 14, 1955)	1.50	2.00
5d brown (September 21, 1955)	5.00	3.00
6d purple (December 20, 1955)	3.50	1.00
6d deep purple (May 8, 1958)	3.00	1.00
7d pale green (April 23, 1956)	30.00	7.00
8d magenta (December 21, 1955)	4.00	1.25
9d myrtle-green (December 15, 1955)	12.00	2.00
10d blue (September 22, 1955)	10.00	2.00
11d brown-red (October 28, 1955)	0.50	1.25
1/- bistre (November 3, 1955)	6.50	0.50
1/3 deep green (March 27, 1956)	14.00	1.00
1/6 grey-blue (March 27, 1956)	20.00	0.75
Set	100.00	25.00
Wmk inverted	14.00	7.00
Wmk sideways	14.00	9.00

Booklet panes	*Wmk Upright*	*Inverted*
Pane of two ½d	3.00	-
Pane of four ½d	4.00	4.00
Pane of six ½d	2.00	3.50
Pane of two 1d	3.50	-
Pane of three 1d with three labels reading:		
PACK YOUR PARCELS SECURELY/		
ADDRESS YOUR LETTERS CORRECTLY/		
POST EARLY IN THE DAY	30.00	35.00
Pane of four 1d	4.00	4.00
Pane of six 1d	2.50	3.00
Pane of two 1½d	3.50	-
Pane of four 1½d	4.00	4.00
Pane of six 1½d	2.00	2.00
Pane of six 2d deep brown	13.00	65.00
Pane of six 2d brown	8.00	22.50
Pane of six 2½d	3.00	3.00
Pane of four 3d	10.00	15.00
Pane of six 3d	6.00	20.00

C) As before but Wmk: Multiple St. Edward's Crown.

½d orange (November 25, 1958)	0.10	0.10
chalky paper (July 15, 1963)	2.00	2.50
Wmk inverted	0.30	0.10
chalky paper and Wmk inverted	1.50	2.00
Wmk sideways	0.25	0.15

1d blue (November 1958)	0.10	0.10
Wmk inverted	0.20	0.20
Wmk sideways	0.60	0.35
1½d green (December 1958)	0.15	0.15
Wmk inverted	1.00	0.40
Wmk sideways	4.50	3.50
2d brown (December 4, 1958)	0.10	0.10
Wmk inverted	75.00	40.00
Wmk sideways	0.50	0.40
2½d carmine (type 1) (October 4, 1961)	0.10	0.40
Wmk sideways	0.20	0.25
2½d carmine (type 2) (November 1958)	0.35	0.20
chalky paper (July 15, 1963)	0.30	0.25
Wmk inverted	3.50	0.90
chalky paper & Wmk inverted	0.30	0.25
Wmk sideways	0.40	0.50
3d violet (November 1958)	0.15	0.10
Wmk inverted	0.25	0.20
Wmk sideways	0.25	0.15
4d blue (October 29, 1958)	0.50	0.25
4d deep blue (April 28, 1965)	0.20	0.12
Wmk inverted	0.35	0.20
Wmk sideways	0.35	0.15
4½d red-brown (February 9, 1959)	0.12	0.12
5d brown (November 10, 1958)	0.20	0.10
6d deep purple (December 23, 1958)	0.25	0.10
7d pale green (November 26, 1958)	0.50	0.20
8d magenta (February 24, 1960)	0.35	0.10
9d myrtle-green (March 24, 1959)	0.35	0.20
10d blue (November 18, 1958)	0.75	0.25
1/- bistre (October 30, 1958)	0.35	0.25
1/3 deep green (June 17, 1959)	0.35	0.15
1/6 grey-blue (December 16, 1958)	3.00	0.15
Set	5.00	1.50
Wmk inverted	80.00	42.00
Wmk sideways	5.50	4.00

Booklet panes	*Wmk Upright*	*Inverted*
Pane of three ½d and one 2½d (chalky paper)	8.00	8.00
Pane of four ½d	2.50	2.50
Pane of six ½d	1.25	2.00
Pane of four 1d	2.50	2.50
Pane of six 1d	1.50	2.50
Pane of four 1½d	2.50	2.50
Pane of six 1½d	5.00	6.00
Pane of six 2d	40.00	£500
Pane of four 2½d (chalky paper)	1.00	1.00
Pane of six 2½d	3.00	15.00
Pane of four 3d	2.00	2.00
Pane of six 3d	1.50	1.50
Pane of six 4d deep blue	1.50	1.50

	Wmk Sideways
Pane of two ½d se-tenant with two 2½d (type 2)	1.00
Pane of four ½d	2.00
Pane of two 1d se-tenant with two 3d to left	5.00
Pane of two 1d se-tenant with two 3d to right	5.00
Pane of four 1d	3.00
Pane of four 1½d	25.00
Pane of four 3d	2.00
Pane of four 4d	2.00

■ Graphite-lined issue

Designs as above, but with black graphite lines on the back. All values have two vertical lines, except for the 2d which has just one line, on the right as viewed from the back.

A) Wmk: St. Edward's Crown and E2R upright. Released on November 19, 1957.

½d orange	0.20	0.20
1d blue	0.20	0.20
1½d green	1.25	0.50
2d brown	1.00	1.25
2½d carmine (type 2)	4.50	3.50
3d violet	0.75	0.50
Set	6.75	5.50
First day cover		75.00

B) Wmk: Multiple St. Edward's Crown.

½d orange (June 15, 1959)	5.00	5.00
Wmk inverted	1.00	1.25
1d blue (December 18, 1958)	1.00	1.00
Wmk inverted	1.00	0.75
1½d green (August 4, 1959)	60.00	50.00
Wmk inverted	20.00	20.00
2d brown (December 4, 1958)	4.75	2.50
2½d carmine (type 2) (June 9, 1959)	6.00	6.00
Wmk inverted	35.00	30.00
3d violet (November 24, 1958)	0.60	0.45
Wmk inverted	0.55	0.40
4d blue (April 29, 1959)	3.25	3.25
4½d red-brown (June 3, 1959)	3.50	2.25
Set	70.00	55.00
Wmk inverted	60.00	50.00

Booklet panes	Wmk Upright	Inverted
Pane of six ½d	20.00	12.00
Pane of six 1d	7.50	7.00
Pane of six 1½d	£500	£125
Pane of six 2½d	30.00	£300
Pane of six 3d	4.00	4.00

■ Phosphor-graphite issue

Designs as above, but with phosphor bands on the front in addition to the graphite lines on the back. All values have two bands, except for the 2d which has just one band to the left.

A) Wmk: St. Edward's Crown and E2R upright. Released on November 18, 1959.

½d orange	3.00	3.00
1d blue	9.00	9.00
1½d green	2.50	3.00
2d brown	95.00	90.00

B) Wmk: Multiple St. Edwards Crown.

2d brown	4.00	3.00
2½d carmine (type 2)	10.00	10.00
3d violet	14.00	7.50
4d blue	8.00	5.00
4½d red-brown	25.00	20.00
Set	50.00	40.00
First day cover		75.00

■ Phosphor issue

Designs as above, but without graphite lines. All values have two phosphor bands on the front, except where stated. Released on June 22, 1960 except where stated. Wmk: Multiple St. Edward's Crown.

½d orange	0.15	0.15
Wmk inverted	1.00	1.00
Wmk sideways	5.00	7.50
1d blue	0.10	0.10
Wmk inverted	0.35	0.30
Wmk sideways	0.40	0.50
1½d green	0.12	0.20
Wmk inverted	11.00	9.00
Wmk sideways	10.00	7.50
2d brown (one band)	14.00	12.00
2d brown (October 4, 1961)	0.20	0.10
Wmk sideways	0.30	0.25
2½d carmine (type 2)	0.20	0.20
Wmk inverted	£160	£140
2½d carmine (type 2, one band)	1.50	0.50
Wmk inverted	35.00	30.00
2½d carmine (type 1, one band)	40.00	35.00
3d violet	0.50	0.35
Wmk inverted	0.80	0.50
Wmk sideways	1.25	0.55
3d violet (April 29, 1965) (one band at left)	0.30	0.40
Wmk inverted	60.00	60.00
Wmk sideways	4.00	4.00
3d violet (one band at right)	0.30	0.40
Wmk inverted	6.00	6.50
Wmk sideways	4.00	4.00
Se-tenant pair	0.60	1.50
Se-tenant pair with Wmk inverted	65.00	65.00
Se-tenant pair with Wmk sideways	8.00	10.00
3d violet (December 8, 1966) (one band)	0.25	0.25
Wmk inverted	3.00	3.50
Wmk sideways	0.40	0.50
4d blue	2.75	3.25
4d deep blue (April 28, 1965)	0.15	0.25
Wmk inverted	0.25	0.20
Wmk sideways	0.35	0.25
4½d red-brown (September 13, 1961)	0.15	0.25
5d brown (June 9, 1967)	0.20	0.25
6d deep purple (June 27, 1960)	0.20	-
7d pale green (February 15, 1967)	0.20	0.25
8d magenta (June 28, 1967)	0.20	0.25
9d myrtle green (December 29, 1966)	0.50	0.25
10d blue (December 30, 1966)	0.50	0.40
1/- bistre (June 28, 1967)	0.40	0.20
1/3 deep green	1.00	1.00
1/6 grey-blue (December 12, 1966)	2.00	2.00

Set (one of each value)		4.50	5.00
Wmk inverted		£180	£170
Wmk sideways		15.00	18.00

Booklet panes	Wmk Upright	Inverted
Pane of six ½d	3.00	4.00
Pane of six 1d	2.00	2.00
Pane of six 1½d	8.00	30.00
Pane of six 2½d (type 2, two bands)	80.00	£1,100
Pane of six 2½d (type 2, one band)	22.00	£140
Pane of six 3d (two bands)	5.00	5.00
Pane of six 3d (one band at left or right)	20.00	90.00
Pane of six 3d (one centre band)	4.00	15.00
Pane of six 4d	2.00	3.00

	Wmk sideways
Pane of four ½d	35.00
Pane of two 1d se-tenant with two 3d (two bands)	3.00
Pane of two 1d se-tenant with two 3d (one band, left)	11.00
Pane of two 1d se-tenant with two 3d (one band, right)	11.00
Pane of four 1d	5.00
Pane of four 1½d	35.00
Pane of four 3d (two bands)	5.00
Pane of four 4d	1.00

Crowns and orb (2½d)
Rose, daffodil, thistle and shamrock (4d)
Coronation robe (1/3)
Crowns and cipher (1/6)

■ 1953, June 3. Coronation
Des: E.G. Fuller (2½d), M. Goaman (4d), E. Dulac (1/3), M.C.
Farrar-Bell (1/6). Wmk: Multiple Tudor Crown E2R.

Set	10.00	4.25
First day cover		32.00

(*The 1/3 design was reissued with a face value of £1 in
2000 and 2003.)

Carrickfergus Castle (2/6)
Caernarvon Castle (5/-)
Edinburgh Castle (10/-)
Windsor Castle (£1)

■ 1955-1968. Castle high value definitives
Des: L. Lamb. Printed in recess. Perf: 11x12.

A) Wmk: St. Edward's Crown and E2R upright.
i) Printed by Waterlow.

2/6 brown (September 23, 1955)	14.00	2.00
5/- carmine (September 23, 1955)	30.00	3.00
10/- blue (September 1, 1955)	60.00	10.00
£1 black (September 1, 1955)	85.00	20.00
Set	£160	30.00
First day cover		£300
Pictorial cover		£850

ii) Printed by De La Rue.

2/6 (July 17, 1958)	25.00	3.50
5/- (April 30, 1958)	50.00	8.00
10/- (April 25, 1958)	£150	14.00
£1 (April 28, 1958)	£200	30.00
Set	£425	47.00

(*The top perforation tooth of each side of stamps from the
De La Rue printing is narrower than on the Waterlow printing.)

B) Wmk: St. Edward's Crown and E2R upright.
i) Printed by De La Rue.

2/6 (July 22, 1959)	12.00	0.50
5/- (June 15, 1959)	50.00	1.00
10/- (July 21, 1959)	40.00	2.75
£1 (June 23, 1959)	80.00	12.00
Set	£150	15.00

ii) Printed by Bradbury, Wilkinson.

2/6 (July 1, 1963)	0.50	0.15
5/- (September 3, 1963)	2.00	0.40
10/- (October 16, 1963)	3.50	2.50
£1 (November 14, 1963)	9.50	3.00
Set	13.50	7.00

iii) Printed by Bradbury, Wilkinson on chalky paper.

2/6 (May 30, 1968)	0.50	0.75

(*The Queen's diadem is more detailed on the Bradbury,
Wilkinson printing than on the De La Rue printing.)

C) No Wmk. Printed by Bradbury, Wilkinson.

2/6 (July 1, 1968)	0.30	0.40
5/- (April 10, 1968)	1.50	0.75
10/- (April 10, 1968)	6.00	4.00
£1 (December 4, 1967)	7.00	4.50
Set	10.50	10.50

Scout Badge (2½d)
Flying Birds (4d)
Globe within compass (1/3)

■ 1957, August 1. World Scout Jubilee Jamboree
Des: Mary Adshead (2½d), Pat Keely (4d), W. H. Brown (1/3).
Wmk: St Edward's Crown and E2R.

Set	3.75	3.25
First day cover		23.00

(*These stamps were issued in coils as well as normal sheets.)

4d

■ 1957, September 12. Inter-Parliamentary Union Conference
Des: F. Langfield. Wmk: Multiple St. Edward's Crown and E2R.

4d	0.50	0.50
First day cover		82.00

Welsh Dragon (3d)
Games emblem (6d)
Welsh Dragon (1/3)

■ 1958, July 18. British Empire & Commonwealth Games
Des: Reynolds Stone (3d), W.H. Brown (6d), Pat Keely (1/3). Wmk: Multiple St. Edward's Crown and E2R.

Set	1.25	1.25
First day cover		60.00

1660 Postboy (3d)
1660 Posthorn (1/3)

■ 1960, July 7. Anniversary of General Letter Office
Des: Reynolds Stone (3d), Faith Jaques (1/3). Wmk: Multiple St. Edward's Crown.

Set	2.00	1.75
First day cover		32.00

Europa emblem (6d, 1/6)

■ 1960, September 19. Europa (First Anniversary)
Des: P. Rahikainen and Reynolds Stone. Wmk: Multiple St. Edward's Crown.

Set	6.50	3.75
First day cover		28.00

Thrift plant (2½d)
Squirrel and stylised tree (3d)
Thrift plant (1/6)

■ 1961, August 28. Post Office Savings Bank Centenary
Des: P. Gauld (2½d), M. Goaman (3d, 1/6). Wmk: Multiple St. Edward's Crown.
A) Printed on a Timson machine.

Set	1.25	1.25
First day cover		38.00

B) Printed on a Thrissell machine: 2½d, 3d only

Pair	1.50	1.50

(* The portrait on the 2½d is greyer from the Thrissell machine, and that on the 3d is much clearer on the Timson printing.)

CEPT emblem (2d)
Doves and emblem (4d)
Doves and emblem (10d)

■ 1961, September 18. CEPT Conference
Des: M. Goaman and T. Kurperschoek. Wmk: Multiple St. Edward's Crown.

Set	0.25	0.25
First day cover		4.00

Roof of Westminster Hall (6d)
Palace of Westminster (1/3)

■ 1961, September 23. Commonwealth Parliamentary Conference
Des: Faith Jaques. Wmk: Multiple St. Edward's Crown.

Set	1.25	1.25
First day cover		20.00

Boxes bearing arrows (2½d)
Arrows over the British Isles (3d)
Joining arrows (1/3)

■ 1962, November 14. National Productivity Year
Des: D. Gentleman. Wmk: Multiple St. Edward's Crown, inverted on 2½d and 3d values.
A) Non-phosphor issue.

Set	1.25	1.00
First day cover		25.00

B) Phosphor issue (one band on 2½d, three bands on 3d, 1/3).

Set	14.00	12.50
First day cover		95.00

Ears of Wheat (2½d)
Three Children (1/3)

■ 1963, March 21. Freedom From Hunger
Des: M. Goaman. Wmk: Multiple St. Edward's Crown, inverted on both values.
A) Non-phosphor issue.

Set	1.25	1.25
First day cover		20.00

B) Phosphor issue (one band on 2½d, three bands on 1/3).

Set	14.00	12.25
First day cover		32.00

1863 Paris Postal Conference Centenary (6d)

■ 1963, May 7. Paris Postal Conference Centenary
Des: Reynolds Stone. Wmk: Multiple St. Edward's Crown, inverted.
A) Non-phosphor issue.

6d	0.20	0.25
First day cover		10.00

B) Phosphor issue (three bands).

6d	3.75	3.75
First day cover		30.00

Bee on flowers (3d)
Selection of wildlife (4½d)

■ 1963, May 16. National Nature Week
Des: S. Scott (3d), M. Goaman (4½d). Wmk: Multiple St. Edward's Crown.
A) Non-phosphor issue.

Set	0.15	0.20
First day cover		14.00

B) Phosphor issue (three bands).

Set	1.75	1.75
First day cover		32.00

Helicopter over boat (2½d)
Lifeboat (4d)
Lifeboatmen (1/6)

■ 1963, May 31. International Lifeboat Conference
Des: D. Gentlemen. Wmk: Multiple St. Edward's Crown.
A) Non-phosphor issue.

Set	1.75	1.75
First day cover		20.00

B) Phosphor issue (one band on 2½d, three bands on 4d, 1/6).

Set	25.00	15.00
First day cover		36.00

Red Cross (3d, 1/3, 1/6 with different borders)

■ 1963, August 15. Red Cross Centenary Congress
Des: H. Bartram. Wmk: Multiple St. Edward's Crown.
A) Non-phosphor issue.

Set	3.00	3.00
First day cover		22.00

B) Phosphor issue (three bands).

Set	35.00	26.00
First day cover		60.00

Cable over globe (1/6)

■ 1963, December 3. Opening of Compac Cable
Des: P. Gauld. Wmk: Multiple St. Edward's Crown.
A) Non-phosphor issue.

1/6	1.50	1.25
First day cover		15.00

B) Phosphor issue (three bands).

1/6	8.50	8.00
First day cover		35.00

Puck and Bottom (3d)
Feste (6d)
Romeo and Juliet (1/3)
Henry V (1/6)
Hamlet (2/6)

■ 1964, April 23. Shakespeare Festival
Des: D. Gentleman (3d to 1/6); C. and R. Ironside (2/6). Printed in recess by Bradbury, Wilkinson (2/6). Perf: 11x12 (2/6). Wmk: Multiple St. Edward's Crown.
A) Non-phosphor issue.

Set	2.25	2.50
First day cover		6.00

B) Phosphor issue (three bands on 3d, 6d, 1/3, 1/6).

Set	6.50	6.75
First day cover		9.00

Flats, Richmond Park (2½d)
Shipbuilding, Belfast (4d)
Forest Park, Snowdonia (8d)
Nuclear Reactor, Dounreay (1/6)

■ 1964, July 1. International Geographical Congress
Des: D. Bailey. Wmk: Multiple St. Edward's Crown.
A) Non-phosphor issue.

Set	2.25	2.25
First day cover		12.00

B) Phosphor issue (one band on 2½d, three bands on 4d, 8d, 1/6).

Set	13.00	11.00
First day cover		25.00

Spring Gentian (3d)
Dog Rose (6d)
Honeysuckle (9d)
Fringed Water Lily (1/3)

■ 1964, August 5. International Botanical Congress
Des: M. and S. Goaman. Wmk: Multiple St. Edward's Crown.
A) Non-phosphor issue.

Set	2.25	2.50
First day cover		12.00

B) Phosphor issue (three bands).

Set	15.00	11.00
First day cover		25.00

Forth Road Bridge (3d)
Forth Road and Railway Bridges (6d)

■ 1964, September 4. Opening of the Forth Road Bridge
Des: A. Restall. Wmk: Multiple St. Edward's Crown.
A) Non-phosphor issue.

Set	0.25	0.30
First day cover		3.50

B) Phosphor issue (three bands).

Set	2.50	2.75
First day cover		10.00

Sir Winston Churchill (4d, 1/3 with slightly different designs)

■ 1965, July 8. Churchill Commemoration
Des: D. Gentleman and R. Dease. Wmk: Multiple St. Edward's Crown.

A) Non-phosphor issue.

Set	0.25	0.30
First day cover		2.50

B) Phosphor issue (three bands).

Set	1.50	1.50
First day cover		5.00

C) Printed on a Timson machine

4d	1.25	1.25

(* The Timson printing shows far more details on the portrait of Churchill.

Seal of Simon de Montfort (6d)
Parliament Buildings (2/6)

■ 1965, July 19. 700th Anniversary of Simon de Montfort's Parliament
Des: S.R. Black (6d), Professor R. Guyatt (2/6). Wmk: Multiple St. Edward's Crown.

A) Non-phosphor issue.

Set	0.65	0.65
First day cover		8.00

B) Phosphor issue (three bands): 6d only

6d	0.50	0.60
First day cover		16.00

Salvation Army Band (3d)
Three Salvation Army members (1/6)

■ 1965, August 9. Centenary of Salvation Army
Des: M.C. Farrar-Bell (3d), G. Trenaman (1/6). Wmk: Multiple St. Edward's Crown.

A) Non-phosphor issue.

Set	0.60	0.60
First day cover		11.00

B) Phosphor issue: 3d (one band), 1/6 (three bands).

Set	1.35	1.25
First day cover		20.00

Carbolic Spray (4d)
Joseph Lister (1/-)

■ 1965, September 1. Centenary of Joseph Lister's Discovery of Antiseptic Surgery
Des: P. Gauld (4d), F. Ariss (1/-). Wmk: Multiple St. Edward's Crown.

A) Non-phosphor issue.

Set	0.50	0.60
First day cover		7.00

B) Phosphor issue (three bands).

Set	1.50	1.50
First day cover		9.00

Trinidad Carnival Dancers (6d)
Canadian Folk Dancers (1/6)

■ 1965, September 1. Commonwealth Arts Festival
Des: D. Gentleman and Rosalind Dease. Wmk: Multiple St. Edward's Crown.

A) Non-phosphor issue.

Set	0.60	0.70
First day cover		9.50

B) Phosphor issue (three bands).

Set	1.70	1.75
First day cover		14.00

Spitfires (4d)
Pilot in Hurricane (4d)
Overlapping wings (4d)
Spitfires attacking Heinkel bomber (4d)
Spitfire attacking Stuka bomber (4d)
Tail wing of Dornier bomber (4d)
Anti-aircraft artillery (9d)
St Paul's Cathedral (1/3)

■ **1965, September 13. 25th Anniversary of the Battle of Britain**
Des: D. Gentleman and R. Dease (4d, 1/3), A. Restall (9d). Wmk: Multiple St. Edward's Crown. Six 4d values se-tenant.
A) Non-phosphor issue.

Set	4.50	5.00
First day cover		12.00

B) Phosphor issue (three bands).

Set	7.00	7.00
First day cover		15.00

Post Office Tower (3d)
Post Office Tower and Nash Terrace (1/3)

■ **1965, October 8. Opening of the Post Office Tower**
Des: C. Abbott. Wmk: Multiple St. Edward's Crown.
A) Non-phosphor issue.

Set	0.25	0.30
First day cover		4.00

B) Phosphor issue (one band on the 3d, three bands on the 1/3).

Set	0.40	0.50
First day cover		5.00

UN emblem (3d)
ICY emblem (1/6)

■ **1965, October 25. 20th Anniversary of United Nations and International Co-operation Year**
Des: J. Matthews. Wmk: Multiple St. Edward's Crown.
A) Non-phosphor issue.

Set	0.50	0.60
First day cover		7.00

B) Phosphor issue (one band on the 3d, three bands on the 1/6).

Set	1.50	1.60
First day cover		9.00

Telecommunications (9d)
Radio Waves (1/6)

■ **1965, November 15. International Telecommunication Union Centenary**
Des: A. Restall. Wmk: Multiple St. Edward's Crown.
A) Non-phosphor issue.

Set	0.75	0.75
First day cover		8.50

B) Phosphor issue (three bands).

Set	2.75	3.00
First day cover		13.00

Robert Burns (4d)
Robert Burns (portrait by Nasmyth) (1/3)

■ **1966, January 25. Robert Burns**
Des: G.F. Huntly. Wmk: Multiple St. Edward's Crown.
A) Non-phosphor issue.

Set	0.30	0.40
First day cover		2.50

B) Phosphor issue (three bands).

Set	1.25	1.25
First day cover		3.50

Westminster Abbey (3d)
Roof of Westminster Abbey (2/6)

■ 1966, February 28. 900th Anniversary of Westminster Abbey

Des: Sheila Robinson (3d), Bradbury Wilkinson (2/6). Printed in recess by Bradbury Wilkinson (2/6). Wmk: Multiple St. Edward's Crown. Perf: 11 x 12 (2/6)
A) Non-phosphor issue.

Set	0.50	0.50
First day cover		3.25

B) Phosphor issue (one band on the 3d).

3d	0.15	0.20
First day cover		8.00

Sussex Downs (4d)
Antrim, Northern Ireland (6d)
Harlech Castle (1/3)
The Cairngorms (1/6)

■ 1966, May 2. Landscapes

Des: L. Rosoman. Wmk: Multiple St. Edward's Crown.
A) Non-phosphor issue.

Set	0.50	0.60
First day cover		3.50

B) Phosphor issue (three bands).

Set	0.50	0.60
First day cover		4.50

Two footballers (4d)
Four footballers (6d)
Saving the ball (1/3)

■ 1966, June 1. World Cup

Des: D. Gentleman (4d), W. Kempster (6d), D. Caplan (1/3).
Wmk: Multiple St. Edward's Crown.
A) Non-phosphor issue.

Set	0.40	0.40
First day cover		9.00

B) Phosphor issue (two bands on the 4d, three bands on the 6d, 1/3).

Set	0.30	0.40
First day cover		11.50

Black-headed Gull (4d)
Blue Tit (4d)
Robin (4d)
Blackbird (4d)

■ 1966, August 8. British Birds

Des: J. Norris Wood. Wmk: Multiple St. Edward's Crown. All four values in se-tenant blocks.
A) Non-phosphor issue.

Se-tenant block of four	0.50	0.60
First day cover		4.00

B) Phosphor issue (three bands).

Se-tenant block of four	0.40	0.60
First day cover		4.50

Two footballers and legend 'ENGLAND WINNERS' (4d)

■ 1966, August 18. England's World Cup Victory

As June 1 issue, but with inscription 'ENGLAND WINNERS'.
Non-phosphor only.

4d	0.15	0.15
First day cover		7.50

Jodrell Bank Radio Telescope (4d)
Jaguar 'E' type and Mini cars (6d)
Hovercraft (1/3)
Windscale Nuclear Reactor (1/6)

■ 1966, September 19. British Technology

Des: D. and A. Gillespie (4d, 6d), A. Restall (1/3, 1/6). Wmk: Multiple St. Edward's Crown.
A) Non-phosphor issue.

Set	0.40	0.55
First day cover		1.75
B) Phosphor issue (three bands).		
Set	0.45	0.65
First day cover		2.50

Scenes from the Bayeux Tapestry (4d, six different designs)
Norman Ship (6d)
Norman horseman attacking Harold's troops (1/3)

■ 1966, October 14. 900th Anniversary of the Battle of Hastings

Des: D. Gentleman. Wmk: Multiple St. Edward's Crown, sideways on 1/3 value. Six 4d values se-tenant.
A) Non-phosphor issue.

Set	1.00	1.25
First day cover		2.50
B) Phosphor issue (three bands on the 4d, 6d, four bands on the 1/3).		
Set	1.00	1.25
First day cover		3.50

King of the Orient (3d)
Snowman (1/6)

■ 1966, December 1. Christmas

Des: Miss T. Shemza (3d), J. Berry (1/6), both aged six. Wmk: Multiple St. Edward's Crown, upright on both values.
A) Non-phosphor issue.

Set	0.15	0.20
First day cover		1.25
B) Phosphor issue (one band on the 3d, two bands on the 1/6).		
Set	0.15	0.25
First day cover		1.25

(* Phosphor 3d can be found with band at left or right).

Loading freight on a ship (9d)
Loading freight on an aeroplane (1/6)

■ 1967, February 20. European Free Trade Association

Des: C. Abbott. Wmk: Multiple St. Edward's Crown.
A) Non-phosphor issue.

Set	0.15	0.20
First day cover		4.00
B) Phosphor issue (three bands).		
Set	0.15	0.20
First day cover		4.00

Hawthorn and Bramble (4d)
Bindweed and Viper's Bugloss (4d)
Daisy, Buttercup and Coltsfoot (4d)
Bluebell, Anemone and Red Campion (4d)
Dog Violet (9d)
Primrose (1/9)

■ 1967, April 24. British Wild Flowers

Des: Keeble Martin (4d), Mary Grierson (9d, 1/9). Wmk: Multiple St. Edward's Crown. Four 4d values se-tenant.
A) Non-phosphor issue.

Set	0.60	0.75
First day cover		2.00
B) Phosphor issue (three bands).		
Set	0.35	0.75
First day cover		2.00

'Master Lambton' by Lawrence (4d)
'Mares and Foals in a Landscape' by Stubbs (9d)
'Children Coming Out of School' by Lowry (1/6)

■ 1967, July 10. British Paintings
No Wmk. Two phosphor bands.

Set	0.20	0.30
First day cover		1.50

Gipsy Moth IV (1/9)

■ 1967, July 24. Sir Francis Chichester's Single-Handed Voyage Around the World
Des: M. and S. Goaman. No Wmk. Three phosphor bands.

1/9	0.10	0.15
First day cover		0.60

Radar screen (4d)
Penicillin Mould (1/-)
Jet Engine (1/6)
Television Equipment (1/9)

■ 1967, September 19. British Discovery & Invention
Des: C. Abbott (4d, 1/-), Negus and Sharland (1/6, 1/9). Wmk: Multiple St. Edward's Crown. Three phosphor bands on the 4d.

Set	0.25	0.30
First day cover		1.25

'The Adoration of the Shepherds' by the School of Seville (3d)
'Madonna and Child' by Murillo (4d)
'The Adoration of the Shepherds' by Louis Le Nan (1/6)

■ 1967, October 18-November 27. Christmas
No Wmk. 3d has one central phosphor band.
3d released on November 27, 4d on October 18, 1/6 on November 27.

Set	0.15	0.20
First day cover		1.75

Tarr Steps (4d)
Aberfeldy Bridge (9d)
Menai Bridge (1/6)
M4 Viaduct (1/9)

■ 1968, April 29. British Bridges
Des: J. Matthews (4d, 1/9), A. Restall (9d), L. Rosoman (1/6). No Wmk. Two phosphor bands.

Set	0.25	0.30
First day cover		1.25

Trades Union Congress (4d)
Votes for Women (9d)
Royal Air Force: Sopwith Camel (1/-)
James Cook Signature and 'Endeavour' (1/9)

■ 1968, May 29. Anniversaries
Des: D. Gentleman (4d), C. Abbott (others). No Wmk.

Set	0.25	0.30
First day cover		2.25

'Queen Elizabeth I' by an unknown artist (4d)
'Pinkie' by Lawrence (1/-)
'Ruins of St Mary le Port' by Piper (1/6)
'The Hay Wain' by Constable (1/9)

■ 1968, August 12. British Paintings.
No Wmk.

Set	0.25	0.30
First day cover		0.75

Boy and Girl and Rocking Horse (4d)
Girl and Doll's House (9d)
Boy and Train Set (1/6)

■ 1968, November 25. Christmas
Des: Rosalind Dease. No Wmk.
A) Printed on a Rembrandt machine.

Set	0.20	0.20
First day cover		0.70

B) Printed on a Thrissell machine (4d only).

4d	0.15	0.20

(* The Thrissell printing can be distinguished by the boy's
pullover having a more mottled appearance.)

'Queen Elizabeth 2' (5d)
Elizabethan Galleon (9d)
East Indiaman (9d)
'Cutty Sark' (9d)
SS 'Great Britain' (1/-)
RMS 'Mauretania' (1/-)

■ 1969, January 15. British Ships
Des: D. Gentleman. No Wmk. Three 9d ivalues in se-tenant strip.
Two 1/- values in se-tenant pair.

Set	0.75	1.20
First day cover		1.75

Concorde over Great Britain and France (4d)
Silhouettes of Concorde (9d)
Nose and Tail of Concorde (1/6)

■ 1969, March 3. First Flight of Concorde
Des: Michael and Sylvia Goaman (4d), D. Gentleman (9d, 1/6).
No Wmk.

Set	0.75	0.50
First day cover		2.00

First Transatlantic Flight: Vickers 'Vimy', Alcock & Brown (5d)
Europa/CEPT (9d)
International Labour Organisation: hand holding wrench (1/-)
NATO: Flags (1/6)
First England-Australia Flight: Vickers 'Vimy', route on globe (1/9)

■ 1969, April 2. Anniversaries
Des: P. Sharland (5d, 1/-, 1/6), Michael and Sylvia Goaman (9d, 1/9).
No Wmk.

Set	0.45	0.60
First day cover		1.50

Durham Cathedral (5d)
York Minster (5d)
St Giles' Cathedral, Edinburgh (5d)
Canterbury Cathedral (5d)
St Paul's Cathedral (9d)
Liverpool Metropolitan Cathedral (1/6)

■ 1969, May 28. British Cathedrals
Des: P. Gauld. No Wmk. Four 5d values se-tenant.

Set	0.75	0.85
First day cover		1.50

The King's Gate, Caernarvon Castle (5d)
The Eagle Tower, Caernarvon Castle (5d)
Queen Eleanor's Gate, Caernarvon Castle (5d)
Celtic Cross, Margam Abbey (9d)
Prince of Wales (1/-)

■ 1969, July 1. Investiture of the Prince of Wales
Des: D. Gentleman. No Wmk. Three 5d values se-tenant.

Set	0.40	0.70
First day cover		1.00

Gandhi and Flag of India (1/6)

■ 1969, August 13. Gandhi Centenary Year
Des: Biman Mullick.

1/6	0.15	0.15
First day cover		0.50

National Giro symbol (5d)
Telephone Dials (9d)
Pulse Code Modulation (1/-)
Automatic Sorting (1/6)

■ 1969, October 1. Post Office Technology
Des: D. Gentleman. Printed in litho by De La Rue. No Wmk.
Perf: 13½x14.

Set	0.40	0.40
First day cover		1.00

The Herald Angel (4d)
The Three Shepherds (5d)
The Three Kings (1/6)

■ 1969, November 26. Christmas
Des: F. Wegner. No Wmk.

Set	0.20	0.20
First day cover		0.60

Fife Harling (5d)
Cotswold Limestone (9d)
Welsh Stucco (1/-)
Ulster Thatch (1/6)

■ 1970, February 11. Rural Architecture
Des: D. Gentleman (5d, 9d), Sheila Robinson (1/-, 1/6). No Wmk.

Set	0.40	0.50
First day cover		1.00

Signing the Declaration of Arbroath (5d)
Florence Nightingale and Patients (9d)
Signing the International Co-operative Alliance (1/-)
Sailing of the 'Mayflower' (1/6)
Royal Astronomical Society: Sir William and Sir John Herschel with Francis Bailey (1/9)

■ **1970, April 1. Anniversaries**
Des: F. Wegner (5d, 9d, 1/6), Marjorie Seynor (1/-, 1/9).
No Wmk.

Set	0.40	0.50
First day cover		1.50

Mr Pickwick and Sam (5d)
Mr and Mrs Micawber (5d)
David Copperfield and Betsey Trotwood (5d)
Oliver Twist asking for more (5d)
Grasmere (1/6)

■ **1970, June 3. Literary Anniversaries**
Des: Rosalind Dease. No Wmk. Four 5d vaues se-tenant.

Set	0.75	0.80
First day cover		1.50

Runners (5d)
Swimmers (1/6)
Cyclists (1/9)

■ **1970, July 15. British Commonwealth Games**
Des: A. Restall. Printed in litho by De La Rue. No Wmk. Perf: 13½x14.

Set	0.50	0.70
First day cover		1.20

Penny Black (line-engraved) (5d)
1/- green (embossed) (9d)
4d carmine (surface-printed) (1/6)

■ **1970, September 18. Philympia 1970**
International Stamp Exhibition
Des: D. Gentleman. No Wmk.

Set	0.40	0.40
First day cover		1.25

The Angel appearing to the Shepherds (4d)
Mary, Joseph and Jesus (5d)
The Wise Men bringing gifts (1/6)

■ **1970, November 25. Christmas**
Des: Sally Stiff (based on the De Lisle Psalter). No Wmk.

Set	0.25	0.25
First day cover		0.75

Introductory Offer 20% OFF whatever you Order
Go to www.arrowfile.com/BSM1013

SAFE **:arrowfile** ✦ **Lighthouse** **hawid**

Protect, Organise & Display Your Treasured Collection!

Over 100 Stamp, Coin & Collectable Archival Pocket Sheets to choose from including
Arrowfile, Compact, Grande, Folio, Kanzlei, Optima, Vario, Numis & much much more....

Stamp Stock Books

Stamp Drying Accessories

Binder Albums

Large Format Albums

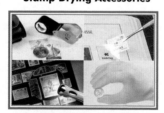

Stamp Accessories

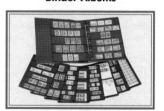

Archival Pocket Sheets

Banknote Albums

FDC & Postcard Albums

Coin Cases & Boxes

MONEY BACK 100% GUARANTEE

For the latest FREE :arrowfile Catalogue ring 0844 855 1100

For a Fast and Efficient Service and all your other Archival Storage Requirements including:
Photos | CD/DVDs | Scrapbooking | Collectables | Genealogy | Portfolios & much more
Go to www.arrowfile.com/BSM1013

PRE-DECIMAL MACHIN DEFINITIVES

In this section, prices are given for unmounted mint (left) and fine used (right). Exceptions are made where used prices are not applicable, for example booklet panes and gum varieties.

The Machin head of Queen Elizabeth II is so-called because it is from a sculpture by Arnold Machin. All designs in the series are similar, but small differences can be found in the head itself and in its setting in the design.

There are also varieties in the number and positioning of phosphor bands.

4d sepia

■ 1967-1969. Definitives

Des: A. Machin. Printed in photogravure by Harrisons. No wmk. Head 1 with two phosphor bands except where stated

A) Gum Arabic.

3d violet (August 8, 1967) (one band)	0.30	-
4d sepia (June 5, 1967)	0.35	-
head 2	£2,000	-
4d red (one centre band)	17.50	-
9d green (August 8, 1967)	0.45	-
1/- pale violet (June 5, 1967)	0.40	-
1/- deep violet	1.50	-
1/6 green, deep blue (August 8, 1967)	0.70	-
1/9 orange, black (June 5, 1967)	1.25	-
First day cover (4d, 1/-, 1/9)		1.25
First day cover (3d, 9d, 1/6)		1.25

Coil stamps (August 27, 1969)

1d olive (head 2, one band)	0.50	-

2d brown (head 2, one band)	0.30	0.30
3d violet (head 2, one band)	0.30	-
4d red (head 2, one band)	0.30	-
Se-tenant coil of two **2d**, one **1d**, one **3d** and one **4d**	1.00	1.10

Booklet panes

Pane of six **4d** sepia (head 1)	11.00	-
Pane of six **4d** red (head 1)	£100	-

B) PVA gum.

½d orange (February 5, 1968)	0.20	0.10
1d olive (February 5, 1968)	0.30	0.10
head 2	0.25	0.10
head 2 (one centre band)	0.30	0.30
2d brown (February 5, 1968)	0.20	0.10
setting 2	0.20	0.30
3d violet (one centre band)	0.20	0.10
head 2 (one centre band)	3.00	0.10
3d violet	0.35	0.10
head 2	0.50	0.10
4d sepia (shades)	0.35	0.10
head 2	0.35	0.10
4d sepia (one centre band)	0.35	0.20
head 2 (one centre band)	0.30	0.10
4d red (January 6, 1969) (one centre band)	0.30	0.20
head 2 (one centre band)	0.20	0.10
head 2 (one band at left)	20.00	0.80
head 2 (one band at right)	20.00	0.90
5d blue (July 1, 1968)	0.30	0.30
head 2	0.25	0.15
head 2 (two bands on 'all over' phosphor)	£275	-
6d purple (February 5, 1968)	0.30	0.20
head 2	12.00	7.50
7d green (July 1, 1968) (head 2)	0.50	0.30
8d red (July 1, 1968)	0.40	0.25
8d light-blue (January 6, 1969) (head 2)	0.60	0.25
9d green	0.50	0.20
10d brown (July 1, 1968)	0.70	0.30
1/- deep violet	0.40	0.20
1/6 green, deep blue	0.80	0.20
phosphor-coated paper	1.00	0.45
1/9 orange, black	3.00	0.30
Set (one of each value)	3.00	2.00
First day cover (½d, 1d, 2d, 6d)		1.00
First day cover (5d, 7d, 8d, 10d)		1.25
First day cover (4d red, 8d light blue)		1.00

Booklet panes of four

Four **4d** sepia (head 2, two bands)	1.00	-
Four **4d** sepia (head 2, one centre band)	2.00	-
Four **4d** red (head 2, one centre band)	2.00	-
Two **1d** left of two **3d** (head 2, two bands)	2.50	-
Two **1d** right of two **3d** (head 2, two bands)	2.50	-
Two **4d** sepia (head 2, one centre band) with two labels reading '£4,315 FOR YOU AT AGE 55' and 'SEE OTHER PAGES'	1.00	-
Two **4d** red (head 2, one centre band) with two labels reading '£4,315 FOR YOU AT AGE 55' and 'SEE OTHER PAGES'	2.00	-

Booklet panes of six

Six **1d** olive (head 2, two bands)	1.25	
Six **3d** violet (head one, centre band)	15.00	-
Six **4d** sepia (head 1, two bands)	1.00	
Six **4d** sepia (head 1, one centre band)	1.50	-
Six **4d** red (head 1, one centre band)	2.00	-
Six 4d red (head 2, one centre band)	1.25	-
Six **5d** blue (head 2, two bands)	1.00	-
Four **1d** olive (one centre band) with		
two **4d** sepia (head 2, one centre band)	3.50	-
Four **1d** olive (two bands) with two		
4d red (head 2, one left band)	3.50	-

Booklet panes of 15 (all head 2)

Six **1d** olive (two bands) with three **4d** red (one		
band at left), three **4d** red (one band at right)		
and three **5d** blue, attached to recipe label	10.00	-
Fifteen **4d** red (one centre band) attached		
to a label headed 'Stuffed Cucumber'	2.50	-
Fifteen **4d** red (one centre band) attached		
to a label headed 'Method'	2.50	-
Fifteen **5d** blue (two bands) attached		
to a recipe label	3.00	-

(*These panes come from the £1 Stamps For Cooks booklet and can be found with just four holes in the binding margin, where stapled together, or with a larger number of equally spaced holes, where stitched.)

5/- brown-red

■ **1969, March 5. High values**
Des: A. Machin. Printed in recess by Bradbury, Wilkinson.
Perf: 12.

2/6 brown	0.35	0.20
5/- brown-red	1.50	0.50
10/- deep blue	4.00	5.00
£1 black	3.00	1.50
Set	8.00	4.00
First day cover		7.50

Salisbury Stamp Fair

at

The Medieval Hall, West Walk
Cathedral Close, Salisbury SP1 2EY

Friday 10th February 11am - 4pm
Saturday 11th February 10am - 3.30pm

FREE ADMISSION   **REFRESHMENTS**
BUY   **SELL**   **EXCHANGE**

Wide range of material available: GB inc. Machins & Wildings
Commonwealth - Europe - World - Thematics - Postal History

For further details please telephone 01406 350896

DECIMAL MACHIN DEFINITIVES

In this section, prices are given for unmounted mint (left) and fine used (right). Exceptions are made where used prices are not applicable, for example in the case of booklet panes and gum varieties.

All stamps have fluorescent coated paper unless otherwise stated

Gum

These stamps can be found with three different gums:

Gum Arabic is either colourless or yellow in appearance and is very shiny.

Polyvinyl alcohol gum (PVA) is likewise colourless but has a matt appearance.

Polyvinyl alcohol with dextrin gum (PVAD) is also matt, but has a blueish or greenish tinge.

In recent years self-adhesive definitives have become more common.

Phosphor

As with the earlier pre-decimal definitives and special issues, the phosphor at first was applied in the form of 'bands'.

When you hold a stamp up to the light and look along the surface, the paper itself appears shiny while the bands have a dull appearance.

Most stamps have two phosphor bands, on the two vertical edges; others have just one, which can be central or down the left or right vertical edge.

The width of the phosphor bands can vary, as can the size of the printing screen used to apply them, but these differences are beyond the scope of this publication.

In recent times, booklet panes, where stamps of the second-class rate (requiring a single phosphor band) have been printed adjacent to other stamps (needing two phosphor bands), have been found with the phosphor printed as bars rather than bands. Whereas bands extend across the perforations to the next stamp, these bars stop at the edge of the stamp design.

The term *all over phosphor* means that the phosphor was printed over the entire surface of the stamp, rather than in the form of bands. In some cases it was printed onto the paper before the stamp design was printed; in other cases it was printed above the stamp design. You can positively identify all-over phosphor from certain marginal stamps, where the phosphor will be seen to end in the sheet margin.

The term *no phosphor* is usually applied to stamps discovered with the phosphor omitted in error; such errors are outside the scope of this publication. However, two values have been printed without phosphor in the normal course of events: the 50p and 75p, both with PVAD gum.

Paper

At first these stamps were printed on what is now known as *original coated paper,* which gives a dull violet reaction when the front of the stamp is viewed ultra-violet light.

This was replaced by *fluorescent coated paper,* which gives a bright reaction under ultra-violet light, and then by *phosphor-coated paper,* which adds the after-glow of phosphor.

With phosphor coated paper, the phosphor is included with the coating of the surface of the paper. This makes the stamp appear uniformly shiny. Note that most stamps intended to have phosphor bands have been found with the phosphor omitted, which also produces a uniformly shiny surface, so those with phosphor coated paper can only be positively identified by their reaction under ultra-violet light.

The appearance of stamps with phosphor coated paper can vary considerably, due to variations in their drying time after printing. The differences range from dull to very shiny. A dull appearance is listed in this guide as *Phosphor Coated Paper I* (PCPI), and a highly glazed appearance as *Phosphor Coated Paper II* (PCPII).

Some stamps have been found with the fluorescent brightener omitted (with phosphor coated paper). These still give the phosphor afterglow, but the paper gives a dull violet reaction similar to that found with original coated paper.

Attempts to standardise the paper have produced what is known as *Advanced Coated Paper* (ACP), which has been used for a number of National and Country definitives. The visual difference between ACP and PCPI is slight, but the former gives a brighter reaction under ultra-violet light.

Printers and processes

Many of the Machin decimal definitives have been printed in photogravure by Harrisons. But some of the work has been undertaken by John Waddington, House of Questa, Walsall, Enschedé and De La Rue. Initially lithography was used, but Royal Mail then decided that it preferred the photogravure process

In 1979 the 10p definitive was printed on a Chambon press at Harrisons which produced sheets of 200 stamps, comprising two panes of 100 stamps separated by a horizontal gutter. Stamps from this printing have either two phosphor bands on top of phosphor coated paper or two phosphor bands on top of fluorescent coated paper.

Value position and portrait types

Changes can be noted in the position of the value in relation to the Queen's portrait, and the position of the portrait in relation to the base of the stamp.

Booklet panes

At first booklets were held together by stitching, so that a number of small holes can be found in the binding margin on the left hand side of panes. Later, the panes were stuck into booklet covers by the binding margins; in many such cases, panes can be found with the binding margin to the left or to the right.

In the case of stitched booklets, the booklet panes are recorded separately. Where the panes are stuck into the covers, most collectors prefer these as complete booklets, so the separate panes are not recorded.

Many of the early decimal booklet panes included labels se-tenant with the stamps in the pane, adjacent to the binding margin. At first these panes were perforated between the labels and the margin, but later they were not.

In 1987, as an experiment to counter complaints about the poor guillotining of panes, two booklet panes were produced with imperforate sides. These produce stamps with either the left or right-hand edge imperforate.

A further experiment of 1987 was to introduce booklets with 'bar codes' on the back cover, and with a window in the front cover, so that the stamp content could be ascertained. The panes in these booklets have a margin surrounding the stamps, and as such are listed separately.

Coils

There are two different types of coils from which stamps may be found.

Some coils contain just one value, with the stamps joined either horizontally or vertically. Today, these usually comprise the basic 1st or 2nd class letter rate stamps, and are prepared for use by businesses. They are not separately listed, but where the source of a particular stamp is given as 'coils', this refers to the single value version.

Other coils contain a mixture of values joined as a se-tenant strip. These have been produced for sale through vending machines, although two cases are known of coils specially produced for a commercial mailing shot. These are referred to here as 'se-tenant coils', and they are also separately listed.

Cartons

In an experiment staged in Scotland in 1976-78, 1st and 2nd-class definitives (including Country stamps) were sold in cartons from vending machines. Sold at 30p or 60p, they contained either 6½p and 8½p, or 7p and 9p stamps.

LOW VALUES WITHOUT ELLIPTICAL PERFORATIONS, 1971-96

Des. A. Machin. Printed in photogravure by Harrisons, no Wmk, Perf: 15x14, except where stated.

■ ½p turquoise, February 15, 1971
A) gum Arabic, two phos bands

i. original coated paper	0.30	-	se-tenant coils
ii. original coated paper with silicone	30.00	-	se-tenant coils
iii. fluorescent coated paper	0.20	-	sheets
iv. fluorescent coated paper with silicone	0.40	-	se-tenant coils

B) PVA gum, two phos bands

i. original coated paper	0.20	-	sheets, se-tenant coils, booklets
ii. fluorescent coated paper	0.40	-	sheets, booklets
C) PVA gum, one band at left	40.00	20.00	£1 Wedgwood booklet
D) PVAD gum, two phos bands	0.20	0.15	sheets, se-tenant coils, booklets
E) PVAD gum, one centre band	0.20	0.15	se-tenant coils, booklets

F) PVAD gum, phos-coated paper

i. PCPI	0.20	0.20	sheets, se-tenant coils
ii. PCPII	0.25	0.30	sheets
iii. fluorescent brightener omitted (poor gum)	£125	30.00	se-tenant coils
iv. fluorescent brightener omitted (good perfs and gum)	£950	-	se-tenant coils

■ 1p purple, February 15, 1971
A) gum Arabic, two phos bands

i. original coated paper	0.30	-	se-tenant coils
ii. original coated paper with silicone	30.00	-	se-tenant coils
iii. fluorescent coated paper	0.60	-	coils
iv. fluorescent coated paper with silicone	0.60	-	se-tenant coils

B) PVA gum, two phos bands

i. original coated paper	0.20	-	sheets
ii. fluorescent coated paper	1.25	-	sheets, booklets

C) PVAD gum, two phos bands

i. value low	0.40	0.30	10p booklets
ii. value in intermediate position	0.40	0.35	10p se-tenant coils, 50p booklets,
iii. value high	0.30	0.30	sheets, 5p se-tenant coils
D) PVAD gum, one centre phos band			
i. portrait above bottom margin	0.20	0.15	se-tenant coils
ii. portrait closer to bottom margin	0.50	0.30	se-tenant coils, 10p, 50p booklets,
E) PVAD gum, all over phos	0.30	0.20	sheets
F) PVAD gum, phos-coated paper			
i. PCPI, portrait above bottom margin	0.20	0.20	sheets
ii. PCPI, portrait closer to bottom margin	0.30	0.15	sheets, se-tenant coils
iii. PCPII	0.40	0.25	sheets
iv. ACP	0.30	0.25	sheets
G) PVAD gum, one phos band at left	1.00	0.80	50p booklet
H) PVAD gum, one phos band at right	2.50	2.25	£5 P&O booklet

■ 1½p black, February 15, 1971

A) PVA gum, two phos bands			
i. original coated paper	0.25	0.15	sheets, booklets
ii. fluorescent coated paper	0.90	0.70	sheets, booklets
B) PVAD gum, two phos bands	0.50	0.30	sheets, booklets

■ 2p green, February 15, 1971

A) gum Arabic, two phos bands			
i. original coated paper	2.00	-	se-tenant coils
ii. original coated paper with silicone	135.00	-	se-tenant coils
iii. fluorescent coated paper with silicone	2.00	-	se-tenant coils
B) PVA gum, two phos bands			
i. original coated paper	0.20	-	sheets, booklets
ii. fluorescent coated paper	1.50	-	sheets, booklets
C) PVAD gum, two phos bands			
i. portrait above bottom margin	0.30	0.20	sheets, se-tenant coils, booklets
ii. portrait close to bottom margin	0.60	0.60	booklets
D) PVAD gum, all over phos	0.30	0.15	sheets
E) PVAD gum, phos-coated paper			
i. PCPI	0.20	0.20	sheets
ii. PCPII	0.25	0.15	sheets
F) PVAD gum, phos-coated paper, litho by Questa, perf 13½x14	0.25	0.20	sheets
G) PVAD gum, phos-coated paper, litho by Questa, perf 15x14	0.40	0.30	sheets
H) PVAD, phos-coated paper, ACP, litho by Questa, perf 15x14	0.40	0.40	sheets

■ 2p deep green, February 23, 1988

A) PVAD gum, phos paper	0.60	0.60	sheets, booklets
B) PVAD gum phos paper, litho by Walsall	0.80	0.70	booklets

■ 2½p pink, February 15, 1971

A) gum arabic, one centre phos band	0.30	-	sheets, coils
B) PVA gum, one centre phos band			
i. original coated paper	0.30	0.20	sheets, coils, booklets,
ii. fluorescent coated paper	0.50	0.40	sheets, booklets
C) PVA gum, one phos band at left			
i. original coated paper	5.00	1.50	50p booklets,
ii. fluorescent coated paper	2.00	1.20	50p, £1 Wedgwood booklets
D) PVA gum, one phos band at right	2.50	1.50	£1 Wedgwood booklet
E) PVAD gum, two phos bands	0.40	0.40	sheets
F) PVAD gum, one centre phos band	0.30	0.20	sheets

■ 2½p rose, January 14, 1981

A) PVAD gum, phos-coated paper			
i. PCPI	0.50	0.20	sheets, se-tenant coils
ii. PCPII	0.30	0.20	sheets,

iii. fluorescent brightener omitted | 30.00 | 30.00 | se-tenant coils
B) PVAD gum, two phos bands | 0.45 | 0.30 | 50p booklets

■ 3p blue, February 15, 1971

A) gum Arabic, two phos bands			
i. original coated paper	45.00	-	coils
ii. fluorescent coated paper	0.60	-	sheets, coils
B) gum arabic, one centre phos band	0.40	-	sheets
C) PVA gum, two phos bands			
i. original coated paper	0.30	0.20	sheets, coils, booklets
ii. fluorescent coated paper	0.40	0.30	sheets, booklets
iii. phos-coated paper	£1,200	-	only two examples known
D) PVA gum, one centre phos band	0.60	-	sheets, booklets
E) PVAD gum, one centre phos band	0.30	0.20	sheets, coils, booklets

■ 3p pink, October 22, 1980

A) PVAD gum, phos-coated paper			
i. PCPI	0.30	0.20	sheets, se-tenant coils
ii. PCPII	0.40	0.20	
iii. fluorescent brightener omitted	5.00	4.00	se-tenant coils
iv. ACP	0.50	0.20	sheets, £4 Royal Mint booklet
B) PVAD gum, two phos bands	0.30	0.20	50p, £4 SG booklets

■ 3½p olive green, February 15, 1971

A) PVA gum, two phos bands			
i. original coated paper	0.40	0.20	sheets
ii. fluorescent coated paper	2.00	-	sheets, 35p booklets
B) PVAD gum, two phos bands			
i. original coated paper	£150	50.00	sheets
ii. fluorescent coated paper	0.60	0.25	sheets, coils, 35p, 50p booklets
C) PVAD gum, one centre phos band	0.35	0.30	sheets, coils, 35p, 85p booklets

■ 3½p light red-brown, March 30, 1983

A) PVA gum, two phos bands			
i. PCPI	0.40	0.30	sheets,
ii. ACP	1.10	0.60	sheets, £4 Royal Mint booklet
B) PVAD gum, one centre phos band	1.25	0.60	50p booklets

■ 4p bistre, February 15, 1971

A) gum arabic, two phos bands	0.30	-	sheets
B) PVA gum, two phos bands			
i. original coated paper	0.30	0.20	sheets
ii. fluorescent coated paper	3.50	-	sheets
C) PVAD gum, two phos bands	0.30	0.20	sheets

■ 4p blue, January 30, 1980

A) PVA gum, two phos bands, litho by Waddingtons	0.20	0.15	sheets
B) PVAD gum, phos-coated paper, litho by Waddingtons	0.30	0.20	sheets
C) PVAD gum, phos-coated paper, litho by Questa, perf 15x14	0.30	0.45	sheets
D) PVAD gum, two phos bands	1.50	0.85	50p booklets
E) PVAD gum, phos-coated paper			
i. PCPI	0.35	0.25	se-tenant coils
ii. fluorescent brightener omitted (perfect gum)	£370	35.00	se-tenant coils
iii. PCPI, value high	0.35	0.20	se-tenant coils
F) PVAD gum, one centre phos band	0.75	0.70	50p booklets
G) PVAD gum, one phos band at left	1.35	1.15	£5 booklet
H) PVAD gum, one phos band at right	1.50	1.30	£5 booklet

■ 4p bright blue, July 26, 1988

A) PVAD gum, phos paper, litho by Questa	0.45	0.50	sheets
A) PVAD gum, phos paper	0.30	0.25	sheets and coils

■ 4½p grey-blue, October 24, 1973

A) PVAD gum, two phos bands	0.50	0.25	sheets, coils, 45p, 85p booklets
B) PVAD gum, two phos bands on all-over phos	0.65	-	sheets

■ 5p violet, February 15, 1971

A) PVA gum, two phos bands			
i. original coated paper	0.30	0.20	sheets
ii. fluorescent coated paper	3.50	-	sheets
B) PVAD gum, two phos bands	0.40	0.20	sheets
C) PVAD gum, phos-coated paper			
i. PCPI	0.65	0.50	sheets
ii. PCPI, value high	0.50	0.35	sheets
D) PVAD gum, phos-coated paper, litho by Questa	0.30	0.20	sheets
E) PVA gum, phos-coated paper, litho by Questa	0.50	1.40	sheets

■ 5p red-brown, January 27. 1982

A) PVAD gum, phos-coated paper, litho by Questa, perf 13½x14	0.40	0.30	sheets
B) PVAD gum, phos-coated paper, litho by Questa, perf 15x14	0.50	0.40	sheets
C) PVAD gum, ACP, litho by Questa, perf 15x14	0.45	0.40	sheets
D) PVAD gum, one centre phos band	1.20	1.20	50p booklet

■ 5½p deep purple, October 24, 1973

A) PVAD gum, two phos bands	0.50	0.40	sheets
B) PVAD gum, one centre phos band	0.40	0.30	sheets

■ 6p light green, February 15, 1971

A) gum arabic, two phos bands	2.25	-	sheets
B) PVA gum, two phos bands			
i. original coated paper	0.30	-	sheets, se-tenant coils
ii. fluorescent coated paper	25.00	-	sheets
C) PVAD gum, two phos bands	0.30	0.20	sheets, se-tenant coils, 10p booklet

■ 6p olive, September 10, 1991

A) PVAD gum, phos paper	0.30	0.20	sheets

■ 6½p green-blue, September 7, 1974

A) PVA gum, two phos bands	30.00	-	sheets
B) PVAD gum, two phos bands	0.40	0.30	sheets
C) PVAD gum, one centre phos band			
i. portrait above bottom margin	0.40	0.30	sheets
ii. portrait close to bottom margin	0.40	0.25	sheets, coils, 65p booklets
D) PVAD gum, one phos band at left	1.00	0.30	50p booklets
E) PVAD gum, one phos band at right	1.10	0.30	50p booklets

■ 7p red-brown, January 15, 1975

A) PVAD gum, two phos bands	0.40	0.30	sheets
B) PVAD gum, one centre phos band			
i. portrait above bottom margin	0.40	0.30	sheets, coils
ii. portrait close to bottom margin	0.50	0.30	sheets, coils, se-tenants coils, booklets
C) PVAD gum, one phos band at left	0.50	0.45	50p booklets
D) PVAD gum, one phos band at right	0.80	0.50	50p booklets

■ 7p brick-red, October 29, 1985

A) PVAD gum, phos-coated paper	1.50	0.90	sheets

■ 7½p brown, February 15, 1971

A) PVA gum, two phos bands			
i. original coated paper	0.50	0.40	sheets
ii. fluorescent coated paper	3.00	-	sheets
B) PVAD gum, two phos bands	0.40	0.25	sheets

■ 8p red, October 24, 1973

A) PVAD gum, two phos bands	0.30	0.20	sheets
B) PVAD gum, one centre phos band, printed by Harrisons			
i. portrait high, value low	0.35	0.25	sheets
ii. portrait low, value high	0.50	0.30	sheets, coils, booklets
C) PVAD gum, one centre phos band, printed by Enschedé	0.35	0.25	sheets
D) PVAD gum, one phos band at left	0.50	0.30	50p booklets
E) PVAD gum, one phos band at right	0.50	0.30	50p booklets

■ 8½p lime green, September 24, 1975

A) PVAD gum, two phos bands			
i. value high	0.40	0.25	sheets, coils, 85p booklets
ii. value low	0.45	0.35	50p booklets
B) PVAD gum, phos-coated paper	0.40	0.35	sheets

■ 9p orange and black, February 15, 1971

A) PVA gum, two phos bands			
i. original coated paper	0.90	0.80	sheets
ii. fluorescent coated paper	2.50	-	sheets
B) PVAD gum, two phos bands	1.00	0.90	sheets

■ 9p violet, February 25, 1976

A) PVAD gum, two phos bands	0.50	0.40	sheets, coils, 50p, 90p, £1.60 booklets

■ 9½p purple, February 25, 1976

A) PVAD gum, two phos bands	0.35	0.30	sheets

■ 10p yellow and orange, August 11, 1971

A) PVA gum, two phos bands	0.50	-	sheets
B) PVAD gum, two phos bands	0.50	0.50	sheets

■ 10p orange, February 25, 1976

A) PVAD gum, two phos bands			
i. base of value above edge of bust	0.40	0.20	sheets, £1.80 booklets
ii. base of value at edge of bust	0.30	0.25	50p booklets
iii. re-drawn (narrower) value	10.50	10.00	£4 Heritage booklet
B) PVAD gum, all-over phos	0.60	0.30	sheets, £1 booklets
C) PVAD gum, phosphor coated paper, PCPI	0.60	0.45	sheets
D) PVAD gum, ACP	0.40	0.25	sheets
E) PVAD gum, one centre phos band	0.35	0.20	sheets, £1, £2.20, £3 booklets
F) PVAD gum, one phos band at left	0.60	0.50	50p, £3 booklets
G) PVAD gum, one phos band at right	0.60	0.50	50p booklets
H) PVAD gum, two phos bands, PCPI, Chambon press	0.50	-	sheets
gutter pair	1.25	-	sheets
I) PVAD gum, two phos bands, fluoresc-coated paper, Chambon	0.45	0.35	sheets
gutter pair	1.00	1.50	sheets
J) PVAD gum, one centre phos band, PCPI	1.00	-	sheets

■ 10½p yellow, February 25, 1976

A) PVAD gum, two phos bands	0.50	0.40	sheets

■ 10½p blue, April 26, 1978

A) PVAD gum, two phos bands	0.50	0.40	sheets

■ 11p orange-pink, February 25, 1976

A) PVAD gum, two phos bands	0.40	0.30	sheets
B) PVAD gum, phos-coated paper, PCPI	0.60	0.50	sheets

■ 11½p sepia, August 15, 1979

A) PVAD gum, phos-coated paper PCPI	0.50	0.30	sheets

■ 11½p mushroom, January 14, 1981

A) PVAD gum, one centre phos band	0.30	0.20	sheets, coils, £1.15, £2.55 booklets
B) PVAD gum, one phos band at left	0.50	0.30	50p, £1.30 booklets
C) PVAD gum, one phos band at right	0.50	0.30	50p, £1.30 booklets

■ 12p yellow-green, January 30, 1980

A) PVAD gum, phos-coated paper			
i. PCPI	0.50	0.45	sheets, coils, £1.20 booklet
ii. PCPII	0.80	0.50	sheets
B) PVAD gum, two phos bands	0.50	0.35	50p, £2.20, £3 booklets

■ 12p emerald-green, October 29, 1985

A) PVAD gum, one centre phos band	0.40	0.35	sheets, 50p, £1.20, £5 booklets
B) PVAD gum, one centre phos band, blue star on gummed side	0.50	-	sheets
C) PVAD gum, one centre phos band in ACP-type phos	0.50	0.35	sheets
D) PVAD gum, one phos band at left	0.75	0.50	£1.50, £5 booklets
E) PVAD gum, one phos band at right	0.75	0.50	£1.50, £5 booklets

■ 12½p light green, January 27, 1982

A) PVAD gum, one centre phos band	0.45	0.30	sheets, coils, 50p, £1.25, £4 SG booklets
B) PVAD gum, one centre phos band, PCPI	5.00	-	sheets
C) PVAD gum, one phos band at left	0.60	0.50	50p, £1.43, £1.46, £4 booklets
D) PVAD gum, one phos band at right	0.60	0.50	50p, £1.43, £1.46, £4 booklets
E) PVAD gum, one centre band, blue star on gummed side	0.60	0.50	£2.50 booklet
F) PVAD gum, one centre band, simple blue star on gummed side	0.60	0.40	£2.20 booklet

■ 13p olive, August 15, 1979

A) PVAD gum, phos-coated paper, PCPI	0.45	0.40	sheets

■ 13p light brown, August 28, 1984

A) PVAD gum, one centre phos band	0.50	0.35	sheets, 50p, £1.30, £5 booklets
B) PVAD gum, one centre phos band, blue star on gummed side	0.60	-	£1.20 booklet
C) PVAD gum, one centre phos band in ACP-type phos	0.50	0.35	sheets
D) PVAD gum, one phos band at left	0.65	0.50	50p, £1.54, £4 Heritage, £5 booklets
E) PVAD gum, one phos band at right	0.65	0.50	£1, £1.54, £4 Heritage, £5 booklets
F) PVAD gum, one centre phos band, litho by Questa	0.60	0.45	booklets
G) PVAD gum, one phos band at left, litho by Questa	0.60	0.45	booklets
H) PVAD gum, one phos band at right, litho by Questa	0.60	0.45	booklets

■ 13½p red-brown, January 30, 1980

A) PVAD gum, phosphor coated paper, PCPI	0.60	0.45	sheets

■ 14p grey-blue, January 14, 1981

A) PVAD gum, phos-coated paper			
i. PCPI	0.45	0.30	sheets, coils, £1.40 booklets
ii. PCPII	0.60	0.50	sheets, coils £1.40 booklets
iii. fluorescent brightener omitted	2.50	-	£1.40 booklets
B) PVAD gum, two phos bands	0.60	0.40	50p, £1.30, £2.55 booklets

■ 14p deep blue, August 23, 1988

A) PVAD gum, one centre phos band	0.50	0.35	sheets, booklets
B) PVAD gum, one phos band at right	2.50	2.00	booklets
C) PVAD gum, one centre phos band, litho by Questa	1.50	1.10	booklets
D) PVAD gum, one phos band at right, litho by Walsall	1.50	1.50	booklets

■ 15p blue, August 15, 1979

A) PVAD gum, phos-coated paper			
i. PCPI	0.50	0.45	sheets
ii. PCPII	0.60	0.55	sheets
B) PVAD gum, one phos band at left	2.20	2.00	50p booklets

C) PVAD gum, one centre phos band	0.50	0.30	sheets, coils
D) PVAD gum, one phos band at right	1.50	1.50	£5 booklets

■ **15p bright blue, September 26, 1989**

A) PVAD gum, one centre phos band	0.50	0.50	sheets, coils
B) PVAD gum, one phos band at left	1.50	1.50	50p booklet
B) PVAD gum, one phos band at right	1.50	1.50	£5 London Life booklet

■ **15½p pale purple, January 14, 1981**
A) PVAD gum, phos-coated paper

i. PCPI	0.60	0.45	sheets, coils, £1.55 booklets
ii. PCPI	0.60	0.45	sheets
iii. fluorescent brightener omitted	15.00	-	sheets
iv. advanced coated paper	3.00	2.50	sheets, £1.55 booklets
B) PVAD gum, two phos bands	0.60	0.45	£1.43, £4 SG booklets
C) PVAD gum, two phos bands, blue star on gummed side	0.60	0.45	£2.50 booklets

■ **16p light mushroom, March 30, 1983**

A) PVAD gum, phos-coated paper, PCPI	0.50	0.45	sheets, £1.60, £4 Royal Mint booklets
B) PVAD gum, PCPI and D on gummed side	0.70	0.45	£1.45 booklet
C) PVAD gum, ACP	0.60	0.45	sheets
D) PVAD gum, two phos bands	1.10	1.10	£1.46 booklet

■ **16½p light brown, January 27 1982**
A) PVAD gum, phos-coated paper

i. PCPI	0.75	0.65	sheets
ii. PCPII	3.00	2.50	sheets

■ **17p sage green, January 30, 1980**
A) PVAD gum, phos-coated paper

i. PCPI	0.60	0.45	sheets
ii. PCPII	3.00	2.50	sheets
iii. fluorescent brightener omitted	1.50	-	sheets

■ **17p steel blue, March 30, 1983**

A) PVAD gum, PCPI	0.70	0.45	sheets, £1.70, £4 Heritage booklets
B) PVAD gum, PCPI, D on gummed side	1.00	-	£1.55 booklet
C) PVAD gum, ACP	0.60	0.45	sheets, £1.70, £5 booklets
D) PVAD gum, two phos bands	0.60	0.45	50p, £1.50, £1.54, £4 Heritage, £5 booklets
E) PVAD gum, two phos bands, stars on gummed side	0.70	0.45	50p booklet

■ **17p deep blue, September 4, 1990**

A) PVAD gum, one centre phos band	0.75	0.60	sheets
B) PVAD gum, one phos band at left	0.95	0.95	booklets
C) PVAD gum, one phos band at right	3.20	3.00	booklets
D) PVAD gum, one centre phos band, litho by Questa	0.70	0.65	booklets

■ **17½p light brown, January 30, 1979**
A) PVAD gum, phos-coated paper

i. PCPI	0.65	0.50	sheets
ii. PCPII	2.00	1.75	sheets

■ **18p violet, January 14, 1981**
A) PVAD gum, phos-coated paper

i. PCPI	0.65	0.50	sheets
ii. PCPII	0.70	0.60	sheets

■ **18p grey-green, August 28, 1984**

A) PVAD gum, ACP	0.65	0.40	sheets
B) PVAD gum, two phos bands	1.25	0.65	50p, £1 booklets

C) PVAD gum, phos-coated paper	0.70	0.60	£1.80 booklet
D) PVAD gum, phos paper, litho by Questa	0.80	0.75	booklets
E) PVAD gum, two phos bands, litho by Questa	3.75	4.00	booklets

■ 18p bright green, September 10, 1991

A) PVAD gum, one centre phos band	0.50	0.45	sheets
B) PVAD gum, one centre phos band, litho by Questa	0.80	0.70	booklets
C) PVAD gum, one phos band at left, litho by Questa	1.50	1.35	booklets
D) PVAD gum, one phos band at right, litho by Questa	1.00	0.90	booklets

■ 19p orange-red, August 23, 1988

A) PVAD gum, phos paper	1.50	1.00	sheets, booklets
B) PVAD gum, phos paper, litho by Questa	1.50	1.40	booklets
C) PVAD gum, two phos bands, litho by Walsall	1.50	1.50	booklets

■ 19½p olive grey, January 27, 1982

A) PVAD gum, phosphor coated paper, PCPI	1.75	1.75	sheets

■ 20p dull purple, February 25, 1976

A) PVA gum, two phos bands, litho by Waddingtons	1.00	0.90	sheets
B) PVAD gum, phos-coated paper, litho by Waddingtons	1.15	1.00	sheets
C) as above but dull purple and sepia	3.00	2.00	sheets
D) PVAD gum, phos-coated paper, litho by Questa, perf 15x14	1.00	0.50	sheets
E) PVAD gum, two phos bands	0.70	0.50	sheets
F) PVAD gum, phos-coated paper			
i. PCPI	0.80	0.50	sheets
ii. PCPII	0.70	0.60	sheets

■ 20p turquoise, August 23, 1988

A) PVAD gum, phos paper	0.80	0.50	sheets

■ 20p brownish-black, September 26, 1989

A) PVAD gum, phos paper	1.00	0.90	sheets, booklets
B) PVAD gum, two phos bands	1.00	0.90	sheets

■ 20½p bright blue, March 30, 1983

A) PVAD gum, phos-coated paper, PCPI	1.00	0.90	sheets

■ 22p deep blue, October 22, 1980

A) PVAD gum, phos-coated paper			
i. PCPI	0.70	0.50	sheets
ii. PCPII	0.70	0.50	sheets
B) PVAD gum, experimental coated paper	2.50	2.00	sheets

■ 22p yellow-green, August 28, 1984

A) PVAD gum, ACP	0.80	0.50	sheets
B) PVAD gum, two phos bands, litho by Questa	5.00	4.50	booklets

■ 22p orange-red, September 4, 1990

A) PVAD gum, two phos bands	0.80	0.70	sheets
B) PVAD gum, phos paper	1.50	1.50	sheets
C) PVAD gum, phos paper, litho by Questa	0.70	0.50	booklets

■ 23p rose, March 30, 1983

A) PVAD gum, phos-coated paper, PCPI	1.30	1.20	sheets

■ 23p bright green, August 23, 1988

A) PVAD gum, phos paper	1.00	1.00	sheets

■ 24p light purple, August 28, 1984

A) PVAD gum, ACP	1.50	1.40	sheets

■ 24p red, September 26, 1989

A) PVAD gum, phos paper	1.30	1.20	sheets

■ 24p chestnut, September 10, 1991

A) PVAD gum, phos paper	0.75	0.75	sheets
B) PVAD gum, phos paper, litho by Questa	1.00	0.40	booklets
C) PVAD gum, two phos bands, litho by Questa	1.20	1.20	booklets
D) PVAD gum, phos paper, litho by Walsall	1.00	0.90	booklets

■ 25p purple, January 14, 1981

A) PVAD gum, phos-coated paper

i. PCPI	2.00	1.10	sheets
ii. PCPII	1.50	1.30	sheets

■ 25p rose red, February 6, 1996

A) PVAD gum, two phos bands	5.50	5.50	coils

■ 26p red, January 27, 1982

A) PVAD gum, phos-coated paper, PCPI	0.75	0.60	sheets
B) PVAD gum, ACP	0.75	0.50	sheets
C) PVAD gum, two phos bands	4.00	4.00	£5 P&O booklet
D) PVAD gum, phos paper, narrow value	3.50	3.00	£1.04 booklet

■ 26p drab, September 4, 1990

A) PVAD gum, phos paper	1.00	0.90	sheets

■ 27p chestnut, August 23, 1988

A) PVAD gum, phos paper	1.00	0.90	sheets, booklets

■ 27p violet, September 4, 1990

A) PVAD gum, phos paper	1.00	0.90	sheets

■ 28p blue, March 30, 1983

A) PVAD gum, phos-coated paper, PCPI	1.00	0.90	sheets
B) PVAD gum, ACP	1.00	0.90	sheets

■ 28p ochre, August 23, 1988

A) PVAD gum, phos paper	1.25	1.15	sheets

■ 28p blue-grey, September 10, 1991

A) PVAD gum , phos paper	1.10	1.00	sheets

■ 29p sepia, January 27, 1982

A) PVAD gum, phos-coated paper

i. PCPI	2.50	2.00	sheets
ii. PCPII	5.00	4.00	sheets

■ 29p mauve, September 26, 1989

A) PVAD gum, phos paper	1.50	1.30	sheets
B) PVAD gum, two phos bands, litho by Walsall	2.50	2.50	booklets
C) PVAD gum, phos paper, litho by Walsall	4.00	4.00	booklets

■ 30p olive, September 26, 1989

A) PVAD gum, phos paper	1.25	1.15	sheets

■ 31p purple, March 30, 1983

A) PVAD gum, phos-coated paper, PCPI	1.20	1.10	sheets
B) PVAD gum, ACP	1.10	1.00	sheets
C) PVAD gum, two phos bands	7.00	7.00	£5 British Rail Booklet

■ 31p ultramarine, September 4, 1990

A) PVAD gum, phos paper	1.10	0.90	sheets
B) PVAD gum, phosphor paper, litho by Walsall	1.30	1.00	booklets

■ 32p green-blue, August 23, 1988

A) PVAD gum, phos paper	1.50	0.90	sheets

■ 33p emerald, September 4, 1990

A) PVAD gum, phos paper	1.40	0.30	sheets
B) PVAD gum, phos paper, litho by Questa	2.00	2.00	booklets
C) PVAD gum, two phos bands, litho by Questa	1.20	1.00	booklets
D) PVAD gum, phos paper, litho by Walsall	1.00	1.00	booklets

■ 34p sepia, August 28, 1984

A) PVAD gum, phos-coated paper	1.10	1.00	sheets
B) PVAD gum, two phos bands	5.50	5.00	£5 Times booklet
C) PVAD gum, ACP	1.40	1.25	sheets
D) PVAD gum, two phos bands, litho by Questa	4.50	4.50	booklets

■ 34p blue-grey, September 26, 1989

A) PVAD gum, phos paper	1.50	1.50	sheets

■ 34p mauve, September 10, 1991

A) PVAD gum, phos paper	1.50	1.30	sheets

■ 35p sepia, August 23, 1988

A) PVAD gum, phos paper	1.50	1.30	sheets

■ 35p yellow, September 10, 1991

A) PVAD gum, phos paper	1.15	1.10	sheets

■ 37p rosine, September 26, 1989

A) PVAD gum, phos paper	2.00	1.00	sheets

■ 39p mauve, September 10, 1991

A) PVAD gum, phos paper	1.75	0.50	sheets
B) PVAD gum, two phos bands, litho by Questa	1.20	1.00	booklets
C) PVA gum, phos paper, litho by Walsall	1.10	1.00	booklets

■ 50p dull brown, February 2, 1977

A) PVAD gum, two phos bands	1.50	0.50	sheets
B) PVAD gum, no phos	1.50	0.70	sheets

■ 50p ochre, March 13, 1990

A) PVAD gum, phos paper	1.40	0.50	sheets
B) PVAD gum, two phos bands	1.50	0.50	sheets

■ 75p deep grey, January 30, 1980

A) PVAD gum, no phos, litho by Questa, perf 13½x14	2.00	2.00	sheets
B) PVA gum, no phos, litho by Questa, perf 15x14	3.00	1.50	sheets
C) PVAD gum, no phos, litho by Questa, perf 15x14	3.75	2.00	sheets
D) PVA gum, no phos, litho by Questa: perf 15x14 on paper supplied by Coated Paper Ltd	3.75	-	sheets

■ 75p grey and black, February 23, 1988

A) PVA gum, litho by Questa	5.00	4.00	sheets

■ 75p grey and black, July 26, 1988

A) PVAD gum, no phosphor	2.00	0.60	sheets

First day cover February15, 1971	
(½p, 1p, 1½p, 2p, 2½p, 3p, 3½p, 4p, 5p, 6p, 7½p, 9p)	4.00
First day cover August 11, 1971	
(10p)	0.75
First day cover October 24, 1973	
(4½p, 5½p, 8p)	0.75
First day cover September 4, 1974	
(6½p)	1.25
First day cover January15, 1975	
(7p)	1.00
First day cover September 24, 1975	
(8½p)	1.00
First day cover February 25, 1976	
(9p, 9½p, 10p, 10½p, 11p, 20p)	2.25
First day cover February 2, 1977	
(50p)	1.50
First day cover April 26, 1978	
(10½p)	0.75
First day cover August 15, 1979	
(11½p, 13p, 15p)	1.00
First day cover January 30, 1980	
(4p, 12p, 13½p, 17p, 17½p, 75p)	1.60
First day cover October 22, 1980	
(3p, 22p)	1.00
First day cover January 14, 1981	
(2½p, 11½p, 14p, 15½p, 18p, 25p)	1.25
First day cover January 27, 1982	
(5p, 12½p, 16½p, 19½p, 26p, 29p)	2.00
First day cover March 30, 1983	
(3½p, 16p, 17p, 20½p, 23p, 31p)	3.00
First day cover August 28, 1984	
(13p, 18p, 22p, 24p, 34p)	2.50
First day cover October 29, 1985	
(7p, 12p)	1.25
First day cover August 23, 1988	
(14p, 19p, 20p, 23p, 27p, 28p, 32p, 35p)	3.00
First day cover September 26, 1989	
(15p, 20p, 24p, 29p, 30p, 34p, 37p)	3.00
First day cover September 4, 1990	
(10p, 17p, 22p, 26p, 27p, 31p, 33p)	3.50
First day cover September 10, 1991	
(6p, 18p 24p, 28p, 34p, 35p, 39p)	3.25
First day cover February 6, 1996	
(25p)	2.00

BOOKLET PANES WITHOUT ELLIPTICAL PERFORATIONS, 1971-93

From stitched booklets and prestige stamp books.

■ Panes of four with PVA gum

Two **2p** with two ½p	
vertically se-tenant	5.50
horizontally se-tenant, original coated paper	8.00
horizontally se-tenant, fluorescent coated paper	3.00
Two **1p** with two 1½p	
vertically se-tenant	5.50
horizontally se-tenant, original coated paper	5.00
horizontally se-tenant, fluorescent coated paper	3.00

■ Panes of six with PVA gum

Five ½p with label 'B ALAN LTD for GB STAMPS'	
perforated label	3.50
imperforate label	3.50
Five ½p with label 'LICK battery failure'	
perforated label	3.50
imperforate label	3.50
Five ½p with label 'MAKE YOUR LUCKY FIND PAY'	
imperforate label only	1.25
Four **2½p** (one centre band) with labels	
'UNIFLO STAMPS' and 'STICK FIRMLY'	
perforated label	3.50
imperforate label	3.50
Five **2½p** (one centre band) with label 'STICK FIRMLY'	
perforated label	3.50
imperforate label	3.50
Five **2½p** (one centre band) with label 'TEAR OFF to ESSO'	
perforated label	3.50
imperforate label	4.50
Five **2½p** (one centre band) with label 'STAMP COLLECTIONS'	
imperforate label only	2.75
Four **2½p** (one centre band) with labels 'DO YOU	
COLLECT GB STAMPS' and 'BUYING OR SELLING'	
imperforate label only	2.75
Five **2½p** (one centre band) with label 'B ALAN'	
imperforate label only	2.50
Five **3p** (two bands) with label '£4,315 FOR YOU'	
perforated label	1.75
imperforate label, original coated paper	1.75
imperforate label, fluorescent coated paper	3.00
Four **3p** (two bands) with two 2½p (one band at left)	
original coated paper	9.50
fluorescent coated paper	5.00
Six **3p** (two bands)	
original coated paper	4.50
fluorescent coated paper	2.50
Five **3p** (one centre band) with blank label	
imperforate label only	12.00
Five **3½p** (two bands) with blank label	
imperforate label only	6.50

■ Panes of four with PVAD gum

Two **2p** horizontally se-tenant with two ½p	1.25
Two **1p** horizontally se-tenant with two 1½p	1.50

■ Panes of six with PVAD gum

Five **3p** (one centre band) with blank label	
imperforate label only	8.00
Five **3½p** (two bands) with blank label	
imperforate label only	1.75

Five **3½p** (one centre band) with blank label
imperforate label only | 1.75
Five **4½p** (two bands) with blank label
imperforate label only | 1.75

SE-TENANT COIL STRIPS WITHOUT ELLIPTICAL PERFORATIONS, 1971-95

■ Strips with gum Arabic
One **2p**, two **½p**, two **1p**
original coated paper | 4.00
original coated paper, silicone coated | £200
fluorescent coated paper, silicone coated | 3.50

■ Strips with PVA gum
One **6p**, one **2p**, one **1p**, two **½p** (two bands)
original coated paper | 4.00

■ Strips with PVAD gum
One **2p**, two **½p**, two **1p** (two bands)
fluorescent coated paper | 1.50
One **6p**, one **2p**, one **1p**, two **½p** (two bands)
fluorescent coated paper | 4.50
Two **½p** one **7p**, two **1p** (one centre band)
fluorescent coated paper | 2.00
One **8p**, two **1p**, two labels (one centre band)
fluorescent coated paper | 1.50
One **2½p** rose, three **3p** pink
phosphor-coated paper | 1.20
fluorescent brightener omitted | 40.00
One **½p**, three **4p** blue
phosphor-coated paper | 1.20
fluorescent brightener omitted | £100
perfect gum | £1,500
One **1p** and three **4p** blue
phosphor-coated paper | 1.50
One **2p**, three **4p**
phosphor-coated paper | 2.00
Three **4p**, one **3p**
phosphor-coated paper | 1.75
Three **4p**, one **5p**
phosphor-coated paper | 1.65
Two **5p**, two **4p**
phosphor-coated paper | 1.40
Three **5p**, one **4p**
phosphor-coated paper | 1.25

NON-VALUE INDICATORS WITHOUT ELLIPTICAL PERFORATIONS, 1989-93

From retail stamp books (at least one edge may be imperforate) or prestige stamp books (marked *).

■ 2nd class bright blue (August 22, 1989)
Printed in gravure by Harrison
with one centre phosphor band | 2.00 | 1.55
with one phosphor band at right* | 3.00 | 1.85
Printed in litho by Walsall
with one centre phosphor band | 1.00 | 1.00
Printed in litho by Questa
with one centre phosphor band | 1.25 | 0.50
with one phosphor band at left* | 1.00 | 1.05
with one phosphor band at right* | 2.25 | 1.00

■ 2nd class deep blue (August 7, 1990)
Printed in gravure by Harrison
with one centre phosphor band | 1.00 | 0.55
Printed in litho by Walsall
with one centre phosphor band | 1.00 | 1.00
Printed in litho by Questa
with one centre phosphor band | 1.25 | 0.90
with one phosphor band at left* | 1.25 | 1.30

■ 1st class brownish black (August 22, 1989)
Printed in gravure by Harrison
on phosphor paper | 2.50 | 0.70
with two phosphor bands* | 2.50 | 2.00
Printed in litho by Walsall
with two phosphor bands | 1.50 | 1.35
Printed in litho by Questa
on phosphor paper | 2.50 | 1.10

■ 1st class orange red (August 7, 1990)
Printed in gravure by Harrison
on phosphor paper | 1.10 | 0.65
Printed in litho by Walsall
on phosphor paper. Perf: 14 | 1.10 | 0.65
on phosphor paper. Perf: 13 | 2.00 | 1.70
Printed in litho by Questa
on phosphor paper | 1.20 | 0.85
with two phosphor bands* | 1.75 | 1.00

First day cover August 22, 1989
(2nd bright blue, 1st brownish black | 2.25
First day cover August 7, 1990
(2nd deep blue, 1st orange red) | 2.50

LOW VALUES WITH ELLIPTICAL PERFORATIONS, 1993 to date

With an elliptical perforation towards the lower end of each vertical side.

■ **1993-2005. Printed in gravure by Enschedé**
Issued in sheets except where stated. Two phosphor bands, except where stated.

1p crimson (June 8, 1993)	0.30	0.10
2p deep green (April 11, 1995)	0.30	0.10
4p new blue (December 14, 1993)	0.35	0.10
5p claret (June 8, 1993)	0.35	0.20
6p lime green (April 27, 1993)	0.35	0.35
10p orange (June 8, 1993)	0.40	0.40
20p sea green (December 14, 1993)	0.80	0.50
25p salmon pink (October 10, 1995)	0.85	0.80
29p light grey (October 26, 1993)	0.90	0.70
30p grey-green (July 27, 1993)	0.95	0.70
31p deep purple (June 25, 1996)	0.90	0.75
35p deep yellow (August 17, 1993)	1.00	0.75
35p lime-green (April 5, 2005) (phos band)	0.80	0.80
35p lime-green (February 23, 2006)		
from Brunel prestige stamp book	1.50	1.50
36p ultramarine (October 26, 1993)	1.00	0.80
37p amethyst (June 25, 1996)	1.10	0.80
38p rosine (October 26, 1993)	1.20	0.80
39p magenta (June 25, 1996)	1.10	0.95
40p turquoise (February 23, 2006)		
from Brunel prestige stamp book	1.50	1.50
41p stone (October 26, 1993)	1.40	0.85
42p olive-grey (May 25, 2004)		
from Glory of the Garden prestige book	1.50	1.50
43p chocolate-brown (June 25, 1996)	1.50	1.10
47p turquoise green (May 25, 2004)		
from Glory of the Garden prestige book	1.50	1.50
50p ochre (December 14, 1993)	1.50	1.20
50p ochre (September 21, 2006)		

from Victoria Cross prestige stamp book	1.50	1.50
63p emerald (June 25, 1996)	1.60	1.30
£1 bluish-violet (August 22, 1995)	2.75	2.50
Stamp card (£1 stamp)	7.50	15.00

■ **1994-1996. Printed in litho by Questa**
Issued in booklets and prestige stamp books. Two phosphor bands, except where stated.

1p crimson (July 8, 1995)		
from £1 booklets	0.75	0.55
6p lime-green (July 26, 1994)		
from Northern Ireland prestige stamp book	6.50	5.00
10p deep orange (April 25, 1995)		
from National Trust prestige stamp book	2.50	2.00
19p olive green (July 26, 1994) (phos band at left)		
from Northern Ireland prestige stamp book		
and National Trust prestige stamp book	1.00	0.80
(April 25, 1995) (phos band at right)		
from National Trust prestige stamp book	1.20	0.80
20p bright green (July 8, 1996) (centre phos band)		
from £1 and £2 booklets	1.75	1.30
25p salmon-pink (July 26, 1994)		
from £1 and £2 booklets, and Northern Ireland		
and National Trust prestige stamp books	0.90	0.60
26p red-brown (July 8, 1996)		
from £1 and £2 booklets	0.80	0.80
30p grey-green (April 25, 1995)		
from National Trust prestige stamp book	2.00	2.00
35p deep yellow (April 25, 1995)		
from National Trust prestige stamp book	1.50	1.50
41p drab (April 25, 1995)		
from National Trust prestige stamp book	1.50	1.50

■ **1998-1999. Printed in gravure by Questa**
Issued in booklets and prestige stamp books. Two phosphor bands, except where stated.

1p crimson (December 1, 1998)		
from £1 booklets and World Changers		
prestige stamp book	0.75	1.00
2p myrtle-green (April 26, 1999)		
from £1 booklets	0.60	0.50
19p olive green (Apr 26, 1999) (centre phos band)		
from £1 and £2 booklets		
and World Changers PSB	0.80	0.80
20p bright green (Dec 1, 1998) (centre phos band)		
from £1 and £2 stamp booklets	10.00	1.20
26p red-brown (December 1, 1998)		
from £1 and £2 booklets and		
World Changers prestige stamp book	0.70	0.70

■ **1993-1996. Printed in litho by Walsall**
Issued in booklets. Two phosphor bands.

25p salmon-pink (November 1, 1993)		
from £1 booklets	1.20	1.00
35p deep yellow (November 1, 1993)		
from £1.40 booklets	1.50	1.00
37p amethyst (July 8, 1996)		
from £1.48 booklets	2.00	3.00
41p stone (November 1, 1993)		
from £1.64 booklets	1.50	1.00

60p slate-blue (March 19, 1996)
from £2.40 booklets 3.00 3.50
63p emerald (July 8, 1996)
from £2.52 booklets 2.25 3.00

■ 1997-2005. Printed in gravure by Walsall

Issued in booklets and prestige stamp books. Two phosphor bands, except where stated.

10p deep orange (October 13, 1998)
from Breaking Barriers prestige stamp book 1.50 1.35
19p olive-green (Feb 15, 2000) (phos band at right)
from Special By Design prestige stamp book 1.00 1.10
30p grey-green (May 5, 1998)
from £1.20 booklet 0.95 0.70
37p amethyst (August 26, 1997)
from £1.48 booklets 0.85 0.80
38p ultramarine (April 26, 1999)
from £1.52 booklet 1.00 0.90
38p ultramarine (February 15, 2000) (perf: 14)
from Special By Design prestige stamp book 1.50 1.50
39p grey (February 24, 2005)
from Bronte prestige stamp book 1.50 1.50
40p grey-blue (April 27, 2000)
from £1.60 booklet 1.00 1.00
42p olive grey (February 24, 2005)
from Bronte prestige stamp book 1.50 1.50
43p chocolate brown (October 13, 1998)
from Breaking Barriers prestige stamp book 1.50 1.50
50p ochre (October 18, 2005)
from Battle of Trafalgar prestige stamp book 1.50 1.50
63p emerald (August 26, 1997)
from £2.52 booklets 1.50 1.50
64p sea-green (April 26, 1999)
from £2.56 booklets 1.50 1.50
65p greenish blue (April 27, 2000)
from £2.60 booklets 1.50 1.50
68p grey-brown (October 18, 2005)
from Battle of Trafalgar prestige stamp book 1.50 1.50

■ 1993-2010. Printed in gravure by Harrisons and later by De La Rue

Issued in sheets. Two phosphor bands, except where stated.

1p crimson (April 1, 1997) 0.30 0.10
2p deep green (May 27, 1997) 0.30 0.10
4p new blue (May 27, 1997) 0.30 0.10
5p claret (May 27, 1997) 0.30 0.20
6p lime green (April 1, 1997) 0.35 0.10
7p light grey (April 20, 1999) 2.25 0.90
7p bright magenta (April 1, 2004) 0.50 0.15
8p deep yellow (April 25, 2000) 0.35 0.30
9p deep orange (April 5, 2005) 0.35 0.25
10p orange (May 8, 1997) 0.40 0.35
12p turquoise (August 1, 2006) 0.40 0.30
14p salmon pink (August 1, 2006) 0.75 0.35
15p shocking pink (April 1, 2008) 0.50 0.35
16p bright pink (March 27, 2007) 0.50 0.35
17p olive green (March 31, 2009) 0.50 0.30
19p olive (Oct 26, 1993) (one phos band) 0.45 0.40
20p bright green
(June 25, 1996) (centre phos band) 0.45 0.35

(September 23, 1997) (phos band at right) 1.00 1.10
(April 20, 1999) (two phos bands) 0.45 0.50
22p stone (March 31, 2009) 0.65 0.35
25p salmon-pink
(October 26, 1993) (phos coated paper) 0.60 0.60
(December 20, 1994) 0.60 0.60
26p reddish brown (June 25, 1996) 0.60 0.60
26p gold (April 29, 1997) 0.60 0.55
30p grey-green (May 12, 1997) 0.65 0.65
31p deep mauve (August 26, 1997) 0.65 0.70
33p slate-blue (April 25, 2000) 0.65 0.65
35p yellow (Nov 1, 1993) (phos coated paper) 5.00 3.50
35p sepia (April 1, 2004) 1.00 0.75
35p lime-green (April 26, 2005) 0.85 0.75
37p amethyst (July 8, 1996) 1.00 1.05
37p bright mauve (August 7, 1997) 0.80 0.45
37p deep grey (July 4, 2002) 0.80 0.80
37p olive green (March 28, 2006) 0.85 0.45
38p ultramarine (April 20, 1999) 0.70 0.70
39p magenta (May 12, 1997) 0.80 0.85
39p grey (April 1, 2004) 1.20 1.00
40p greyish blue (April 20, 1999) 0.75 0.80
40p turquoise (April 1, 2004) 1.20 1.00
41p drab (Nov 1, 1993) (phos coated paper) 5.50 4.50
41p rosine (April 20, 1999) 0.85 0.90
42p olive-grey (July 4, 2002) 0.85 0.85
43p chocolate-brown (July 8, 1996) 1.10 1.10
43p brown (March 21, 1997) 4.50 3.50
43p emerald (April 1, 2004) 0.90 0.95
44p stone (April 20, 1999) 3.00 0.75
44p ultramarine (March 28, 2006) 0.95 0.75
45p mauve (April 20, 1999) 0.80 0.85
46p light brown (April 5, 2005) 1.95 0.80
47p turquoise green (July 4, 2002) 0.85 0.85
48p purple (March 27, 2007) 1.25 1.25
49p rust (March 28, 2006) 0.95 0.80
50p ochre (April 1, 1997) 1.00 0.95
50p grey (March 27, 2007) 1.00 0.95
54p rust (March 27, 2007) 2.75 2.00
56p lime green (April 1, 2008) 1.20 1.20
60p emerald green (March 30, 2010) 1.00 1.00
62p red (March 31, 2009) 1.10 0.85
63p emerald (December 12, 1996) 1.20 1.10
64p sea green (April 20, 1999) 1.20 1.10
65p greenish blue (April 25, 2000) 1.20 1.10
67p rhododendron (March 30, 2010) 1.25 1.25
68p grey-brown (July 4, 2002) 1.95 1.50
72p red (March 28, 2006) 1.40 1.20
78p emerald green (March 27, 2007) 1.50 1.20
81p sea green (April 1, 2008) 1.50 1.25
88p shocking pink (March 30, 2010) 1.50 1.50
90p ultramarine (March 31, 2009) 1.50 1.10
97p mauve (March 30, 2010) 1.60 1.60
£1 bluish-violet (April 1, 1997) 1.60 1.90
£1 ruby (June 5, 2007) 1.95 1.25
£1.48 dark turquoise (March 30, 2010) 2.00 2.00
Stamp cards (one of each value current in September 2008, including non-value indicators; 24 in total) 15.00 15.00
(* The 2p, 5p, 37p deep grey, 46p, 48p and £1 ruby also appear in

prestige stamp books, and the £1 ruby and £1 bluish-violet in a miniature sheet of 2007.)

■ 2009. Printed in litho by De La Rue

Issued in prestige stamp books.

5p deep claret (February 12, 2009)
from Darwin prestige stamp book · 1.75 · 1.75
10p orange (February 12, 2009)
from Darwin prestige stamp book · 1.50 · 1.50
48p purple (February 12, 2009)
from Darwin prestige stamp book · 1.80 · 1.80

■ 2009. Printed in litho by Cartor

Issued in prestige stamp books.

1p crimson (September 17, 2009)
from Royal Navy Uniforms prestige book · 1.15 · 1.00
5p deep claret (February 25, 2010) wrong font*
from Classic Album Covers prestige book · 1.75 · 1.75
5p deep claret (May 13, 2010)
from Britain Alone prestige book · 1.75 · 1.75
10p orange-brown (February 25, 2010)
from Classic Album Covers
and Britain Alone prestige books · 2.00 · 2.00
16p bright pink (January 13, 2009)
from Design Classics prestige stamp book · 2.00 · 2.00
17p olive green (August 18, 2009)
from Treasures of the Archive and
Royal Navy Uniforms prestige books · 1.25 · 1.25
20p bright green (February 25, 2010)
from Classic Album Covers prestige book · 1.50 · 1.50
22p stone (August 18, 2009)
from Treasures of the Archive, Classic Album
Covers and Royal Sociiety prestige books · 1.95 · 1.75
50p grey (January 13, 2009)
from Design Classics prestige stamp book · 2.00 · 2.00
54p rust (February 25, 2010) wrong font*
from Classic Album Covers and
Royal Society prestige books · 2.80 · 2.50
60p emerald-green (May 13, 2010)
from Britain Alone prestige book · 2.50 · 2.50
62p red (August 18, 2009)
from Treasures of the Archive and
Classic Album Covers prestige books · 1.95 · 1.95
90p ultramarine (September 17, 2009)
from Royal Navy Uniforms prestige book · 2.70 · 2.70
(* Two prestige stamp books in 2010 included definitives
using the wrong font for the '5' of 5p and '54' of 54p.)

First day cover October 26, 1993
(19p, 25p, 29p, 36p, 38p, 41p) · 4.00
First day cover August 9, 1994
(60p) · 2.00
First day cover August 22, 1995
(£1) · 2.50
First day cover June 25, 1996
(20p, 26p, 31p, 37p, 39p, 43p, 63p) · 4.25
First day cover April 21, 1997
(26p, together with 1st gold) · 2.50
First day cover April 20, 1999
(7p, 38p, 44p, 64p) · 4.00

First day cover April 25, 2000
(8p, 33p, 40p, 41p, 45p, 65p) · 4.50
First day cover July 4, 2002
(37p, 42p, 47p, 68p) · 5.00
First day cover May 6, 2003
(34p) · 1.20
First day cover April 1, 2004
(7p, 35p, 39p, 40p, 43p) · 7.50
First day cover April 5, 2005
(9p, 35p, 46p) · 2.50
First day cover March 28, 2006
(37p, 44p, 49p, 72p) · 6.50
First day cover August 1, 2006
(12p, 14p, together with Pricing in Proportion stamps) · 3.75
First day cover March 27, 2007
(16p, 48p, 50p, 54p, 78p) · 6.50
First day cover June 5, 2007
(£1) · 2.00
First day cover April 1, 2008
(15p, 56p, 81p) · 5.00
First day cover March 31, 2009
(17p, 22p, 62p, 90p) · 5.50
First day cover March 30, 2010
(60p, 67p, 88p, 97p, £1.46, with Europe, Worldwide NVIs) · 7.50

NON-VALUE INDICATORS WITH ELLIPTICAL PERFORATIONS, 1993-2000

Issued in booklets or coils. 2nd class stamps have one centre phosphor band; the others have two phosphor bands, except where stated.

■ 1993-1999. Printed in gravure by Harrison

2nd bright blue (September 7, 1993) · 0.80 · 0.50
1st orange-red*
(April 6, 1993) (phos coated paper) · 1.00 · 0.55
(April 4, 1995) (two phosphor bands) · 1.10 · 0.65
1st gold (April 21, 1997)* · 1.20 · 0.75

E deep blue (October 5, 1999)	1.50	0.85
Stamp card (1st gold)	0.75	3.00

■ 1993. Printed in litho by Walsall

2nd bright blue (April 6, 1993)	1.00	0.60
1st orange-red (April 6, 1993)	1.20	0.60

■ 1997-1999. Printed in gravure by Walsall

2nd bright blue (April 29, 1997)	1.00	0.80
1st gold (April 21, 1997)	1.20	0.80
1st orange-red (August 26, 1997)	0.75	0.60
E deep blue (January 19, 1999)	1.50	0.70

■ 1993. Printed in litho by Questa

2nd bright blue (April 6, 1993)	1.00	0.65
1st orange-red (April 6, 1993)	1.25	0.80

■ 1998-2000. Printed in gravure by Questa

2nd bright blue (Dec 1, 1998) (perf: 14)	1.00	0.75
2nd bright blue (Apr 27, 2000) (perf: 15x14)	1.00	0.65
1st orange-red (Dec 1, 1998) (perf: 14)	1.10	0.80
1st orange-red (Apr 27, 2000) (perf: 15x14)	1.10	0.80

First day cover April 6, 1993	
(2nd bright blue, 1st orange-red)	5.00
First day cover April 21, 1997	
(1st gold, together with 26p)	2.50
First day cover January 19, 1999	
(E deep blue)	2.00

(* The 2nd class bright blue printed in gravure by Enschedé and Walsall, the 1st class orange-red printed in gravure by Questa, the 1st class gold printed in gravure by De La Rue, Enschedé, Questa and Walsall, and the E deep blue printed in gravure by Enschedé and Questa are also found in prestige stamp books.)

NON-VALUE INDICATORS IN GREETINGS CARD SHEETLETS, 1994-97

Small sheets including one 1st class orange-red stamp sold in conjunction with greetings cards, through Boots and other retail outlets.

■ 1994-1995. Printed in litho by Questa

1st sheetlet with Boots logo (Aug 17, 1994)	2.00	2.00
1st sheetlet with no logo (Sep 11, 1995)	1.30	1.20

■ 1997. Printed in litho by Enschedé

1st sheetlet with no logo (Apr 29, 1997)	1.25	1.15

SELF-ADHESIVES, 1993-2010

All with elliptical perforations except where otherwise stated.

■ 1993, October 19

Des: Jeffery Matthews. Printed in litho by Walsall. Horizontal format. Issued only in booklets of 20.

1st orange-red	1.30	1.20
Stamp card	9.00	8.00
First day cover		2.50

■ 1997, March 18

Des: Jeffery Matthews. Printed in gravure by Enschedé. Horizontal format with 'st' or 'nd' in large size. Issued only in rolls of 100.

2nd bright blue	1.30	1.20
1st orange-red	1.30	1.20
First day cover		3.50

■ 1998, April 6

Printed in gravure by Enschedé in rolls of 200, by Walsall in business sheets of 100 and booklets, by Questa in business sheets of 100 (1st class only) and by Enschedé in business sheets of 100. Perf: 15 x 14 except where stated.

2nd bright blue	1.30	1.20
2nd bright blue (Perf: 14½ x 14)	£125	£125

1st orange-red	1.30	1.50
1st orange-red (Perf: 14½ x 14)	£125	£125

(* Perf: 14½ x 14 stamps were printed only by Walsall, and sold only individually through Royal Mail's Tallents House)

■ 2002, June 5

Printed in gravure by De La Rue, Questa and Walsall in retail stamp booklets, and by Enschedé and Walsall in business sheets of 100.

1st gold	1.20	0.80

■ 2002, July 4. Overseas rates

Printed in gravure by Walsall. Issued only in retail books.

E deep blue	1.60	1.00
42p olive-grey	3.50	1.00
68p grey-brown	4.50	1.50

■ 2003-2010. Overseas rates with airmail chevrons

Des: Sedley Place. Printed in gravure by Walsall. Issued only in booklets, although individual stamps were sold through Royal Mail's Tallents House.

Europe up to 40g (March 27, 2003)	1.90	0.85
Europe up to 20g (March 30, 2010)	1.50	1.00
Worldwide up to 40g (March 27, 2003)	2.50	1.25
Worldwide up to 20g (March 30, 2010)	2.00	1.25
Worldwide Postcard (April 1, 2004)	1.30	1.25
First day cover (March 27, 2003)		4.25
First day cover (April 1, 2004)		3.25
First day cover (March 30 2010, with other values)		7.50

■ 2006. Pricing in Proportion

Des: Mike Dempsey. Printed in gravure by De La Rue.

2nd blue (August 1, 2006)	1.00	0.40
2nd Large blue (August 1, 2006)	1.30	0.60
1st gold (August 1, 2006)	1.20	0.50
1st Large gold (August 1, 2006)	1.60	0.80
First day cover (together with 12p, 14p)		3.75

(* All four values also appear printed in gravure by De La Rue, and the 1st class printed in gravure by Enschedé, in prestige stamp books.)

SELF-ADHESIVES WITH EXTRA SECURITY FEATURES, 2009 to date

Stamps feature U-shaped security slits, and/or an iridescent overlay text inscribed 'Royal Mail' but including variant letters which indicate the source of the stamp (where it is not from counter sheets), and from 2010 the year of production.

Source codes are MFIL or FOYAL (booklet panes of four), MSIL (booklet panes of six), MTIL (booklet panes of 12), MCIL (booklets that include special issues), MPIL (prestige stamp books), MBIL or ROYBL (business sheets) and MRIL (rolls). On booklet panes of four and business sheets, the entire word does not appear.

Year codes are MA10 (2010), M11L or MA11 (2011), and M12L (2012).

■ 2009, February 17

Printed in gravure by De La Rue (sheets and 2nd, 2nd Large, 1st and 1st Large business sheets) or Walsall (2nd, 2nd Large, 1st and 1st Large booklets). With slits and overlay text.

2nd blue	0.80	0.60
2nd Large blue	1.10	0.85
1st gold	1.00	0.65
1st Large gold	1.50	0.90
50p grey	1.00	0.75
£1 ruby	1.80	1.50
First day cover		5.00

(* The 2nd class exists with no date code, from counter sheets, business sheets and booklets, with date codes '10' or '11' from counter sheets, business sheets and booklets, or with date code '12' from business sheets and booklets.)

(* The 2nd Large exists with no date code, from counter sheets, business sheets and booklets, or with date codes '10' or '11' from counter sheets, business sheets and booklets.)

(* The 1st class exists with no date code, from counter sheets, business sheets and booklets, with date codes '10' or '11' from counter sheets, business sheets, booklets and prestige stamp books, or with date code '12' from booklets.)

(* The 1st Large exists with no date code, from counter sheets, business sheets and booklets, or with date codes '10' or '11' from counter sheets, business sheets and booklets.)

(* The 50p exists with no date code, from counter sheets, or with date codes '10' or '11', from prestige stamp books.

(* The £1 exists with no date code, or with date codes '11' or '12'.)

■ 2009, November 17. Recorded/Signed For
Printed in gravure by De La Rue. With slits and overlay text.

1st orange-red and yellow	2.50	2.00
1st Large orange-red and yellow	2.95	2.50
First day cover		5.00

(* These stamps exist with no date code, or with date code '10'.)

■ 2010, May 13
Printed in gravure by De La Rue. With overlay text but without slits. Issued only in rolls.

2nd blue	0.75	0.75
1st gold	1.00	1.00

(The 1st gold also exists from rolls with slits but without overlay text.)

■ 2010, October 26. Special Delivery
Printed in gravure by De La Rue. With slits and overlay text.

1st up to 100g silver and blue	8.25	7.50
1st up to 500g blue and silver	9.50	8.00
First day cover		15.00

■ 2011, March 8
Printed in gravure by De La Rue. With slits but without overlay text.

1p dark maroon	0.10	0.10
2p dark green	0.10	0.10
5p ash pink	0.10	0.10
10p light tan	0.20	0.20
20p light green	0.40	0.40
First day cover		2.00

(* The 5p and 10p also exist from a prestige stamp book.)

■ 2011, March 29
Printed in gravure by De La Rue. With slits and overlay text.

68p sea green	1.20	1.20
76p bright pink	1.30	1.30
£1.10 lime green	2.00	2.00
£1.65 sage green	2.50	2.50
First day cover		7.00

(* The 68p and 76p exist with date code '11' or '12'. The £1.10 and £1.65 have only been reported with date code '11'.)

■ 2012, April 25
Printed in gravure by De La Rue. With slits and overlay text.

87p orange	1.50	1.50
£1.28 emerald green	2.50	2.50
£1.90 rhododendron	3.50	3.50
First day cover		9.50

(* The Royal Mail first day cover also included the 1st Large Diamond Jubilee definitive.)

HIGH VALUES, 1970 to date

■ 1970, June 17. Large format
Des: Arnold Machin. Printed in recess by Bradbury, Wilkinson.
No wmk. Perf: 12.

10p cerise, phos paper	1.00	0.90
20p olive-green	0.90	0.60
50p ultramarine	1.00	0.40
phosphor paper (Feb 1, 1973)	2.00	1.00
£1 black (Dec 6, 1972)	3.50	1.00
First day cover (10p, 20p, 50p)		2.50
First day cover (£1)		2.50

(* Initially the £1 was identical to that issued in 1969, although
printed in sheets of 100 instead of 40. However, in 1972 it was
re-released with the denomination in a different typeface.)

■ 1977, February 2
Des: Arnold Machin. Printed in photogravure by Harrison. Perf:
14x15.

£1 olive, deep green	2.50	0.30
£1.30 steel blue, buff (Aug 3, 1983)	5.00	4.50
£1.33 lilac, deep blue (Aug 28, 1984)	6.00	6.00
£1.41 deep blue, pale blue, green (Sep 17, 1985)	6.00	6.00
£1.50 rose-lilac, blue-black (Sep 2, 1986)	5.00	4.00
£1.60 buff, blue-green (Sep 15, 1987)	5.00	4.50
£2 emerald, deep purple	6.00	0.50
£5 pink, blue	10.00	2.50
Set	40.00	24.00
Gutter pair	£100	
Traffic light gutter pair	£110	

First day cover (£1, £2, £5)		12.00
First day cover (£1.30)		7.00
First day cover (£1.33)		7.00
First day cover (£1.41)		7.00
First day cover (£1.50)		6.00
First day cover (£1.60)		6.50

■ 1999, March 9. Small format
Printed in intaglio by Enschedé. Engraved by C. Slania.

£1.50 red, **£2** blue, **£3** violet, **£5** brown		
Set	25.00	15.00
First day cover		20.00

■ 2000, April 11
Printed in intaglio by De La Rue.

£1.50 red, **£2** blue, **£3** violet, **£5** brown		
Set	25.00	15.00
First day cover		30.00

■ 2003, July 1
Printed in gravure by De La Rue.

£1.50 brown-red, **£2** blue-green, **£3** mauve, **£5** grey-blue		
Set	18.50	14.50
First day cover		20.00

■ 2009, February 17. Added security features
Printed in gravure by De La Rue. Self-adhesive, with security slits
and iridescent overlay text.

£1.50 brown-red, **£2** blue-green, **£3** mauve, **£5** azure		
Set	16.00	15.00
First day cover		20.00

SPECIAL ISSUES, 1990 to date

■ **1999, February 6. Large-format Machin-head designs**

Issued only in the Profile On Print prestige stamp book.

A) Embossed and litho printed by Walsall. Self-adhesive.

1st pale grey		1.60	1.40

B) Recess printed by Enschedé. Engraved by C. Slania. Two phosphor bands.

1st grey-black		1.60	1.40

C) Printed in typography by Harrison. Two phosphor bands.

1st black		1.60	1.40

■ **1990, January 10. 150th Anniversary of the Penny Black**

Des: Jeffery Matthews. Issued in sheets and booklets; the stamps from booklets can have one or more edges imperforate.

A) Printed in photogravure by Harrison, from sheets and booklets and, where marked *, from the London Life prestige stamp book

15p bright blue (one centre phos band)	1.00	0.75
(one phos band at left)*	2.75	2.00
(one phos band at right)*	3.25	3.00
20p brownish-black and cream (phos paper)	1.00	0.65
(two phos bands)*	2.00	2.00
29p mauve (phosphor paper)	1.50	1.10
(two phosphor bands)*	6.00	5.00
34p blue-grey	1.50	1.25
37p rosine	1.50	1.25
First day cover		7.00

B) Printed in litho by Walsall, only from booklets

15p bright blue (one centre phos band)	1.20	0.90
20p brownish-black and cream (phos paper)	1.20	0.90

C) Printed in litho by Questa, only from booklets

15p bright blue (one centre phos band)	1.25	1.30
20p brownish-black (phos paper)	1.20	0.90

D) Printed in gravure by Walsall, only from the Special by Design prestige stamp book

1st brownish black and cream	1.20	1.00

E) Printed in litho by Cartor, only from the Treasures of the Archive prestige stamp book

1st brownish black	1.30	1.10
20p brownish black	1.10	1.00

■ **2000, January 6. Millennium definitive**

Des: R. Scholey.

Printed in gravure by Harrison. Perf: 15 x 14. Issued in sheets.

1st olive-brown		1.20	0.70
First day cover			2.50

Printed in gravure by Walsall. Perf: 15 x 14. Issued in retail books.

1st olive-brown		1.20	0.70

Printed in gravure by Walsall. Perf: 14. Issued in the Special By Design and Treasury Of Trees prestige stamp books.

1st olive-brown		1.25	0.90

Printed in gravure by Questa. Perf: 14. Issued in retail stamp booklets.

1st olive-brown		1.20	0.70

Printed in gravure by Questa. Perf: 15 x 14. Issued in the Queen Elizabeth The Queen Mother prestige stamp book.

1st olive-brown		1.30	1.00

■ 2000, May 22. Stamp Show 2000 Exhibition Souvenir

Des: Jeffery Matthews. Printed by De La Rue. Phosphor paper. Miniature sheet comprising 4p blue, 5p claret, 6p lime green, 10p orange, 31p purple, 39p magenta, 64p sea-green, £1 bluish violet, plus the Royal Mail crest and the Jeffery Matthews colour palette.

Miniature sheet	10.00	10.00
First day cover		20.00

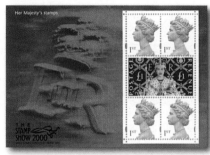

■ 2000, May 23. Her Majesty's Stamps. Stamp Show 2000

Des: Delaney Design Consultants. Printed in gravure by De La Rue. Comprising four 1st class Millennium definitives, plus the 1953 Coronation design by Edmund Dulac, with face value £1.

Miniature sheet	18.00	18.00
First day cover		20.00
Stamp cards	16.00	25.00

EXHIBITION SOUVENIR

■ 2010, May 8. London 2010 Festival of Stamps Exhibition Souvenir

Printed by De La Rue. Two phosphor bands. Miniature sheet comprising 1p, 2p, 5p, 9p, 10p, 20p, 60p, 67p, 88p. 97p, £1.46, plus a label featuring the London 2010: Festival of Stamps logo

Miniature sheet	7.00	7.00
First day cover		7.50

In June 1967 Royal Mail introduced a new definitive stamp design. Arnold Machin's bas-relief portrait of HM The Queen has been acknowledged as a classic icon of British design.

Amold Machin 1911–1999

■ 2011, September 14. Centenary of the Birth of Arnold Machin

Printed by Cartor. Miniature sheet comprising ten 1st class gold, with security overlay but no slits.

Miniature sheet	10.00	9.00
First day cover		8.50

■ 2012, February 6. Diamond Jubilee definitives

Printed in gravure by De La Rue (counter sheets, 1st class business sheets) or Walsall (booklets, 1st class and 1st Large business sheets). Self-adhesive. With slits and overlay text reading 'Diamond Jubilee'.

1st diamond blue	0.90	0.90
First day cover		2.00
1st Large diamond blue (April 25)	1.50	1.50
First day cover		2.50

(*The 1st class value also appears, printed by Walsall with normal gum, in the Diamond Jubilee prestige stamp book and miniature sheet. The 1st Large value was released early by a number of post offices; the Royal Mail first day cover for this stamp also included the 87p, £1.28 and £1.90 definitives.)

QUEEN ELIZABETH II DECIMAL SPECIAL ISSUES

In this section, prices are quoted in two columns: unmounted mint (left) and fine used (right). Most issues, as well as gutter pairs and stamp cards, are priced for complete sets only except where stated.

Except where otherwise stated, all stamps were printed in photogravure by Harrison. Gutter pairs and traffic-light gutter pairs appear from November 1972, blue-tinted polyvinyl alcohol dextrin (PVAD) gum from November 1973 and phosphor-coated paper from September 1979.

'A Mountain Road' by Flanagan (3p)

'Deer's Meadow' by Carr (7½p)
'Slieve na brock' by Middleton (9p)

■ 1971, June 16. Ulster Paintings
Des: S. Rose.

Set	0.50	0.60
First day cover		1.25

John Keats (3p)

Thomas Gray (5p)
Sir Walter Scott (7½p)

■ 1971, July 28. Literary Anniversaries
Des: Rosalind Dease.

Set	0.50	0.60
First day cover		1.40

British Legion: Servicemen and a nurse (3p)

City of York: A Roman Centurion (7½p)
Rugby Football Union: Rugby Players (9p)
■ 1971, August 25. Anniversaries

Des: F. Wegner.

Set	0.50	0.60
First day cover		1.25

University College, Aberystwyth (3p)

University of Southampton (5p)
University of Leicester (7½p)
University of Essex (9p)

■ 1971, September 22. Modern University Buildings
Des: N. Jenkins.

Set	0.85	1.00
First day cover		1.25

'Dream of the Wise Men' (2½p)

'Adoration of the Magi' (3p)
'Ride of the Magi' (7½p)

■ 1971, October 13. Christmas
Des: Clarke, Clement and Hughes based on stained glass windows at Canterbury Cathedral.

Set	0.40	0.50
First day cover		1.25

Sir James Clarke Ross (3p)

Sir Martin Frobisher (5p)
Henry Hudson (7½p)
Captain Scott (9p)

■ 1972, February 16. Polar Explorers
Des: Marjorie Seynor.

Set	0.80	0.90
First day cover		1.40

Tutankhamun (3p)

Coastguard (7½p)
Ralph Vaughan Williams (9p)

■ 1972, April 26. Anniversaries
Des: Rosalind Dease (3p), F. Wegner (7½p), C. Abbott (9p)
Set   0.50   0.60
First day cover   1.40
St. Andrew's, Greensted-juxta-Ongar, Essex (3p)

All Saints, Earls Barton, Northants (4p)
St. Andrew's, Lethringsett, Norfolk (5p)
St. Andrew's, Helpringham, Lincs (7½p)
St. Mary the Virgin, Huish Episcopi, Somerset (9p)

■ 1972, June 21. Village Churches
Des: R. Maddox.
Set   1.10   1.35
First day cover   2.00
Microphones (3p)

Horn Loudspeaker (5p)
Colour Television (7½p)
Oscillator and Spark Transmitter (9p)

■ 1972, September 13. 50th Anniversary of the BBC
Des: D. Gentleman.
Set   0.75   0.90
First day cover   1.45
Angel with trumpet (2½p)

Angel with lute (3p)
Angel with harp (7½p)

■ 1972, October 19. Christmas
Des: Sally Stiff.
Set   0.30   0.40
First day cover   1.25
Queen Elizabeth II and Prince Phillip (3p), (20p)

■ 1972, November 20, Royal Silver Wedding
Des: J. Matthews from photograph by Norman Parkinson.
All-over phosphor (3p), no phosphor (20p).
i) Printed on a Rembrandt machine
Set   0.90   0.80
First day cover   1.25
ii) Printed on a Jumelle machine.
3p deep blue, brown, silver   0.25   0.25
Gutter pair   0.40
Traffic light gutter pair   10.00
(* The portraits tend to be lighter on the Jumelle printing)
Jigsaw pieces representing Europe (3p), (5p)

■ 1973, January 3, European Communities
Des: P. Murdoch.
Set   0.75   0.85
First day cover   1.25
Oak Tree (9p)

■ **1973, February 28. British Trees**
Des: D. Gentleman.

9p multicoloured	0.20	0.25
First day cover		1.25

David Livingstone (3p)

H.M. Stanley (3p)
Francis Drake (5p)
Walter Raleigh (7½p)
Charles Sturt (9p)

■ **1973, April 18. British Explorers**
Des: Marjorie Seynor. All-over phosphor.

Set	1.10	1.00
First day cover		1.40

About to bat (3p)

Watching the ball (7½p)
Leaving the wicket (9p)

■ **1973, May 16. County Cricket**
Des: E Ripley, based on drawings by Harry Furniss of W.G. Grace.

Set	1.00	1.00
First day cover		1.25
Stamp card (of 3p design)	50.00	

Self portrait of Joshua Reynolds (3p)

Self portrait of Henry Raeburn (5p)
'Nelly O'Brien' by Reynolds (7½p)
'Rev. R. Walker' by Raeburn (9p)

■ **1973, July. British Painters**
Des: S. Rose.

Set	0.70	0.80
First day cover		1.25

Court Masque Costumes (3p)

St Paul's church, Covent Garden (3p)
Prince's Lodging, Newmarket (5p)
Court Masque Stage Scene (5p)

■ **1973, August 15. 400th Anniversary of Birth of Inigo Jones**
Des: Rosalind Dease. Printed in litho and typo by Bradbury, Wilkinson.

Set	0.60	1.00
First day cover		1.25
Stamp card (of 3p St Paul's)	£140	£200

Palace of Westminster from Whitehall (8p)

Palace of Westminster from Millbank (10p)

■ **1973, September 12. Commonwealth Parliamentary Conference**
Des: R. Downer. Printed in recess and litho by Bradbury, Wilkinson.

Set	0.40	0.50
First day cover		1.25
Stamp card (of 8p design)	25.00	£175

Princess Anne and Captain Mark Phillips (3½p), (20p)

■ 1973, November 14. Royal Wedding
Des: C. Clements and E. Hughes based on photograph by Lord Lichfield

Set	0.50	0.55
Gutter pair	1.50	
Traffic light gutter pair	65.00	
First day cover		1.25
Stamp card (of 3½p design)	5.00	20.00

(* The 3½p exists from sheets guillotined in the wrong place giving incorrect inscriptions within the gutter: priced at £30.)

Good King Wenceslas (five different 3p designs)
Good King Wenceslas, the Page and the Peasant (3½p)

■ 1973, November 28. Christmas
Des: D. Gentleman. 3p values have one phosphor band. These stamps exist with either gum Arabic (3p), PVA gum (3½p) or dextrin gum (both values); prices are the same.

Set	1.50	1.70
First day cover		1.20

Horse Chestnut (10p)

■ 1974, February 27. British Trees
Des: D. Gentleman.

10p	0.25	0.25
Gutter pair	1.00	
Traffic light gutter pair	50.00	
First day cover		1.25
Stamp card	85.00	75.00

First Motor Fire Engine 1904 (3½p)
Fire Engine 1863 (5½p)
Steam Fire Engine (8p)
Fire Engine 1766 (10p)

■ 1974, April 24. Fire Engines
Des: D. Gentleman. Dextrin gum except where stated.

3½p with PVA gum	0.90	–
Set	0.75	0.80
Gutter pairs	2.50	
Traffic light gutter pairs	40.00	
First day cover		2.00
Stamp card (of 3½p)	65.00	75.00

P&O Packet Steamer 'Peninsular' (3½p)
Coronation Airmail 1911 (5½p)
Blue Airmail Van (8p)
Imperial Airways Flying boat (10p)

■ 1974, June 12. Centenary of the UPU
Des: Rosalind Dease.

Set	0.50	0.75
Gutter pairs	1.75	
Traffic light gutter pairs	35.00	
First day cover		1.20

Robert the Bruce (4½p)
Owain Glyndwr (5½p)
Henry V (8p)
The Black Prince (10p)

■ 1974, July 10. Medieval Warriors
Des: F. Wegner.

Set	0.70	0.80
Gutter pairs	3.00	
Traffic light gutter pairs	45.00	
First day cover		1.75
Stamp card (set)	16.00	70.00

Lord Warden of the Cinque Ports (4½p)
Prime Minister (5½p)
Secretary for War and Air (8p)
War Correspondent in South Africa (10p)

■ 1974, October 9. Birth Centenary of Winston Churchill
Des: C. Clements and E. Hughes.

8p with PVA gum	0.50	–
Set	0.90	0.85
Gutter pairs	1.75	
Traffic light gutter pairs	24.00	
First day cover		1.20
Stamp card (of 5½p)	2.50	17.00

'Adoration of the Magi' (3½p)
'The Nativity' (4½p)
'Virgin and Child' (8p)
'Virgin and Child' (10p)

■ 1974, November 27. Christmas
Des: Peter Hatch Partnership based on church roof bosses.

3½p with phos band to right	0.20	0.25
Set	0.50	0.60
Gutter pairs	2.25	
Traffic light gutter pairs	25.00	
First day cover		1.25

Invalid in Wheelchair (4½p + 1½p)

■ 1975, January 22. Health and Handicap Charities
Des: P. Sharland. Surcharge donated to charity.

4½p + 1½p	0.15	0.15
Gutter pair	0.30	
Traffic light gutter pair	1.00	
First day cover		0.50

'Peace: Burial at Sea' (4½p)
'Snowstorm' (5½p)
'The Arsenal, Venice' (8p)
'St. Laurent' (10p)

■ 1975, February 19. Bicentenary of the Birth of Turner
Des: S. Rose.

Set	0.50	0.60
Gutter pairs	1.25	
Traffic light gutter pairs	6.00	
First day cover		1.00
Stamp card (of 5½p)	20.00	17.00

Charlotte Square, Edinburgh (7p)
The Rows, Chester (7p)
Royal Observatory, Greenwich (8p)
St. George's Chapel, Windsor (10p)
National Theatre, London (12p)

■ 1975, April 23. European Architectural Heritage Year
Des: P. Gauld.

Set	0.80	1.00
Gutter pairs	3.00	
Traffic light gutter pairs		12.00
First day cover		1.50
Stamp cards (7p and 8p)	6.00	25.00

Sailing Dinghies (7p)
Racing Keel Boats (8p)
Cruising Yachts (10p)
Multihulls (12p)

■ 1975, June 11. Sailing

Des: A. Restall. Printed in photogravure and recess by Harrison.

Set	0.60	0.75
Gutter pairs	1.50	
Traffic light gutter pairs	16.00	
First day cover		1.20
Stamp card (of 8p)	4.00	15.00

(* The 7p exists from sheets guillotined in the wrong place, giving gutter pairs with the wrong inscriptions, priced at £45.)

Stephenson's 'Locomotion' (7p)
Waverley Class (8p)
Caerphilly Class (10p)
High Speed Train (12p)

■ 1975, August 13. Railways

Des: B. Cracker.

Set	0.80	0.80
Gutter Pairs	2.25	
Traffic light gutter pairs	7.00	
First day cover		1.50
Stamp cards (set)	25.00	35.00

Palace of Westminster (12p)

■ 1975, September 3. Inter-Parliamentary Union Conference

Des: R. Downer

12p	0.25	0.25
Gutter pair	0.60	
Traffic light gutter pair	2.00	
First day cover		0.75

Emma and Mr. Woodhouse (8½p)
Catherine Morland (10p)
Mr. Darcy (11p)
Mary and Henry Crawford (13p)

■ 1975, October 22. Jane Austen Birth Bicentenary

Des: Barbara Brown.

Set	0.70	0.70
Gutter pairs	1.40	
Traffic light gutter pairs	5.50	
First day cover		1.25
Stamp cards (set)	10.00	30.00

Angel with harp and lute (6½p)
Angel with mandolin (8½p)
Angel with horn (11p)
Angel with trumpet (13p)

■ 1975, November 25. Christmas

Des: R. Downer. Dextrin gum except where stated. The 8½p has the phosphor in the green printing ink

6½p with PVA gum	0.50	-
Set	0.65	0.75
Gutter pairs	1.40	
Traffic light gutter pairs	5.50	
First day cover		1.00

Housewife with telephone (8½p)
Policeman with telephone (10p)
District Nurse with telephone (11p)
Industrialist with telephone (13p)

■ 1976, March 10. Centenary of First Telephone Conversation

Des: P. Sharland.

Set	0.75	0.80
Gutter pairs	1.50	
Traffic light gutter pairs	5.50	
First day cover		1.00

Mining coal: Thomas Hepburn (8½p)
Machinery: Robert Owen (10p)
Sweeping a chimney: Lord Shaftesbury (11p)
Prison bars: Elizabeth Fry (13p)

■ 1976, April 28. Social Reformers
Des: D. Gentleman.

Set	0.70	0.80
Gutter pairs	1.50	
Traffic light gutter pairs	5.50	
First day cover		1.00
Stamp card (of 8½p)	3.00	10.00

Benjamin Franklin (11p)

■ 1976, June 2. American Bicentennial
Des: P. Sharland.

11p	0.25	0.25
Gutter pair	0.50	
Traffic light gutter pair	1.75	
First day cover		1.00
Stamp card	3.50	10.00

Elizabeth of Glamis (8½p)
Grandpa Dickson (10p)
Rosa Mundi (11p)
Sweet Briar (13p)

■ 1976, June 30. Roses
Des: Kristin Rosenberg.

Set	0.70	0.80
Gutter pairs	1.50	
Traffic light gutter pairs	7.00	
First day cover		1.25
Stamp cards	15.00	25.00

Archdruid (Royal National Eisteddfod) (8½p)
Morris Dancing (10p)
Highland Gathering (11p)
Harpist (Royal National Eisteddfod) (13p)

■ 1976, August 4. Cultural Traditions
Des: Marjorie Seynor.

Set	0.70	0.80
Gutter pairs	1.50	
Traffic light gutter pairs	6.00	
First day cover		1.00
Stamp cards	9.00	17.00

'The Canterbury Tales' (8½p)
'The Tretyse of Love' (10p)
'The Game and Playe of Chesse (11p)
Printing Press (13p)

■ 1976, September 29. 500th Anniversary of British Printing
Des: R. Gay.

Set	0.70	0.75
Gutter pairs	1.50	
Traffic light gutter pairs	5.50	
First day cover		1.00
Stamp cards	7.00	17.00

Virgin and Child (6½p)
Angel (8½p)
Angel with Shepherds (11p)
The Three Kings (13p)

■ **1976, November 24. Christmas.**
Des: Enid Marx (based on English embroideries)

6½p with one phos band	0.15	0.10
Set	0.80	0.70
Gutter pairs	1.50	
Traffic light gutter pairs	6.50	
First day cover		1.00
Stamp cards	2.50	17.00

Lawn Tennis (8½p)
Table Tennis (10p)
Squash (11p)
Badminton (13p)

■ **1977, January 12. Racket Sports**
Des: A. Restall.

Set	0.75	0.70
Gutter pairs	1.75	
Traffic light gutter pairs	4.50	
First day cover		1.25
Stamp cards	4.50	17.00

Steroids (8½p)
Vitamin C (10p)
Starch Chromatography (11p)
Salt Crystallography (13p)

■ **1977, March 2. Centenary of the Royal Institute of Chemistry**
Des: J. Karo.

Set	0.65	0.65
Gutter pairs	1.75	
Traffic light gutter pairs	4.50	
First day cover		1.25
Stamp cards	4.50	10.00

ER (8½p, 9p, 10p, 11p, 13p)

■ **1977, May 11. Silver Jubilee.**
Des: Professor R. Guyatt. 9p issued on June 15.

Set	0.80	0.75
Gutter pairs	1.80	
Traffic light gutter pairs	4.50	
First day cover (8½p, 10p, 11p, 13p)		1.00
First day cover (9p)		0.50
Stamp cards	5.00	11.00

Symbol of Pentagons (13p)

■ **1977, June 8. Commonwealth Heads of Government Meeting**
Des: P. Murdoch. Printed in photogravure and recess by Harrison.

13p	0.25	0.25
Gutter pair	0.50	
Traffic light gutter pair	1.25	
First day cover		0.50
Stamp card	2.00	2.00

Hedgehog *Erinaceus europaeus*

Hedgehog (9p)
Hare (9p)
Red Squirrel (9p)
Otter (9p)
Badger (9p)

■ 1977, October 5. Wildlife.
Des: P Oxenham. All multicoloured

Se-tenant strip of five	0.90	1.20
Gutter strip	1.25	
Traffic light gutter strip	3.50	
First day cover		1.40
Stamp cards	3.00	5.00

(* Gutter strips normally comprise a strip of four designs separated from the fifth design by the gutter.)

THE TWELVE DAYS OF CHRISTMAS

Three French Hens, two Turtle Doves and a Partridge in a Pear Tree (7p)
Six Geese, five Gold Rings, four Colley Birds (7p)
Eight Maids, seven Swans (7p)
Ten Pipers, nine Drummers (7p)
Twelve Lords, eleven Ladies (7p)
A Partridge and Pears (9p)

■ 1977, November 23. Christmas
Des: D. Gentleman based on the Christmas song 'The Twelve Days of Christmas'. The 7p values, issued se-tenant, have one phosphor band.

Set	0.75	0.85
Gutter pairs	1.50	
Traffic light gutter pairs	4.00	
First day cover		1.25
Stamp cards	2.25	5.00

(* Gutter pairs of the 7p values comprise two horizontal se-tenant strips of the stamps separated by a horizontal gutter.)

OIL

North Sea Oil (9p)
Coal Pithead (10½p)
Natural Gas Flame (11p)
Electricity (13p)

■ 1978, January 25. Energy
Des: P. Murdoch.

Set	0.65	0.75
Gutter pairs	1.50	
Traffic light gutter pairs	2.50	
First day cover		1.25
Stamp cards	1.75	4.00

Tower of London-The White Tower

Tower of London (9p)
Holyroodhouse (10½p)
Caernarvon Castle (11p)
Hampton Court (13p)

■ 1978, March 1. Historic Buildings
Des: R. Maddox; miniature sheet by J. Matthews

Set	0.75	0.80
Gutter pairs	1.60	
Traffic light gutter pairs	2.50	
First day cover		1.25
Stamp cards	2.00	4.00
Miniature sheet (one of each value)	0.75	0.85
Miniature sheet first day cover		1.25

(* The miniature sheet was sold at 53½p, the extra 10p being donated to assist the finances of staging the International Stamp Exhibition. London 1980, which the sheet itself publicised.)

State Coach (9p)
St. Edward's Crown (10½p)
Sovereign's Orb (11p)
Imperial State Crown (13p)

■ 1978, May 31. 25th Anniversary of the Coronation
Des: J. Matthews.

Set	0.75	0.75
Gutter pairs	1.60	
Traffic light gutter pairs	2.50	
First day cover		1.25
Stamp cards	2.50	3.00

Shire Horse (9p)
Shetland Pony (10½p)
Welsh Pony (11p)
Thoroughbred (13p)

■ 1978, July 5. Horses
Des: P. Oxenham.

Set	0.70	0.75
Gutter pairs	1.50	
Traffic light gutter pairs	2.50	
First day cover		1.25
Stamp cards	3.25	3.00

Penny Farthing and Safety Bicycle of 1884 (9p)
Touring bicycles (10½p)
Small-Wheel Bicycles (11p)
Road-racers (13p)

■ 1978, August 2. Cycling
Des: F. Wegner.

Set	0.70	0.75
Gutter pairs	1.60	
Traffic light gutter pairs	2.50	
First day cover		1.25
Stamp cards	2.00	3.00

Dancing around a Christmas Tree (7p)
The Waits (9p)
Carol Singers (11p)
Carrying the Boar's Head (13p)

■ 1978, November 22. Christmas
Des: Faith Jaques. 7p has one phosphor band.

Set	0.70	0.75
Gutter pairs	1.25	
Traffic light gutter pairs	2.50	
First day cover		1.25
Stamp cards	1.50	3.00

Old English Sheepdog (9p)
Welsh Springer Spaniel (10½p)
West Highland Terrier (11p)
Irish Setter (13p)

■ 1979, February 7. British Dogs
Des: P. Barrett.

Set	0.70	0.75
Gutter pairs	1.25	
Traffic light gutter pairs	2.25	
First day cover		1.25
Stamp cards	2.50	5.00

Primrose (9p)
Daffodil (10½p)
Bluebell (11p)
Snowdrop (13p)

■ 1979, March 21. Spring Flowers
Des: P. Newcombe.

Set	0.70	0.75
Gutter pairs	1.50	
Traffic light gutter pairs	2.25	
First day cover		1.25
Stamp cards	2.50	3.00

Hands placing 'flag' voting papers into ballot boxes
(9p, 10½p, 11p, 13p, designs vary slightly)

■ 1979, May 9. Direct Elections to the European Assembly
Des: S. Cliff.

Set	0.70	0.75
Gutter pairs	1.50	
Traffic light gutter pairs	2.25	
First day cover		1.25
Stamp cards	1.50	3.00

Saddling Mahmoud for the Derby (9p)
The Liverpool Great National Steeple Chase (10½p)
The First Spring Meeting, Newmarket (11p)
Racing at Dorsett Ferry, Windsor (13p)

■ 1979, June 6. Horse Racing
Des: S. Rose.

Set	0.70	0.75
Gutter pairs	1.50	
Traffic light gutter pairs	2.25	
First day cover		1.25
Stamp cards	1.50	3.00

The Tale of Peter Rabbit (9p)
The Wind in the Willows (10½p)
Winnie the Pooh (11p)
Alice's Adventures in Wonderland (13p)

■ 1979, July 11. International Year of the Child
Des: E. Hughes.

Set	1.00	0.85
Gutter pairs	1.75	
Traffic light gutter pairs	2.25	
First day cover		1.25
Stamp cards	3.00	3.00

Sir Rowland Hill (10p)
London Post (11½p)
General Post (13p)
Penny Post (15p)

■ 1979, August 22. Centenary of Death of Sir Rowland Hill

Des: E Stemp; miniature sheet by J. Matthews.

Set	0.75	0.75
Gutter pairs	1.60	
Traffic light gutter pairs	2.25	
First day cover		1.00
Stamp cards	1.50	3.00
Miniature sheet (one of each value)	0.80	0.70
Miniature sheet first day cover		1.25

(* The miniature sheet, issued on October 24, 1979, was sold at 59½p, the extra 10p being donated towards the finances of staging the International Stamp Exhibition, London 1980, which the sheet itself publicised.)

Policeman talking to two children (10p)
Street Patrol (11½p)
Policewoman on horseback (13p)
River police (15p)

■ 1979, September 26. Metropolitan Police 150th Anniversary

Des: B. Sanders.

Set	0.80	0.85
Gutter pairs	1.60	
Traffic light gutter pairs	2.25	
First day cover		1.00
Stamp cards	1.50	3.00

The Kings following the Star (8p)
The Angel appearing to the Shepherd (10p)
The Manger Scene (11½p)
Joseph and Mary travelling to Bethlehem (13p)
The Annunciation (15p)

■ 1979, November 21. Christmas

Des: F. Wegner. 8p has one phosphor band.

Set	0.90	0.90
Gutter pairs	1.80	
Traffic light gutter pairs	2.25	
First day cover		1.00
Stamp cards	1.50	3.00

Kingfisher (10p)
Dipper (11½p)
Moorhen (13p)
Yellow Wagtail (15p)

■ 1980, January 16. Water Birds

Des: Michael Warren.

Set	0.80	0.80
Gutter pairs	2.00	
First day cover		1.25
Stamp cards	2.50	3.00

The Rocket (12p)
First and second class carriages (12p)
Third class carriage and cattle truck (12p)
Open coach on truck and horsebox (12p)
Goods wagon and mail coach (12p)

■ 1980, March 12. 150th Anniversary of the Liverpool & Manchester Railway

Des: D. Gentleman.

Se-tenant strip of five	0.85	1.00
Gutter pairs	2.25	
First day cover		1.25
Stamp cards	3.00	3.00

(* The gutter pairs comprise two horizontal se-tenant strips of the stamps separated by a horizontal gutter.)

INTERNATIONAL STAMP EXHIBITION

Montage of London buildings and monuments (50p)

■ 1980, April 9. London 1980 International Stamp Exhibition

Des: J. Matthews. Printed in recess by Harrisons. No phosphor.

50p	0.80	0.75
Gutter pair	2.00	
First day cover		1.00
Stamp card	0.75	1.50
Miniature sheet	0.80	1.00
Miniature sheet first day cover		1.25

(* The miniature sheet, issued on May 7, 1980, was sold at 75p, the extra 25p being donated towards the finances of staging the International Stamp Exhibition, London 1980. The stamp is known to exist in shades of green, caused by the speed of the ink-drying operation, and fakes of these shades exist.)

Buckingham Palace (10½p)
Albert Memorial (12p)
Royal Opera House (13½p)
Hampton Court (25p)
Kensington Palace (17½p)

■ 1980, May 7. London Landmarks

Des: Sir Hugh Casson.

Set	1.00	1.00
Gutter pairs	2.50	
First day cover		1.25
Stamp cards	1.50	3.00

Charlotte Bronte (12p)
George Eliot (13½p)
Emily Bronte (15p)
Mrs. Gaskell (17½p)

■ 1980, July 9. Famous Women/Europa 1980

Des: Barbara Brown.

Set	0.85	0.80
Gutter pairs	2.50	
First day cover		1.25
Stamp cards	1.75	3.00

Her Majesty Queen Elizabeth The Queen Mother (12p)

■ 1980, August 4. Queen Mother's 80th Birthday

Des: Jeffery Matthews.

12p	0.40	0.30
Gutter pair	1.00	
First day cover		1.00
Stamp card	1.00	1.00

Sir Henry Wood (12p)
Sir Thomas Beecham (13½p)
Sir Malcolm Sargent (15p)
Sir John Barbirolli (17½p)

■ 1980, September 10. British Conductors

Des: Peter Gauld

Set	0.90	0.80
Gutter pairs	2.25	
First day cover		1.25
Stamp cards	1.50	2.50

(*These stamps exist on paper which reveals differences in the degree of 'shine' on the surface.)

Athletics (12p)
Rugby (13½p)
Boxing (15p)
Cricket (17½p)

■ 1980, October 10. Sports Centenaries

Des: Robert Goldsmith. Printed in litho by Questa.

Set	0.90	0.90
Gutter pairs	2.25	
First day cover		1.25
Stamp cards	1.50	2.50

Christmas tree (10p)
Candles, ivy and ribbon (12p)
Mistletoe and apples (13½p)
Paper chains with crown and bell (15p)
Holly wreath and ornaments (17½p)

■ 1980, November 10. Christmas

Des: Jeffery Matthews. 10p has one phosphor band.

Set	1.00	1.00
Gutter pairs	2.50	
First day cover		1.25
Stamp cards	1.50	2.75

(*These stamps exist on paper which reveals differences in the degree of 'shine' on the surface.)

St. Valentine's Day (14p)
Morris Dancers (18p)
Lammastide (22p)
Medieval Mummers (25p)

■ 1981, February 6. Folklore/Europa 1981

Des: Fritz Wegner.

Set	1.25	1.25
Gutter pairs	3.50	
First day cover		1.25
Stamp cards	1.50	2.25

Blind Man and Guide Dog (14p)
Deaf and Dumb Alphabet (18p)
Person in Wheelchair (22p)
Foot Artist (25p)

■ 1981, March 25. International Year of Disabled People

Des: John Gibbs.

Set	1.20	1.20
Gutter pairs	3.00	
First day cover		1.25
Stamp cards	1.50	2.25

Small tortoiseshell (14p)
Large blue (18p)
Peacock (22p)
Chequered skipper (25p)

■ 1981, May 13. Butterflies

Des: Gordon Beningfield.

Set	1.25	1.25
Gutter pairs	3.50	
First day cover		1.25
Stamp cards	1.50	3.00

Glenfinnan, Scotland (14p)
Derwentwater, England (18p)
Stackpole Head, Wales (20p)
Giant's Causeway, Northern Ireland (22p)
St. Kilda, Scotland (25p)

■ 1981, June 24. British Landscapes

Des: Michael Fairclough.

Set	1.45	1.40
Gutter pairs	3.50	
First day cover		1.20
Stamp cards	1.50	3.00

Prince Charles and Lady Diana Spencer(14p and 25p)

■ 1981, July 22. Wedding of Prince Charles and Lady Diana Spencer

Des: Jeffery Matthews, from a portrait by Lord Snowdon.

Set	1.00	0.75
Gutter pair	2.50	
First day cover		2.00
Souvenir pack	2.00	
Stamp cards	1.75	3.00

(* A folder containing these two stamps with text printed in Japanese, was sold at the international stamp exhibition in Tokyo in 1981. A modified version of this was made available through the British Philatelic Bureau. A folder was also prepared for a promotion with Cadbury Typhoo.)

Expeditions (14p)
Skills (18p)
Service (22p)
Recreation (25p)

■ 1981, August 12. 25th Anniversary of the Duke of Edinburgh's Award Scheme

Des: Philip Sharland. Printed in litho by Waddingtons.

Set	1.25	1.25
Gutter pairs	3.50	
First day cover		1.20
Stamp cards	1.50	2.25

Cockle dredging (14p)
Hauling side trawl (18p)
Lobster potting (22p)
Hauling Seine net (25p)

■ 1981, September 23. Fishing

Des: Brian Sanders.

Set	1.25	1.25
Gutter pairs	3.50	
First day cover		1.20
Stamp cards	1.50	2.25

Father Christmas with sacks of toys (11½p)
The head of Christ (14p)
Angel in flight (18p)
Joseph and Mary with Donkey (22p)
The Three Wise Man on their camels following the star (25p)

■ 1981, November 18. Christmas

Des: Samantha Brown (11½p), Tracy Jenkins (14p), Lucinda Blackmore (18p), Stephen Moore (22p), Sophie Sharp (25p). The 11½p has one phosphor band

Set	1.20	1.20
Gutter pairs	3.00	
First day cover		1.25
Stamp cards	1.50	3.00

Darwin and Giant Tortoises (15½p)
Darwin and Iguanas (19½p)
Darwin and Darwin's Finches (26p)
Darwin and Prehistoric Skulls (29p)

■ 1982, February 10. Centenary of the death of Charles Darwin.

Des: David Gentleman.

Set	1.40	1.30
Gutter pairs	3.50	
First day cover		1.35
Stamp cards	1.50	3.50

Boys' Brigade (15½p)
Girls' Brigade (19½p)
Boy Scouts (26p)
Girl Guides and Brownies (29p)

■ 1982, March 24. Youth Organisations

Des: Brian Sanders.

Set	1.40	1.40
Gutter pairs	3.50	
First day cover		1.25
Stamp cards	1.50	3.50

Ballet (15½p)
Pantomime (19½p)
Shakespearean drama (26p)
Opera (29p)

■ 1982, April 28. British Theatre/Europa

Des: Adrian George.

Set	1.75	1.50
Gutter pairs	5.00	
First day cover		1.50
Stamp cards	2.50	3.50

Henry VIII and Mary Rose (15½p)
Admiral Blake and Triumph (19½p)
Lord Nelson and HMS Victory (24p)
Lord Fisher and HMS Dreadnought (26p)
Viscount Cunningham and HMS Warspite (29p)

■ 1982, June 16. Maritime Heritage

Des: Marjorie Seynor. Printed in recess and photogravure by Harrison.

Set	1.75	1.70
Gutter pairs	5.00	
First day cover		1.60
Stamp cards	1.75	3.50

'Strawberry Thief', 1883 by William Morris (15½p)
'Scarlet Tulips', 1906 by F. Steiner and Co (19½p)
'Cherry Orchard', 1930 by Paul Nash (26p)
'Chevrons', 1973 by Andrew Foster (29p)

■ 1982, July 23. British Textiles
Des: Peter Hatch Patnership.

Set	1.25	1.50
Gutter pairs	3.00	
First day cover		1.50
Stamp cards	3.50	3.50

History of Communications (15½p)
Technology Today (26p)

■ 1982, September 8. Information Technology Year
Des: Brian Delaney and Darrell Ireland.

Set	0.75	0.80
Gutter pair	2.00	
First day cover		1.25
Stamp cards	1.00	3.50

Austin Seven and Metro (15½p)
Ford Model T and Escort (19½p)
Jaguar SS1 and XJ6 (26p)
Rolls Royce Silver Ghost and Silver Spirit (29p)

■ 1982, October 13. British Motor Cars
Des: Stanley Paine. Printed in litho by Questa.

Set	1.40	1.50
Gutter pairs	3.25	
First day cover		1.50
Stamp cards	1.75	3.50

While Shepherds Watched (12½p)
The Holly and the Ivy (15½p)
I Saw Three Ships (19½p)
We Three Kings of Orient Are (26p)
Good King Wenceslas (29p)

■ 1982, November 17. Christmas
Des: Barbara Brown. 12½p has one phosphor band.

Set	1.50	1.50
Gutter pairs	3.50	
First day cover		1.50
Stamp cards	1.75	4.00

Salmon (15½p)
Pike (19½p)
Trout (26p)
Perch (29p)

■ 1983, January 26. British River Fish
Des: Alex Jardine.

Set	1.50	1.50
Gutter pairs	3.50	
First day cover		1.50
Stamp cards	2.50	3.50

Tropical island (15½p)
Hot arid desert (19½p)
Lush arable land (26p)
Cold mountainous region (29p)

■ 1983, March 9. Commonwealth Day
Des: Donald Hamilton Fraser based on an original idea by
Stafford Cliff.

Set	1.50	1.50
Gutter pairs	3.50	
First day cover		1.50
Stamp cards	1.75	3.50

Humber Bridge (16p)
Thames Flood Barrier (20½p)
'Iolair' Emergency Support Vessel (28p)

■ 1983, May 25. Europa: Engineering Achievements
Des: Michael Taylor.

Set	1.25	1.50
Gutter pairs	4.00	
First day cover		1.30
Stamp cards	1.75	3.50

Musketeer and pikeman of the Royal Scots (16p)
The Royal Welch Fusiliers (20½p)
Riflemen of the 95th Rifles: the Royal Green Jacket (26p)
Irish Guards (28p)
The Parachute Regiment (31p)

■ 1983, July 6. The British Army
Des: Eric Stemp.

Set	1.90	1.90
Gutter pairs	5.00	
First day cover		2.00
Stamp cards	1.75	3.50

Sissinghurst (16p)
Biddulph Grange (20½p)
Blenheim (28p)
Pitmedden (31p)

■ 1983, August 24. British Gardens
Des: Liz Butler. Printed in litho by Waddingtons.

Set	1.70	1.50
Gutter pairs	4.00	
First day cover		1.50
Stamp cards	1.75	3.50

Merry-go-round (16p)
Menagerie and fairground rides (20½p)
Side shows (28p)
Trading in farm produce (31p)

■ 1983, October 5. Fairs and Shows
Des: Andrew Restall.

Set	1.40	1.50
Gutter pairs	3.25	
First day cover		1.50
Stamp cards	1.75	3.50

Flurry of birds posting Christmas greetings (12½p)
Chimney pots with a dove and cat (16p)
Dove and blackbird under an umbrella (20½p)
Dove and blackbird under a street lamp (28p)
Hedge sculpture in shape of dove (31p)

■ 1983, November 16. Christmas
Des: Tony Meeuwissen. 12½p has one phosphor band.

Set	1.50	1.60
Gutter pairs	3.50	
First day cover		1.75
Stamp cards	1.75	3.50

Arms of The College of Arms (16p)
Arms of Richard III (20½p)
Arms of The Earl Marshal (28p)
Arms of the City of London (31p)

■ 1984, January 17. Quincentenary of The College of Arms
Des: Jeffery Matthews.

Set	1.50	1.50
Gutter pairs	3.50	
First day cover		1.75
Stamp cards	1.75	3.50

Highland Cow

Highland Cow (16p)
Chillingham Wild Bull (20½p)
Hereford Bull (26p)
Welch Black Bull (28p)
Irish Moiled Cow (31p)

■ 1984, March 6. British Cattle
Des: Barry Driscoll.

Set	1.60	1.75
Gutter pairs	4.00	
First day cover		2.00
Stamp cards	2.50	3.50

Liverpool: International Garden Festival (16p)
Durham: Milburngate Shopping Centre (20½p)
Bristol: Bush House, City Docks Area (28p)
Perth: Commercial Street Housing Scheme (31p)

■ 1984, April 19. Urban Renewal
Des: Trickett and Webb and Ronald Maddox.

Set	1.50	1.50
Gutter pairs	3.50	
First day cover		1.75
Stamp cards	1.75	3.50

Europa 'bridge' and CEPT emblem (16p, 20½p)
Europa abducted by Zeus in the shape of a bull, and the emblem of the European Parliament (16p, 20½p)

■ 1984, May 15. 25th Anniversary of CEPT and Second Direct Elections to European Parliament
Des: J. Larriviere (16p), Fritz Wegner (20½p). The two designs of each value were printed in se-tenant pairs.

Set	2.25	2.50
Gutter pairs	5.50	
First day cover		2.00
Stamp cards	1.75	3.50

Lancaster House and flags of participating nations (31p)

■ 1984, June 5. London Economic Summit
Des: Paul Hogarth.

31p	0.60	0.70
Gutter pair	1.75	
First day cover		1.00
Stamp card	0.50	2.00

The Earth from space (16p)
Navigational chart of the English Channel (20½p)
Aerial photograph of the Greenwich Observatory (28p)
Airy's transit telescope (31p)

■ 1984, June 21. Centenary of the Greenwich Meridian
Des: J. Barney and H. Walker. Printed in litho by Questa.

Set	1.60	1.60
Gutter pairs	4.00	
First day cover		1.60
Stamp cards	1.75	3.50

Original Bath Mail Coach of 1784 (16p)
Attack on the Exeter Mail in 1816 (16p)
The Norwich Mail in a thunderstorm 1827 (16p)
The Holyhead and Liverpool Mails 1828 (16p)
The Edinburgh Mail snowbound in 1831 (16p)

■ 1984, July 31. 200th Anniversary of the First Mail Coach Run from Bristol and Bath to London
Des: Keith Bassford and Stanley Paine. Printed in recess and photogravure by Harrison.

Set	1.50	1.50
Gutter pairs	3.50	
First day cover		1.75
Stamp cards	1.75	4.00

(* Gutter pairs comprise two horizontal se-tenant strips of the five stamps separated by a gutter.)

Education for development (17p)
Promoting the arts (22p)
Technical training (31p)
Language and libraries (34p)

■ 1984, September 25. 50th Anniversary of the British Council
Des: Francis Newell, John Sorrell and Brian Sanders.

Set	1.70	1.50
Gutter pairs	4.00	
First day cover		1.70
Stamp cards	1.75	3.50

(* Sheets of these stamps sold at the international stamp exhibition held in Melbourne, Australia, in September 1984 had the gutter margins overprinted with the exhibition logo.)

Holy Family (13p)
Arrival in Bethlehem (17p)
Shepherd and Lamb (22p)
Virgin and Child (31p)
Offering of Frankincense (34p)

■ 1984, November 20. Christmas
Des: Yvonne Gilbert. 13p has one centre phosphor band.

Set	1.75	1.80
13p (stars printed on back)	0.60	
Gutter pairs	4.00	
First day cover		1.75
Stamp cards	1.75	3.50

(* The 13p was also issued in a booklet, with an all-over five-pointed-star pattern printed on the back.)

Flying Scotsman (17p)
Golden Arrow (22p)
Cheltenham Flyer (29p)
Royal Scot (31p)
Cornish Riviera (34p)

■ 1985, January 22. Famous Trains
Des: Terence Cuneo.

Set	2.75	2.75
Gutter pairs	7.50	
First day cover		2.25
Stamp cards	2.50	5.00

Buff-tailed Bumble Bee (17p)
Seven-Spotted Ladybird (22p)
Wart-biter Bush-cricket (29p)
Stag Beetle (31p)
Emperor Butterfly (34p)

■ 1985, March 12. Insects
Des: Gordon Beningfield.

Set	2.25	2.00
Gutter pairs	6.00	
First day cover		2.00
Stamp cards	1.75	4.50

'Water Music' by Handel (17p)
'The Planet Suite' by Holst (22p)
'The First Cuckoo' by Delius (31p)
'Sea Picture' by Elgar (34p)

■ 1985, May 14. European Music Year. British Composers
Des: Wilson McLean.

Set	2.25	2.50
Gutter pairs	7.00	
First day cover		2.00
Stamp cards	3.00	4.50

RNLI Lifeboat and dinghy in distress (17p)
Beachy Head Lighthouse (22p)
Marecs A Satellite (31p)
Trinity House Buoy (34p)

■ 1985, June 18. Safety at Sea
Des: Newell and Sorell. Printed in litho by Waddingtons.

Set	1.90	1.90
Gutter pairs	5.00	
First day cover		1.75
Stamp cards	1.75	4.50

Datapost motorcyclist and plane (17p)
Postbus in countryside (22p)
Parcel delivery (31p)
Postman delivering letters (34p)

■ 1985, July 30. 350th Anniversary of Royal Mail Service to the Public
Des: Paul Hogarth.

Set	1.75	1.80
17p 'D' pattern printed on gummed side	0.60	
Gutter pairs	4.25	
First day cover		1.75
Stamp cards	1.75	4.50
Booklet (10 x 17p)	3.00	

(* The booklet sold at a discounted price of £1.53. Each stamp had a 'D' pattern printed on the gummed side. The cover shows a Datapost van and plane, and Concorde.)

King Arthur and Merlin (17p)
The Lady of the Lake (22p)
Guinevere and Lancelot of the Lake (31p)
Sir Galahad (34p)

■ 1985, September 3. Arthurian Legend
Des: Yvonne Gilbert.

Set	1.75	1.85
Gutter pairs	4.50	
First day cover		1.75
Stamp cards	1.75	4.50

Peter Sellers from photograph by Bill Brandt (17p)
David Niven by Cornel Lucas (22p)
Charles Chaplin by Snowdon (29p)
Vivien Leigh by Angus McBean (31p)
Alfred Hitchcock by Howard Coster (34p)

■ 1985, October 8. British Film Year
Des: Keith Bassford.

Set	2.75	2.50
Gutter pairs	7.00	
First day cover		2.25
Stamp cards	1.75	5.00

Principal Boy (12p)
Genie (17p)
Pantomime Dame (22p)
Good Fairy (31p)
Pantomime Cat (34p)

■ 1985, November 19. Christmas: Pantomime
Des: Adrian George. 12p has one phosphor band.

Set	2.00	2.00
12p ('stars' on gummed side)	0.55	
Gutter pairs	5.00	
First day cover		2.00
Stamp cards	1.75	4.50
Christmas card pack (50 x 12p)	30.00	

(*The 12p was also issued in a booklet.)

North Sea Drilling Rig and light bulb (17p)
Thermometer and laboratory (22p)
Garden hoe and steelworks (31p)
Loaf of bread and cornfield (34p)

■ 1986, January 14. Industry Year
Des: Keith Bassford. Printed in litho by Questa.

Set	2.00	2.25
Gutter pairs	5.00	
First day cover		1.75
Stamp cards	1.75	3.50

Edmund Halley as the Comet (17p)
The Giotto space probe (22p)
'Maybe twice in a lifetime' (31p)
The Comet's Orbit (34p)

■ 1986, February 18. Halley's Comet
Des: Ralph Steadman.

Set	1.90	2.20
Gutter pairs	4.75	
First day cover		1.75
Stamp cards	1.75	3.50

The Queen at the age of 2, 16 and 26 (17p and 34p)
The Queen at the age of 32, 47 and 56 (17p and 34p)

■ 1986, April 21. The Queen's 60th Birthday
Des: Jeffery Matthews.

Set	2.25	2.50
Gutter pairs	5.00	
First day cover		2.25
Stamp cards	1.75	4.00

Barn Owl (17p)
Pine Marten (22p)
Wild Cat (31p)
Natterjack Toad (34p)

■ 1986, May 20. Europa: Nature Conservation
Des: Ken Lilly.

Set	1.75	1.80
Gutter pairs	5.00	
First day cover		2.00
Stamp cards	1.75	3.50

The peasant working on his land (17p)
The freeman and his craft (22p)
The knight and his retinue (31p)
The lord at head of table (34p)

■ 1986, June 17. Medieval Life. 900th Anniversary of the Domesday Book
Des: Tayburn.

Set	2.00	2.00
Gutter pairs	5.00	
First day cover		2.00
Stamp cards	1.75	3.50

Sprinter's feet on starting blocks (17p)
Oarsman (22p)
Weightlifter with bar (29p)
Man looking through the sights of a rifle (31p)
Hockey player (34p)

■ 1986, July 15. Commonwealth Games
Des: Nick Cudworth.

Set	2.40	2.40
Gutter pairs	6.00	
First day cover		2.25
Stamp cards	2.25	4.00

Prince Andrew and Miss Sarah Ferguson (12p and 17p)

■ 1986, July 22. Royal Wedding
Des: Jeffery Matthews.

Set	0.85	0.75
Gutter pairs	2.00	
First day cover		1.25
Stamp cards	1.50	3.50

Cross on ballot paper (34p)

■ 1986, August 19. Commonwealth Parliamentary Association Conference
Des: John Gibbs. Printed in litho by Questa.

34p	0.75	0.80
Gutter pairs	2.00	
First day cover		1.25
Stamp card	0.60	1.50

Lord Dowding and the Hurricane (17p)
Lord Tedder and the Typhoon (22p)
Lord Trenchard and the DH 9A (29p)
Sir Arthur Harris and the Lancaster (31p)
Lord Portal and the Mosquito (34p)

■ 1986, September 16. Royal Air Force
Des: Brian Sanders.

Set	2.50	2.50
Gutter pairs	6.50	
First day cover		2.50
Stamp cards	1.75	4.00

The Glastonbury Thorn (12p), (13p)
The Tanad Valley Plygain (18p)
The Hebrides Tribute (22p)
The Dewsbury Church Knell (31p)
The Hereford Boy Bishop (34p)

■ 1986, November 18. Christmas. Traditions
Des: Lynda Gray. 12p has one phosphor band and was issued on December 2, 1986; 13p has one phosphor band

Set	2.00	2.00
Gutter Pairs	5.00	
First day covers		2.00
Stamp cards	1.75	4.00
Pack (36 × 13p, with stars on back)	9.00	

(* The 13p was also issued in a booklet, with a star pattern printed on the gummed side; priced at 0.70 for a mint single.)

Gaillardia (18p)
Echinops (22p)
Echeveria (31p)
Colchicum (34p)

■ 1987, January 6. Flowers
Des: Jeffery Matthews from photographs by Alfred Lammer.

Set	2.00	2.00
Gutter pairs	5.00	
First day cover		2.00
Stamp cards	1.75	3.50

(* A card with a Flowers design, stamped and cancelled with the 31p and 34p stamps, was made available at several stamp exhibitions, starting with Capex 87 in Toronto in June 1987.)

Apple (18p)
Planets moving around the sun (22p)
Flask of water and refraction of light (31p)
The earth and an artificial satellite (34p)

■ 1987, March 24. Sir Isaac Newton
Des: Sarah Goodwin.

Set	2.00	2.00
Gutter pairs	5.00	
First day cover		2.00
Stamp cards	1.75	3.50

Willis Faber Dumas Building, Ipswich (18p)
Pompidou Centre, Paris (22p)
Staatgalerie, Stuttgart (31p)
European Investment Bank, Luxembourg (34p)

■ 1987, May 12. British Architects in Europe. CEPT

Des: Minale Tattersfield Studio.

Set	2.00	2.00
Gutter pairs	5.00	
First day cover		2.00
Stamp cards	1.75	3.50

First aid duties in 1887 (18p)
First aid in wartime (22p)
First aid at events (31p)
Transplant organs flights (34p)

■ 1987, June 16. St John Ambulance Centenary

Des: Debbie Cook. Printed in litho by Questa.

Set	2.00	2.00
Gutter pairs	5.00	
First day cover		2.00
Stamp cards	1.75	3.50

Arms of the Lord Lyon, King of Arms (18p)
Arms of His Royal Highness The Duke of
Rothesay (22p)
Arms of the Royal Scottish Academy of Painting,
Sculpture and Architecture (31p)
Arms of The Royal Society of Edinburgh (34p)

■ 1987, July 21. Order of the Thistle

Des: Jeffery Matthews.

Set	1.90	1.90
Gutter pairs	4.75	
First day cover		2.00
Stamp cards	1.75	3.50

Landseer's painting 'Monarch of the Glen', the Great Exhibition,
Grace Darling's Rescue (18p)
Launching of Brunel's 'Great Eastern', Mrs Beeton's Book of
Household Management, Prince Albert (22p)
The Albert Memorial, Benjamin Disraeli, the first ballot
box (31p)
Marconi's broadcast to Paris, Queen Victoria's diamond jubilee,
the Boer War (34p)

■ 1987, September 8. Victorian Britain

Des: Carroll and Dempsey Studio. Printed in recess and
photogravure by Harrison.

Set	1.85	2.00
Gutter pairs	5.00	
First day cover		2.00
Stamp cards	1.75	3.50

Pottery by Bernard Leach (18p)
Pottery by Elizabeth Fritsch (26p)
Pottery by Lucie Rie (31p)
Pottery by Hans Coper (34p)

■ **1987, October 13. Studio Pottery**
Des: Tony Evans.

Set	1.85	1.75
Gutter pairs	4.50	
First day cover		2.00
Stamp cards	3.50	3.50

Decorating the Christmas tree (13p)
Child looking out of a window (18p)
Father Christmas in sleigh and child asleep (26p)
A child reading a book surrounded by toys (31p)
Child playing a recorder and a snowman (34p)

■ **1987, November 17. Christmas**
Des: M. Foreman. 13p has one phosphor band.

Set	2.00	2.00
Gutter pairs	5.00	
First day cover		2.00
Stamp cards	1.75	3.50
Folder (36 x 13p with star on gum)	8.50	

(*The 13p was also issued in a booklet, with a star pattern printed on the gummed side; priced at 0.50 for a mint single.)

Short-spined seascorpion (18p)
Yellow waterlily (26p)
Bewick's Swan (31p)
Morchella esculenta (34p)

■ **1988, January 19. Bicentenary of Linnean Society**
Des: E. Hughes.

Set	2.00	2.00
Gutter pairs	5.00	
First day cover		2.00
Stamp cards	1.75	3.50

Revd William Morgan (18p)
William Salesbury (26p)
Bishop Richard Davies (31p)
Bishop Richard Parry (34p)

■ **1988, March 1. 400th Anniversary of the Welsh Bible**
Des: K. Bowen.

Set	2.00	2.00
Gutter pairs	5.00	
First day cover		2.00
Stamp cards	1.75	3.50

Gymnastics (18p)
Downhill skiing (26p)
Tennis (31p)
Football (34p)

■ **1988, March 22. Sports Organisations**
Des: J. Sutton.

Set	2.00	2.00
Gutter pairs	5.00	
First day cover		2.00
Stamp cards	1.50	3.50

'Mallard' (18p)
'Queen Elizabeth' (26p)
Glasgow tram (31p)
Handley Page H.P.45 'Horatius' (34p)

■ 1988, May 10. Transport and Mail Services. Europa

Des: M. Dempsey.

Set	2.00	2.00
Gutter pairs	5.00	
First day cover		2.00
Stamp cards	1.75	3.50

(* A set of four air cards was issued on March 2, 1993, bearing the Handley Page design as an imprinted 33p value; price £5 mint.)

Settler and clipper (18p)
British and Australian Parliament Buildings
and Queen Elizabeth II (18p)
W. G. Grace and tennis racquet (34p)
Shakespeare, John Lennon and Sydney Opera House (34p)

■ 1988, June 21. Australian Bicentenary

Des: G. Emery. Printed in litho by Questa.

Set of four in two se-tenant pairs	1.70	2.20
Gutter pairs	4.00	
First day cover		2.00
Stamp cards	1.50	3.50

Spanish off The Lizard (18p)
English Fleet leaving Plymouth (18p)
Fighting off the Isle of Wight (18p)
English attacking at Calais (18p)
Armada in the North Sea (18p)

■ 1988, July 19. 400th anniversary of the Spanish Armada

Des: G. Evernden.

Set of five in se-tenant strip	1.60	1.90
Gutter pairs	4.00	
First day cover		2.00
Stamp cards	1.50	3.50

The Owl and the Pussy Cat (19p)
Edward Lear as a bird (27p)
Cat (32p)
There was a Young Lady whose Bonnet... (35p)

■ 1988, September 6. Centenary of the Death of Edward Lear

Des: M. Swatridge and S. Dew.

Set	2.20	2.20
Gutter pairs	5.50	
First day cover		2.00
Stamp cards	2.50	3.50
Miniature sheet (one of each value)	4.50	4.50
First day cover		5.00

(* The miniature sheet, issued on September 27, 1988, was sold with a surcharge to help fund the international stamp exhibition, Stamp World London 90.)

Carrickfergus Castle (£1)
Caernarfon Castle (£1.50)
Edinburgh Castle (£2)
Windsor Castle (£5)

■ 1988, October 18. Castle high value definitives

Engraved by C. Matthews from photographs by Prince Andrew. Recess printed by Harrison.

Set	16.00	4.50
Gutter pairs	35.00	
Gutter blocks of four (centre cross)	75.00	
First day cover		20.00

Journeying to Bethlehem (14p)
Shepherds following the Star (19p)
Three Wise Men (27p)
The Nativity (32p)
The Annunciation (35p)

■ 1988, November 15. Christmas
Des: L. Trickett. 14p has one phosphor band.

Set	1.75	2.20
Gutter pairs	4.00	
First day cover		2.00
Stamp cards	1.50	3.50

Atlantic Puffin (19p)
Avocet (27p)
Oystercatcher (32p)
Northern Gannet (35p)

■ 1989, January 17. Centenary of the Royal Society for the Protection of Birds
Des: D. Cordery.

Set	2.00	2.00
Gutter pairs	5.00	
First day cover		1.75
Stamp cards	1.50	4.00

Teddy Bear (19p)
Rose (19p)
Cupid (19p)
Yachts (19p)
Fruit (19p)

■ 1989, January 31. Greetings stamps
Des: P. Sutton. Se-tenant strip of five Issued in booklets in panes of ten containing two of each design.

Se-tenant strip	11.00	13.00
Booklet pane (of 10)	23.00	
Booklet	25.00	
First day cover		11.00
Stamp cards	5.00	10.00

Fruit and vegetables (19p)
Meat (27p)
Dairy products (32p)
Cereals (35p)

■ 1989, March 7. Food and Farming Year
Des: Sedley Place Ltd.

Set	2.00	2.00
Gutter pairs	5.00	
First day cover		2.00
Stamp cards	1.25	3.50

Firework display: Mortar board (19p)
Firework display: Cross on ballot paper (19p)
Firework display: Posthorn (35p)
Firework display: Globe (35p)

■ 1989, April 11. Anniversaries & Events
Des: Lewis Moberly. 19p and 35p issued in se-tenant pairs.

Set (of two se-tenant pairs)	2.25	2.25
Gutter pairs	6.00	
First day cover		2.00
Stamp cards	1.25	4.00

Toy aeroplane and locomotive (19p)
Building bricks (27p)
Board games and dice (32p)
Robot, boat and doll's house (35p)

■ 1989, May 16. Toys and Games. Europa
Des: D. Fern.

Set	2.25	2.00
Gutter pairs	6.00	
First day cover		2.00
Stamp cards	2.50	3.50

Ironbridge, Shropshire (19p)
Tin mine, St Agnes Head, Cornwall (27p)
Cotton Mills, New Lanark, Strathclyde (32p)
Pontcysyllte Aqueduct, Clwyd (35p)

■ 1989, July 4. Industrial Archaeology
Des: R. Maddox.

Set	2.00	2.00
Gutter pairs	5.00	
First day cover		2.00
Stamp cards	1.25	3.50
Miniature sheet	3.50	3.50
First day cover		3.50

(* The miniature sheet, issued on July 25, 1989, contained one
of each value but with the designs in a horizontal format, with a
surcharge to help fund the international stamp exhibition, Stamp
World London 90.)

Snowflake (19p)
Fly (27p)
Blood cells (32p)
Microchip (35p)

■ 1989, September 5. 150th Anniversary of the Royal Microscopical Society
Des: K. Bassford. Printed in litho by Questa.

Set	2.00	2.00
Gutter pairs	5.00	
First day cover		1.75
Stamp cards	1.25	3.50

Royal Mail coach (20p)
The Blues and Royals (20p)
Lord Mayor's coach (20p)
St Paul's Cathedral (20p)
Blues and Royals Drum Horse (20p)

■ 1989, October 17. Lord Mayor's Show
Des: P. Cox.

Set in se-tenant strip	1.70	1.70
Gutter pairs	4.50	
First day cover		1.70
Stamp cards	1.50	4.00

(* The Royal Mail Coach design also appears in the Treasures
of the Archive prestige stamp book issued on August 18, 2009,
printed in litho.)

Peasants, from stained glass window (15p)
Arches and Roundels, West Front (15p+1p)
Octagon Tower (20p+1p)
Arcade from West Transept (34p+1p)
Triple Arch from West Front (37p+1p)

■ 1989, November 14. Christmas. 800th Anniversary of Ely Cathedral

Des: D. Gentleman. 15p and 15p+1p have one phosphor band.

Set	2.25	2.25
Gutter pairs	5.00	
First day cover		1.75
Stamp cards	1.50	4.00

(* Four of the stamps carried a surcharge for charity.)

■ 1990, January 10. 150th Anniversary of the Penny Black

See under Machin decimal definitives

Kitten (20p)
Rabbit (29p)
Duckling (34p)
Puppy (37p)

■ 1990, January 23. 150th Anniversary of the Royal Society for the Prevention of Cruelty to Animals

Des: T. Evans. Printed in litho by Questa.

Set	2.25	2.25
Gutter pairs	5.00	
First day cover		1.75
Stamp cards	1.50	4.00

Teddy Bear (20p)
Dennis the Menace (20p)
Punch (20p)
Cheshire Cat (20p)
The Man in the Moon (20p)
The Laughing Policeman (20p)
Clown (20p)
Mona Lisa (20p)
Queen of Hearts (20p)
Stan Laurel (20p)

■ 1990, February 6. Greetings stamps: Smiles

Des: Michael Peters and Partners. Stamps se-tenant in booklet panes of ten containing one of each design.

Booklet pane (of 10)	12.50	14.00
Booklet	15.00	
First day cover		12.50

Alexandra Palace (20p)
Glasgow School of Art (20p)
British Philatelic Bureau, Edinburgh (29p)
Templeton Carpet Factory, Glasgow (37p)

■ 1990, March 6. Europa and Glasgow 1990 European City of Culture

Des: P. Hogarth.

Set	2.00	2.00
Gutter pairs	6.00	
First day cover		1.75
Stamp cards	1.50	4.00

(* The two 20p designs were issued in separate sheets, not as se-tenant pairs. The 20p Alexandra Palace design also appears as a pane of four in the £5 'London Life' prestige stamp booklet issued on March 20, 1990.)

Export Achievement Award (20p and 37p)
Technological Achievement Award (20p and 37p)

■ 1990, April 10. 25th Anniversary of The Queen's Awards for Export and Technology
Des: S. Broom. Printed in litho by Questa.

Set (in two se-tenant pairs)	1.80	1.80
Gutter pairs	4.50	
First day cover		1.80
Stamp cards	1.50	4.00

Portraits of Queen Victoria and Queen Elizabeth II (20p)

■ 1990, May 3. Stamp World London 90 International Exhibition
Des: Sedley Place Design; engraved by C. Matthews. Printed in recess and photogravure by Harrison.

Miniature sheet	2.50	2.50
First day cover		3.00

(*The border illustrates the 1840 Penny Black and Britannia from the 1913-1934 'Seahorses' series. The sheets were sold at £1 each, the surcharge being used to help fund the exhibition.)

Cycad and Sir Joseph Banks Building (20p)
Stone Pine and Princess of Wales Conservatory (29p)
Willow Tree and Palm House (34p)
Cedar Tree and Pagoda (37p)

■ 1990, June 5. 150th Anniversary of Kew Gardens
Des: P. Leith.

Set	1.75	1.75
Gutter pairs	4.50	
First day cover		1.75
Stamp cards	1.50	4.00

Thomas Hardy and Clyffe Clump, Dorset (20p)

■ 1990, July 10. 150th Anniversary of the Birth of Thomas Hardy
Des: J. Gibbs.

20p	0.40	0.40
Gutter pair	1.00	
First day cover		1.00
Stamp card	0.60	2.50

Queen Elizabeth The Queen Mother (20p)
Queen Elizabeth (29p)
Elizabeth, Duchess of York (34p)
Lady Elizabeth Bowes-Lyon (37p)

■ **1990, August 2. 90th Birthday of Queen Elizabeth, The Queen Mother**
Des: J. Gorham from photographs by Norman Parkinson, Dorothy Wilding, B. Park and Rita Martin.

Set	3.00	3.00
Gutter pairs	7.50	
First day cover		2.50
Stamp cards	2.00	5.00

(* The same designs were used in 2002 in memory of the Queen Mother although the borders were changed to black.)

Victoria Cross (20p)
George Cross (20p)
Distinguished Service Cross and Distinguished Service Medal (20p)
Military Cross and Military Medal (20p)
Distinguished Flying Cross and Distinguished Flying Medal (20p)

■ **1990, September 11. Gallantry Awards**
Des: J. Gibbs and J. Harwood.

Set	2.00	2.00
Gutter pairs	5.00	
First day cover		2.00
Stamp cards	2.00	4.00

(* The 20p also appears on the miniature sheet and in the Prestige stamp book for the Victoria Cross issued on September 21, 2006.)

Armagh Observatory, Jodrell Bank & La Palma Telescopes (22p)
Early telescope and diagram of Moon & Tides by Newton (26p)
Greenwich Old Observatory and astronomical equipment (31p)
Stonehenge, gyroscope and navigation by the stars (37p)

■ **1990, October 16. Astronomy**
Des: J. Fisher. Printed in litho by Questa.

Set	2.00	2.00
Gutter pairs	5.00	
First day cover		2.00
Stamp cards	1.50	4.00

Building a snowman (17p)
Fetching a Christmas tree (22p)
Carol singers (26p)
Tobogganing (31p)
Ice-skating (37p)

■ **1990, November 13. Christmas**
Des: J. Gorham and A. Davidson. 17p has one phosphor band.

Set	2.25	2.25
Gutter pairs	6.00	
First day cover		2.00
Stamp cards	1.75	4.00

(* The 17p was also sold in booklets.)

King Charles Spaniel (22p)
Pointer (26p)
Two Hounds in a Landscape (31p)
A Rough Dog (33p)
Fino and Tiny (37p)

■ **1991, January 8. Dogs: Paintings by George Stubbs**
Des: Carroll, Dempsey and Thirkell Ltd.

Set	2.25	2.25
Gutter pairs	5.50	
First day cover		2.25
Stamp cards	1.50	4.00

Thrush's Nest (1st)
Shooting Star and Rainbow (1st)
Magpies and Charm Bracelet (1st)
Black cat (1st)
Kingfisher and key (1st)
Mallard and frog (1st)
Four-leaf clover, boot and matchbox (1st)
Pot of Gold at the end of the Rainbow (1st)
Butterflies (1st)
Wishing Well and sixpence (1st)

■ 1991, February 5. Greetings stamps: Good Luck

Des: J. Meeuwissen. Issued in booklets in panes of ten containing one of each design.

Booklet pane (of 10)	7.00	7.75
Booklet	8.00	
First day cover		7.50

Michael Faraday (22p)
Charles Babbage (22p)
Sweep of radar of East Anglia (31p)
Gloster Whittle E28/39 airplane over East Anglia (37p)

■ 1991, March 5. Scientific Achievements

Des: P. Till (22p values), J. Harwood (31p, 37p).

Set	2.00	2.00
Gutter pairs	5.00	
First day cover		2.00
Stamp cards	1.75	3.75

■ 1991, March 26. Greetings stamps: Smiles

Designs as for the Greetings stamps of February 6, 1990, but the values in each case changed to 1st. Issued in booklets in panes of ten containing one of each design.

Booklet pane (of 10)	7.00	7.50
Booklet	8.00	
First day cover		7.50

(* These designs were also used for Smilers sheets in 2000 and 2001.)

Man looking at Space (design over two se-tenant 22p values)
Space looking at Man (design over two se-tenant 37p values)

■ 1991, April 23. Europe in Space. Europa

Des: J-M. Folon.

Set of two se-tenant pairs	2.25	2.25
Gutter pairs	6.00	
First day cover		2.25
Stamp cards	1.75	3.75

Fencing (22p)
Hurdling (26p)
Diving (31p)
Rugby (37p)

■ 1991, June 11. World Student Games, Sheffield and World Cup Rugby Championships, London

Des: Huntley Muir Partners.

Set	2.25	2.25
Gutter pairs	6.00	
First day cover		2.25
Stamp cards	1.50	3.75

Silver Jubilee (22p)
Mme Alfred Carrière (26p)
Rosa Moyesii (31p)
Harvest Fayre (33p)
Mutabilis (37p)

■ 1991, July 16. Ninth World Conference of Roses, Belfast

Des: Yvonne Skargon. Printed in litho by Questa.

Set	2.40	2.25
Gutter pairs	6.00	
First day cover		2.25
Stamp cards	2.00	4.00

Iguanodon (22p)
Stegosaurus (26p)
Tyrannosaurus (31p)
Protoceratops (33p)
Triceratops (37p)

■ 1991, August 20. 150th Anniversary of the Identification of Dinosaurs by Owen

Des: B. Kneale.

Set	2.50	2.50
Gutter pairs	6.00	
First day cover		3.00
Stamp cards	1.75	4.00

Map of Hamstreet in 1816 (24p)
Map of Hamstreet in 1906 (28p)
Map of Hamstreet in 1959 (33p)
Map of Hamstreet in 1991 (39p)

■ 1991, September 17. Bicentenary of Ordnance Survey

Des: H. Brown. Printed in recess and litho by Harrison (24p), in litho by Harrison (28p) and in litho by Questa (33p, 39p).

Set	2.25	2.25
Gutter pairs	6.00	
First day cover		2.25
Stamp cards	1.75	4.00

(* Examples of the 28p are known with the denomination of 26p, from supplies printed before an increase in postage rates affected the denominations of this set.)

Adoration of the Magi (18p)
Mary with Jesus in stable (24p)
The Holy Family and angel (28p)
The Annunciation (33p)
The flight into Egypt (39p)

■ 1991, November 12. Christmas

Des: D. Driver. 18p has one phosphor band.

Set	2.25	2.25
Gutter pairs	6.00	
First day cover		2.50
Stamp cards	1.75	4.00

(* The 18p was also sold in booklets.)

Fallow deer (18p)
Hare (24p)
Fox (28p)
Redwing (33p)
Welsh mountain sheep (39p)

■ 1992, January 14. The Four Seasons: Wintertime

Des: J. Gorham and K. Bowen. 18p has one phosphor band.

Set	2.25	2.25
Gutter pairs	5.00	
First day cover		2.25
Stamp cards	1.75	3.75

(* The 39p also appears as a pane of four in the Cymru Wales prestige stamp booklet issued on February 25, 1992.)

Spray of flowers (1st)
Double locket (1st)
Key (1st)
Toy car and cigarette cards (1st)
Compass and map (1st)
Pocket watch (1st)
Penny red stamp and pen (1st)
Pearl necklace (1st)
Marbles (1st)
Starfish and a bucket and spade (1st)

■ 1992, January 28. Greetings stamps: Memories
Des: Trickett and Webb Ltd. Issued in booklets, in panes of ten containing one of each design.

Booklet pane (of 10)	7.00	7.00
Booklet	7.00	
First day cover		7.50

Queen Elizabeth II, in Coronation robes (24p)
Queen Elizabeth II, in Garter robes (24p)
Queen Elizabeth II, with Prince Andrew as a baby (24p)
Queen Elizabeth II, at Trooping of the Colour (24p)
Queen Elizabeth II, with emblem of the Commonwealth (24p)

■ 1992, February 6. 40th Anniversary of the Accession
Des: Why Not Associates. Printed in litho by Questa.

Set (in se-tenant strip)	3.00	3.50
Gutter pairs	7.50	
First day cover		3.25
Stamp cards	2.00	4.00

Tennyson in 1888 (24p)
In 1856 (28p)
In 1864 (33p)
As a young man (39p)

■ 1992, March 10. Centenary of the Death of Alfred, Lord Tennyson
Des: Irene von Treskow.

Set	2.25	2.25
Gutter pairs	5.00	
First day cover		2.25
Stamp cards	1.75	3.75

British Olympic Association logo (24p)
British Paralympic Association symbol (24p)
Santa Maria, Christopher Columbus (24p)
Kaisei, Operation Raleigh (39p)
British Pavilion at Expo '92 in Seville (39p)

■ 1992, April 7. International Events
Des: K. Bassford (BOA, BPA and Expo), K. Bassford and S. Paine (Santa Maria and Kaisei). Printed in litho by Questa and in recess and litho by Harrison. The BOA and BPA designs were issued as a se-tenant pair.

Set	2.50	2.60
Gutter pairs	6.50	
First day cover		2.50
Stamp cards	1.75	4.00

Carrickfergus Castle (£1)
Caernarfon Castle (£1.50)
Edinburgh Castle (£2)
Windsor Castle (£5)

■ **1992, March 24. Castle high value definitives**
As issue of October 18, 1988, but Queen's head is in silhouette printed in optically variable ink which changes colour from gold to green depending on the angle at which it is viewed. In addition, an elliptical perforation is included along the side of each stamp.

Set	19.50	4.00
Gutter pairs	70.00	
Gutter blocks of four (centre cross)	£140	
First day cover		15.00
Stamp cards	10.00	50.00

(* The £1.50, £2 and £5 exist with either blue tinted PVAD gum, or white PVA gum. The date of release of the stamp cards is not the day of issue of the stamps.)

Pikeman (24p)
Drummer (28p)
Musketeer (33p)
Standard bearer (39p)

■ **1992, June 16. 350th Anniversary of the Civil War**
Des: J. Sancha.

Set	2.25	2.25
Gutter pairs	6.00	
First day cover		2.25
Stamp cards	1.75	3.75

Gilbert and Sullivan operas:
The Yeoman of the Guard (18p)
The Gondoliers (24p)
The Mikado (28p)
The Pirates of Penzance (33p)
Iolanthe (39p)

■ **1992, July 21. Gilbert and Sullivan Operas**
Des: Lynda Gray. 18p has one phosphor band.

Set	2.20	2.25
Gutter pairs	5.50	
First day cover		2.25
Stamp cards	1.75	3.75

Acid rain kills (24p)
Ozone layer (28p)
Greenhouse effect (33p)
Bird of hope (39p)

■ **1992, September 15. Protection of the Environment**
Des: C. Hall (24p), L. Fowler (28p), S. Warren (33p) and A. Newton-Mold (39p). All paintings by children, in conjunction with the BBC Television programme Blue Peter.

Set	2.20	2.25
Gutter pairs	5.50	
First day cover		2.00
Stamp cards	1.75	3.75

European Star (24p)

■ **1992, October 13. Single European Market**
Des: D. Hockney.

24p	0.50	0.45
Gutter pair	1.50	
First day cover		1.00
Stamp card	1.00	2.00

Angel Gabriel (18p)
Madonna and Child (24p)
King carrying Gold (28p)
Shepherds (33p)
Kings with Frankincense and Myrrh (39p)

■ 1992, November 10. Christmas
Des: Carroll, Dempsey and Thirkell Ltd. The 18p has one phosphor band.

Set	2.25	2.25
Gutter pairs	6.00	
First day cover		2.25
Stamp cards	1.75	4.00

(* The 18p was also sold in booklets.)

Mute Swan Cob (18p)
Cygnet and Decoy (24p)
Swans and Cygnet (28p)
Eggs in nest (33p)
Young swan (39p)

■ 1993, January 19. 600th Anniversary of Abbotsbury Swannery
Des: David Gentleman. 18p has one phosphor band.

Set	4.00	4.00
Gutter pairs	10.00	
First day cover		4.00
Stamp cards	1.75	5.50

William (1st)
Long John Silver (1st)
Tweedledum and Tweedledee (1st)
Mole and Toad (1st)
Teacher and Wilfred (1st)
Peter Rabbit and Mrs Rabbit (1st)
Snowman and Father Christmas (1st)
The Big Friendly Giant and Sophie (1st)
Bill Badger and Rupert Bear (1st)
Aladdin and the Genie (1st)

■ 1993, February 2. Greetings stamps: Gift Giving
Des: Newell and Sorell. Issued in booklets in panes of ten containing one of each design.

Booklet pane (of 10)	6.50	6.50
Booklet	7.50	
First day cover		7.50
Stamp cards	10.00	15.50

(* The Peter Rabbit and Mrs Rabbit design also appears as a pane of four in the Story of Beatrix Potter prestige stamp book issued on August 10, 1993.)

Decorated dial (24p)
Escapement, Remontoire and Fusée (28p)
Balance, Spring and Temperature compensator (33p)
Movement seen from back (39p)

■ 1993, February 16. 300th Anniversary of the Birth of John Harrison
Des: H. Brown and D. Penny. Printed in litho by Questa.

Set	2.00	2.25
Gutter pairs	5.00	
First day cover		2.25
Stamp cards	1.75	5.00

Britannia (£10)

■ 1993, March 2. £10 Definitive

Des: B. Craddock and Roundel Design Group. Printed in litho by Questa, also including die-stamping and embossing of Braille.

£10	20.00	7.50
First day cover		15.00
Stamp card	4.50	50.00

Dendrobium hellwigianum (18p)
Paphiopedilum Maudiae 'Magnificum' (24p)
Cymbidium lowianum (28p)
Vanda Rothschildiana (33p)
Dendrobium vexillarius var albiviride (39p)

■ 1993, March 16. 14th World Orchid Conference, Glasgow

Des: Pandora Sellars. 18p has one phosphor band.

Set	2.25	2.25
Gutter pairs	5.50	
First day cover		2.25
Stamp cards	2.00	5.50

'Family Group' by Henry Moore (24p)
'Kew Gardens' by Edward Bawden (28p)
'St Francis and the Birds' by Stanley Spencer (33p)
'Still Life: Odyssey I' by Ben Nicholson (39p)

■ 1993, May 11. Contemporary Art. Europa

Des: A. Dastor.

Set	2.25	2.25
Gutter pairs	6.00	
First day cover		2.25
Stamp cards	2.00	5.00

Emperor Claudius (24p)
Emperor Hadrian (28p)
Goddess Roma (33p)
Christ (39p)

■ 1993, June 15. Roman Britain

Des: J. Gibbs.

Set	2.25	2.25
Gutter pairs	6.00	
First day cover		2.25
Stamp cards	2.00	5.00

Grand Union Canal (24p)
Stainforth and Keadby Canal (28p)
Brecknock and Abergavenny Canal (33p)
Crinan Canal (39p)

■ 1993, July 20. Inland Waterways

Des: T. Lewery. Printed in litho by Questa.

Set	2.25	2.25
Gutter pairs	6.00	
First day cover		2.25
Stamp cards	2.00	5.00

Horse Chestnut (18p)
Blackberry (24p)
Hazel (28p)
Rowan (33p)
Pear (39p)

■ 1993, September 14. The Four Seasons: Autumn

Des: Charlotte Knox. 18p has one phosphor band.

Set	2.25	2.25
Gutter pairs	6.00	
First day cover		2.25
Stamp cards	2.00	5.00

SHERLOCK HOLMES & DR.WATSON
"THE REIGATE SQUIRE"

The Reigate Squire (24p)
The Hound of the Baskervilles (24p)
The Six Napoleons (24p)
The Greek Interpreter (24p)
The Final Problem (24p)

■ 1993, October 12. Sherlock Holmes

Des: A. Davidson. Printed in litho by Questa.

Set (in se-tenant strip of five)	2.25	2.50
Gutter pairs	6.00	
First day cover		2.50
Stamp cards	2.00	5.00

Bob Cratchit and Tiny Tim (19p)
Mr and Mrs Fezziwig (25p)
Scrooge (30p)
The Prize Turkey (35p)
Scrooge's nephew (41p)

■ 1993, November 9. Christmas: 'A Christmas Carol' by Charles Dickens

Des: Q. Blake. 19p has one phosphor band.

Set	2.25	2.25
Gutter pairs	6.00	
First day cover		2.75
Stamp cards	3.00	5.50

(*The 19p and 25p were also sold in booklets.)

Class 5 and Class B1 on the West Highland Line (19p)
Class A1 at Kings Cross (25p)
Class 4 at Blythe North (30p)
Class 4 near Wigan Central (35p)
Castle Class crossing Worcester and Birmingham Canal (41p)

■ 1994, January 18. The Age of Steam

Des: B. Delaney, from photographs by Colin Gifford. 19p has one phosphor band.

Set	2.50	3.00
Gutter pairs	6.50	
First day cover		2.50
Stamp cards	3.00	5.50

Dan Dare (1st)
The Three Bears (1st)
Rupert Bear (1st)
Alice (1st)
Noggin and the Ice Dragon (1st)
Peter Rabbit (1st)
Little Red Riding Hood (1st)
Orlando the Marmalade Cat (1st)
Biggles (1st)
Paddington Bear (1st)

■ 1994, February 1. Greetings stamps: Messages

Des: Newell and Sorell. Issued in booklets in panes of ten containing one of each design.

Booklet pane (of 10)	7.50	7.50
Booklet	7.00	
First day cover		8.50
Stamp cards	10.00	15.50

Castell Y Waun/Chirk Castle, Clwyd, Cymru/Wales

Castell Y Waun/Chirk Castle, Clwyd, Wales (19p)
Ben Arkle, Sutherland, Scotland (25p)
Mourne Mountains, County Down, Northern Ireland (30p)
Dersingham, Norfolk, England (35p)
Dolwyddelan, Gwynedd, Wales (41p)

■ 1994, March 1. 25th Anniversary of the Investiture of The Prince of Wales

Paintings by the Prince of Wales. 19p has one phosphor band.

Set	2.50	2.50
Gutter pairs	6.50	
First day cover		2.50
Stamp cards	2.25	5.50

(* The 30p also appears as a pane of four in the Northern Ireland prestige stamp book issued on July 26, 1994.)

Bathing at Blackpool (19p)
Where's My Little Lad (25p)
Wish You Were Here (30p)
Punch and Judy Show (35p)
'The Tower Crane' machine (41p)

■ 1994, April 12. Centenary of Picture Postcards

Des: M. Dempsey and B. Dare. Printed in litho by Questa. 19p has one phosphor band, others have two.

Set	2.50	2.50
Gutter pairs	6.50	
First day cover		2.50
Stamp cards	2.25	5.50

British Lion and French Cockerel (25p and 41p)
Hands over a train (25p and 41p)

■ 1994, May 3. Opening of Channel Tunnel

Des: G. Hardie (Lion & cockerel), J.-P. Cousin (Hands & train)

Set of two se-tenant pairs	2.50	2.50
Gutter pairs	6.50	
First day cover		2.75
Stamp cards	1.75	4.50

Douglas Boston and groundcrew (25p)
HMS Warspite (25p)
Commandos on Gold Beach (25p)
Infantry on Sword Beach (25p)
Tank and infantry (25p)

■ 1994, June 6. 50th Anniversary of D-Day

Des: K. Bassford. Printed in litho by Questa.

Set of five in se-tenant strip	2.75	2.75
Gutter pairs	7.00	
First day cover		2.75
Stamp cards	2.00	5.50

St Andrew's (19p)
Muirfield (25p)
Carnoustie (30p)
Royal Troon (35p)
Turnberry (41p)

■ 1994, July 5. Scottish Golf Courses

Des: P. Hogarth. 19p has one phosphor band.

Set	2.50	2.50
Gutter pairs	6.50	
First day cover		2.50
Stamp cards	2.00	5.50

Royal Welsh Show, Llanelwedd (19p)
Wimbledon Tennis Championships (25p)
Cowes Week (30p)
Test Match at Lord's (35p)
Braemar Gathering (41p)

■ 1994, August 2. The Four Seasons: Summertime

Des: M. Cook. 19p has one phosphor band.

Set	2.25	2.50
Gutter pairs	6.00	
First day cover		2.50
Stamp cards	2.00	5.50

Ultrasonic imaging (25p)
Scanning electron microscopy (30p)
Magnetic resonance imaging (35p)
Computed tomography (41p)

■ 1994, September 27. Medical Discoveries. Europa

Des: P. Vermier and J.-P. Tibbles. Printed in photogravure by
Enschedé.

Set	2.25	2.25
Gutter pairs	6.00	
First day cover		2.50
Stamp cards	2.25	5.50

Mary and Joseph (19p)
Three Wise Men (25p)
Mary with doll (30p)
Shepherds (35p)
Angels (41p)

■ 1994, November 1. Christmas: Children's Nativity Plays

Des: Yvonne Gilbert. 19p has one phosphor band.

Set	2.25	2.50
Gutter pairs	6.00	
First day cover		2.50
Stamp cards	2.50	5.50

(*The 19p and 25p were also sold in booklets.)

Black cat (19p)
Siamese and tabby cat (25p)
Ginger cat (30p)
Tortoiseshell and Abyssinian cat (35p)
Black and white cat (41p)

■ 1995, January 17. Cats

Des: Elizabeth Blackadder. Printed in litho by Questa. 19p has
one phosphor band, others two phosphor bands.

Set	2.40	2.40
Gutter pairs	6.00	
First day cover		2.50
Stamp cards	2.75	7.50

Dandelion (19p)
Chestnut leaves (25p)
Garlic leaves (30p)
Hazel leaves (35p)
Spring grass (41p)

■ 1995, March 14. The Four Seasons: Springtime

Plant sculptures by Andy Goldsworthy. 19p has one phosphor
band, others two phosphor bands.

Set	2.25	2.40
Gutter pairs	6.00	
First day cover		2.50
Stamp cards	2.75	6.50

'La Danse à la Campagne' by Renoir (1st)
'Troilus and Criseyde' by Peter Brookes (1st)
'The Kiss' by Rodin (1st)
'Girls on the Town' by Beryl Cook (1st)
'Jazz' by Andrew Mockett (1st)
'Girls performing a Kathak Dance' (1st)
'Alice Keppel with her daughter' by Alice Hughes (1st)
'Children Playing' by L. S. Lowry (1st)
'Circus Clowns' by Emily Firmin and Justin Mitchell (1st)
'All the Love Poems of Shakespeare' (detail) by Eric Gill (1st)

■ **1995, March 21. Greetings stamps: Art**

Des: Newell and Sorell. Printed in litho by Walsall. Issued in booklets in panes of ten containing one of each design.

Booklet pane (of 10)	6.50	6.50
Booklet	6.50	
First day cover		6.50
Stamp cards	10.00	15.50

Fireplace decoration (19p)
Oak seedling (25p)
Carved table leg (30p)
St David's Head, Dyfed, Wales (35p)
Elizabethan window (41p)

■ **1995, April 11. Centenary of The National Trust**

Des: T. Evans. One phosphor band (19p), two phosphor bands (25p, 35p), phosphor paper (30p, 41p).

Set	2.25	2.25
Gutter pairs	6.00	
First day cover		2.50
Stamp cards	2.75	6.50

(* The 25p also appeared in a pane of six in the National Trust prestige stamp book issued on April 25, 1995.)

British troops and French civilians (19p)
Symbolic hands and Red Cross (19p)
Searchlights in a 'V' over St Paul's Cathedral (25p)
Hand releasing Dove of Peace (25p)
Symbolic hands and United Nations (30p)

■ **1995, May 2. Peace & Freedom. Europa**

Des: J-M. Folon (Red Cross 19p, Dove 25p, 30p), J. Gorham (Troops 19p, Seachlights 25p), One phosphor band (19p), two phosphor bands (others).

Set	2.25	2.25
Gutter pairs	6.00	
First day cover		2.50
Stamp cards	2.75	6.50

(* The design with St Paul's Cathedral was also used as a 1st class stamp in a miniature sheet in 2005.)

The Time Machine (25p)
The First Men in the Moon (30p)
The War of the Worlds (35p)
The Shape of Things to Come (41p)

■ **1995, June 6. Novels of H. G. Wells**

Des: Siobhan Keaney. Printed in litho by Questa.

Set	2.25	2.25
Gutter pairs	6.00	
First day cover		2.50
Stamp cards	2.00	6.50

The Swan, 1595 (25p)
The Rose, 1592 (25p)
The Globe, 1599 (25p)
The Hope, 1613 (25p)
The Globe, 1614 (25p)

■ **1995, August 8. Reconstruction of Shakespeare's Globe Theatre**

Des: C. Hodges. Printed in litho by Walsall.

Set of five in se-tenant strip	2.25	2.50
Gutter pairs	6.00	
First day cover		2.50
Stamp cards	2.75	6.50

■ 1995, August 22. Castle high-value definitive
As issue of March 24, 1992, but new value, replacing the £1.

£3	8.50	1.35
Gutter pair	20.00	
Gutter block of four (centre cross)		40.00
First day cover		5.00
Stamp card	10.00	21.00

(* This stamp exists with either blue tinted PVAD gum or white PVA gum.)

Sir Rowland Hill and Uniform Penny Postage Petition (19p)
Sir Rowland Hill and Penny Black (25p)
Marconi and early wireless (41p)
Marconi and 'Titanic' (60p)

■ 1995, September 5. Pioneers of Communications
Des: The Four Hundred; engraved by C. Slania. Printed in recess and litho by Harrison. 19p has one phosphor band.

Set	2.25	2.25
Gutter pairs	6.00	
First day cover		2.50
Stamp cards	2.25	6.50

Harold Wagstaff (19p)
Gus Risman (25p)
Jim Sullivan (30p)
Billy Batten (35p)
Brian Bevan (41p)

■ 1995, October 3. Centenary of Rugby League
Des: C. Birmingham. One phosphor band (19p), two phosphor bands (others).

Set	2.40	2.50
Gutter pairs	6.00	
First day cover		2.50
Stamp cards	2.75	6.50

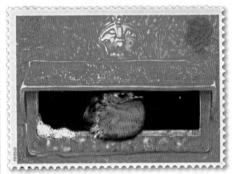

Robin in letter box (19p)
Robin on railings (25p)
Robin on milk bottles (30p)
Robin on road sign (41p)
Robin on front door handle (60p)

■ 1995, October 30. Christmas. Robins
Des: K. Lilly. One phosphor band (19p), two phosphor bands (others).

Set	2.70	2.70
Gutter pairs	7.00	
First day cover		2.75
Stamp cards	3.25	6.50

(* The 19p, 25p and 60p were also sold in booklets, and the 19p was used in Smilers sheets in 2000 and 2001.)

Wee, fleeket, cowran, tim'rous beastie (19p)
O, my Love's like a red, red rose (25p)
Scots, Wha hae wi Wallace bled (41p)
Should auld acquaintance be forgot (60p)

■ 1996, January 25. Bicentenary of Death of Robert Burns
Des: Tayburn Design Consultancy. Printed in litho by Questa. One phosphor band (19p), two phosphor bands (others).

Set	2.40	2.25
Gutter pairs	6.00	
First day cover		2.50
Stamp cards	2.25	6.50

I'm writing to you because you don't listen to a word I say .. (1st)
More! Love (1st)
Sincerely (1st)
Do you have something for the human condition? (1st)
Mental floss (1st)
4:55pm. Don't ring (1st)
Dear lottery prize winner (1st)
Fetch this, fetch that. Let the cat do it. (1st)
My day starts before I'm ready for it (1st)
The cheque in the post (1st)

■ 1996, February 26. Greetings stamps: Cartoons

Des: M. Wolff. Printed in litho by Walsall. All-over phosphor.
Issued in booklets in panes of ten containing one of each design.

Booklet pane (of 10)	7.00	7.00
Booklet	9.00	
First day cover		6.50
Stamp cards	10.00	15.50

Muscovy Duck (19p)
Lapwing (25p)
White-front Goose (30p)
Bittern (35p)
Whooper Swan (41p)

■ 1996, March 12. 50th Anniversary of the Wildfowl and Wetlands Trust

Des: Moseley Webb, from paintings by C. F. Tunnicliffe. 19p has one phosphor band.

Set	2.25	2.50
Gutter pairs	6.00	
First day cover		2.75
Stamp cards	3.25	6.50

Odeon (19p)
Laurence Olivier and Vivien Leigh (25p)
Cinema ticket (30p)
Pathé News (35p)
'Big Screen Showing' (41p)

■ 1996, April 16. Centenary of Cinema

Des: The Chase. One phosphor band (19p), two phosphor bands (others).

Set	2.40	2.50
Gutter pairs	6.00	
First day cover		2.75
Stamp cards	4.00	6.50

Dixie Dean (19p)
Bobby Moore (25p)
Duncan Edwards (30p)
Billy Wright (35p)
Danny Blanchflower (41p)

■ 1996, May 14. European Football Championships

Des: H. Brown. Printed in litho by Questa. One phosphor band (19p), two phosphor bands (others).

Set	2.75	2.75
Gutter pairs	7.00	
First day cover		3.00
Stamp cards	4.50	6.50

(* All of the stamps in this set also appeared as panes in the European Football Championships prestige stamp booklet, issued on May 14, 1996.)

Athlete (26p)
Throwing the Javelin (26p)
Basketball (26p)
Swimming (26p)
Athlete and Olympic rings (26p)

■ 1996, July 9. Olympic Games and Paralympic Games

Des: N. Knight. Printed in litho by Questa.

Set (in se-tenant strip of five)	2.25	2.40
Gutter pairs	6.00	
First day cover		2.50
Stamp cards	2.50	6.50

Dorothy Hodgkin (20p)
Margot Fonteyn (26p)
Elizabeth Frink (31p)
Daphne du Maurier (37p)
Marea Hartman (43p)

■ 1996, August 6. Famous Women. Europa

Des: Stephanie Nash. One phosphor band (20p), two phosphor bands (others).

Set	2.50	2.60
Gutter pairs	6.50	
First day cover		3.00
Stamp cards	2.00	6.50

Muffin the Mule (20p)
Sooty (26p)
Stingray (31p)
The Clangers (37p)
Dangermouse (43p)

■ 1996, September 3. 50th Anniversary of Children's Television

Des: Tutssels. Printed in photogravure by Enschedé. One phosphor band (20p), two phosphor bands (others).

Set	2.50	2.75
Gutter pairs	6.50	
First day cover		3.00
Stamp cards	3.50	6.50

(* The 20p also appeared in the 75th Anniversary of the BBC prestige stamp booklet issued on September 23, 1997, printed in photogravure by Harrison; priced at £1.00 mint or used.)

Triumph TR3 (20p)
MG TD (26p)
Austin Healey 100 (37p)
Jaguar XK120 (43p)
Morgan Plus 4 (63p)

■ 1996, October 1. Classic Sports Cars

Des: S. Clay. One phosphor band (20p), two phosphor bands (others).

Set	3.00	3.00
Gutter pairs	8.50	
First day cover		3.50
Stamp cards	4.00	6.50

The Three Kings (2nd)
The Annunciation (1st)
The Journey to Bethlehem (31p)
The Nativity (43p)
The Shepherds (63p)

■ 1996, October 28. Christmas
Des: Laura Stoddart. One phosphor band (2nd), two phosphor bands (others).

Set	3.00	3.00
Gutter pairs	8.50	
First day cover		3.50
Stamp cards	3.00	6.50

(* The 2nd class and 1st class were also sold in booklets.)

■ 1996, November 11. Greetings stamps: Cartoons
As issue of February 26, but with two phosphor bands. Issued in booklets in panes of ten containing one of each design

Booklet pane (of 10)	25.00	25.00
Booklet	25.00	

(* These designs were also used for Smilers sheets in 2001 and 2002.)

Iris latifolia (1st)
Gentiana acaulis (1st)
Magnolia grandiflora (1st)
Camellia japonica (1st)
Tulipa (1st)
Fuchsia 'Princess of Wales' (1st)
Tulipa gesneriana (1st)
Gazania splendens (1st)
Hippeastrum rutilum (1st)
Passiflora coerulea (1st)

■ 1997, January 6. Greetings stamps: Flower Paintings
Des: Tutssels. Printed in litho by Walsall. Two phosphor bands. Issued in booklets in panes of ten containing one of each design.

Booklet pane (of 10)	7.00	6.50
Booklet	7.00	
First day cover		10.00
Stamp cards	10.00	15.50

(* The Gentiana acaulis, Tulipa and Iris latifolia designs also appear in the Glory of the Garden prestige stamp book of 2004, and the Tulipa and Iris latifolia designs in the 50th Anniversary of NAFAS booklet of May 21, 2009, in self adhesive form, priced £1.50 the pair. All the designs were also used in a Smilers sheet issued on January 21, 2003.)

King Henry VIII (26p)
Catherine of Aragon (26p)
Anne Boleyn (26p)
Jane Seymour (26p)
Anne of Cleves (26p)
Catherine Howard (26p)
Catherine Parr (26p)

■ 1997, February 21. 450th Anniversary of the Death of King Henry VIII
Des: Kate Stephens. Two phosphor bands. King Henry VIII design issued as a separate stamp in sheets, wives designs in a se-tenant strip

Set	3.50	3.75
Gutter pairs	9.00	
First day cover		4.00
Stamp cards	6.00	6.50

St Columba in boat (26p)
St Columba on Iona (37p)
St Augustine with King Ethelbert (43p)
St Augustine with a model of a cathedral (63p)

■ 1997, March 11. Religious Anniversaries
Des: Claire Melinsky. Printed in photogravure by Enschedé. Two phosphor bands.

Set	2.75	2.75
Gutter pairs	7.00	
First day cover		3.25
Stamp cards	2.00	6.00

Dracula

Dracula (26p)
Frankenstein (31p)
Dr Jekyll and Mr Hyde (37p)
The Hound of the Baskervilles (43p)

■ 1997, May 13. Tales of Horror. Europa

Des: J. Pollock. Printed in photogravure by Walsall. Two phosphor bands.

Set	2.50	2.75
Gutter pairs	6.50	
First day cover		3.00
Stamp cards	2.00	6.00

Supermarine Spitfire MkIIA and Reginald Mitchell (20p)
Avro Lancaster MkI and Roy Chadwick (26p)
De Havilland Mosquito B MkXVI and Ronald Bishop (37p)
Gloster Meteor T Mk7 and George Carter (43p)
Hawker Hunter FGA Mk9 and Sir Sydney Camm (63p)
The faces of the aircraft designers feature in the cloud formations

■ 1997, June 10. British Aircraft Designers

Des: Turner Duckworth. One phosphor band (20p), two phosphor bands (others).

Set	3.25	3.25
Gutter pairs	8.00	
First day cover		3.25
Stamp cards	2.00	6.50

(* The 20p also appears in the Pilot To Plane: RAF Uniforms prestige stamp book issued on September 18, 2008)

Carriage horse (20p)
Lifeguards horse (26p)
Blues and Royals drum horse (43p)
Duke of Edinburgh's horse (63p)

■ 1997, July 8. All The Queen's Horses. 50th Anniversary of the British Horse Society

Des: J.-L. Benard. Printed in litho by Walsall. One phosphor band (20p), two phosphor bands (others).

Set	2.50	2.75
Gutter pairs	7.00	
First day cover		3.00
Stamp cards	3.00	6.00

■ 1997, July 29. Castle high-value definitives

Designs as the £1.50, £2 and £5 of March 24, 1992, and £3 of August 22, 1995, but printed in recess and silk screen (for Queen's portrait) by Enschedé. Engraved by Inge Madlé.

Set	45.00	10.00
Gutter pairs	£125	
Gutter blocks of four (centre cross)	£275	
First day cover		25.00

Haroldswick, Shetland, Scotland

Haroldswick, Shetland (20p)
Painswick, Gloucestershire (26p)
Beddgelert, Gwynedd (43p)
Ballyroney, County Down (63p)

■ 1997, August 12. Sub Post Offices

Des: T. Millington. Printed in photogravure by Enschedé. One phosphor band (20p), two phosphor bands (others).

Set	2.50	2.75
Gutter pairs	7.00	
First day cover		3.00
Stamp cards	2.00	6.00

Enid Blyton's *Malory Towers*

Noddy (20p)
Famous Five (26p)
Secret Seven (37p)
Faraway Tree (43p)
Malory Towers (63p)

■ 1997, September 9. Centenary of the Birth of Enid Blyton
Des: C. Birmingham. Printed in photogravure by Enschedé. One phosphor band (20p), two phosphor bands (others).

Set	2.75	3.00
Gutter pairs	7.00	
First day cover		3.00
Stamp cards	3.50	6.50

Children and Father Christmas pulling Christmas cracker (2nd)
Father Christmas with Christmas cracker (1st)
Father Christmas riding on a Christmas cracker (31p)
Father Christmas with a snowball (43p)
Father Christmas on a chimney (63p)

■ 1997, October 27. Christmas. 150th Anniversary of the Christmas Cracker
Des: M. Thomas (1st) and J. Gorham (others). One phosphor band (2nd), two phosphor bands (others).

Set	3.00	3.00
Gutter pairs	8.00	
First day cover		3.00
Stamp cards	3.50	6.50

(*The 2nd class and 1st class were also sold in booklets, and the 1st class was used for Smilers sheets in 2000 and 2001.)

Queen Elizabeth II and Prince Philip wedding photograph of 1947 (20p and 43p)
Queen Elizabeth II and Prince Philip photographed in 1997 (26p and 63p)

■ 1997, November 13. Royal Golden Wedding
Des: D. Driver (20p, 43p), Lord Snowdon (26p, 63p). One phosphor band (20p), two phosphor bands (others).

Set	3.50	3.50
Gutter pairs	9.50	
First day cover		3.25
Stamp cards	2.75	5.50

Common Dormouse (20p)
Lady's Slipper Orchid (26p)
Song Thrush (31p)
Shining Ram's-horn Snail (37p)
Mole Cricket (43p)
Devil's Bolette (63p)

■ 1998, January 20. Endangered Species
Des: R. Maude. Printed in litho by Questa. One phosphor band (20p), two phosphor bands (others).

Set	4.00	4.00
Gutter pairs	10.00	
First day cover		3.50
Stamp cards	4.00	6.50

By Lord Snowdon (26p)
At British Lung Foundation function (26p)
Wearing tiara (26p)
During visit to Birmingham (26p)
In evening dress (26p)

■ **1998, February 3. Diana, Princess of Wales Memorial**
Des: B. Robinson. Two phosphor bands.

Set (in se-tenant strip of five)	2.25	2.25
Gutter pairs	6.00	
First day cover		3.25

Lion of England and Griffin of Edward III (26p)
Flacon of Plantagenet and Bull of Clarence (26p)
Lion of Mortimer and Yale of Beaufort (26p)
Greyhound of Richmond and Dragon of Wales (26p)
Unicorn of Scotland and Horse of Hanover (26p)

■ **1998, February 24. The Queen's Beasts. 650th Anniversary of the Order of the Garter**
Des: Jeffery Matthews. Printed in recess and litho by Harrison. Two phosphor bands.

Set (in se-tenant strip of five)	2.40	2.50
Gutter pairs	6.00	
First day cover		3.00
Stamp cards	3.50	6.50

■ **1998, March 10. Wilding definitives**
Des: Dew Gibbons Design Group, from original design by G. Knipe. Printed in gravure by Walsall. Issued only in the Wilding Definitives prestige stamp book.

20p light green (phos band at left)	0.70	0.75
20p light green (phos band at right)	0.70	0.75
26p red-brown	0.75	0.80
37p light purple	1.75	1.85

St John's Point Lighthouse (20p)
Smalls Lighthouse (26p)
Needles Rock Lighthouse (37p)
Bell Rock Lighthouse (43p)
Eddystone Lighthouse (63p)

■ **1998, March 24. Lighthouses**
Des: D. Davis and J. Boon. Printed in litho by Questa. One phosphor band (20p), two phosphor bands (others).

Set	3.25	3.25
Gutter pairs	9.00	
First day cover		3.25
Stamp cards	3.00	6.50

Tommy Cooper (20p)
Eric Morecambe (26p)
Joyce Grenfell (37p)
Les Dawson (43p)
Peter Cook (63p)

■ **1998, April 23. Comedians**
Des: Gerald Scarfe. Printed in litho by Questa. One phosphor band (20p), two phosphor bands (others).

Set	3.25	3.25
Gutter pairs	9.00	
First day cover		3.25
Stamp cards	3.00	6.50

(* Examples exist of the 37p design but with the denomination 30p, printed before an increase in postal rates, and issued in error.)

Hands forming the shape of a heart (20p)
Adult holding the hand of a child (26p)
Hands forming a cradle (43p)
Hand taking a pulse (63p)

■ **1998, June 23. 50th Anniversary of the National Health Service**
Des: V. Frost, using photographs by A. Wilson. Printed in litho by Questa. One phosphor band (20p), two phosphor bands (others).

Set	2.50	2.50
Gutter pairs	7.00	
First day cover		3.25
Stamp cards	3.00	6.50

The Hobbit (20p)
The Lion, The Witch and the Wardrobe (26p)
The Phoenix and the Carpet (37p)
The Borrowers (43p)
Through The Looking Glass (63p)

■ **1998, July 21. Children's Fantasy Novels**
Des: P. Malone. Printed in photogravure by De La Rue. One phosphor band (20p), two phosphor bands (others).

Set	3.25	3.25
Gutter pairs	8.50	
First day cover		3.50
Stamp cards	6.00	6.50

Woman in costume of yellow feathers (20p)
Woman in blue costume (26p)
Children in white and gold robes (43p)
Child dressed as a tree (63p)

■ **1998, August 25. Notting Hill Carnival. Europa**
Des: T. Hazael. Printed in photogravure by Walsall. One phosphor band (20p), two phosphor bands (others).

Set	2.75	2.75
Gutter pairs	7.00	
First day cover		3.25
Stamp cards	2.00	6.50

Bluebird of Sir Malcolm Campbell (20p)
Sunbeam of Sir Henry Segrave (26p)
Babs of John G. Parry Thomas (30p)
Railton Mobil Special of John R. Cobb (43p)
Bluebird CN7 of Donald Campbell (63p)

■ **1998, September 29. British Land Speed Records**
Des: Roundel Design Group. Printed in photogravure by De La Rue. One centre phosphor band (20p), two phosphor bands (others).

Set	3.00	3.00
Gutter pairs	7.50	
First day cover		3.25
Stamp cards	2.25	6.50

(* The 20p also appears in the Breaking Barriers prestige stamp book issued on October 13, 1988, but printed in photogravure by Walsall, and with one phosphor band printed on the left or right of the stamp; priced at £1.00 each mint or used)

Angel with hands in blessing (20p)
Angel praying (26p)
Angel playing lute (30p)
Angel playing flute (43p)
Angel praying (63p)

■ 1998, November 2. Christmas. Angels
Des: Irene von Treskow. Printed in photogravure by De La Rue.
One phosphor band (20p), two phosphor bands (others).

Set	3.25	3.25
Gutter pairs	9.00	
First day cover		3.25
Stamp cards	1.75	6.50

(* The 20p and 26p were also sold in booklets.)

During 1999 and 2000 Royal Mail embarked on a programme of special stamp issues to mark the new Millennium. Each design includes the inscription 'Millennium' and the year, and a serial number. The designs for 1999 looked back over the previous Millennium, by exploring 12 different 'tales'. The designs for 2000 are of photographs of projects undertaken to celebrate the Millennium.

Timekeeping: Greenwich Meridian and clock (20p)
Steam Power: worker and blast furnace (26p)
Photography: photograph of leaves (43p)
Computers: computer inside head (63p)

■ 1999, January 12. The Inventors' Tale
Des: David Gentleman (20p), P. Howson (26p), Z. and Barbara Baran (43p), E. Paolozzi (63p). Printed in photogravure by Enschedé (26p), or De La Rue (others). One phosphor band (20p), two phosphor bands (others).

Set	3.00	3.00
Gutter pairs	7.50	
First day cover		4.50
Stamp cards	2.00	6.50

(* The 63p also appears in the World Changers prestige stamp book issued on September 21, 1999, but printed in photogravure by Questa; priced at £2.00 mint or used.)

Jet Travel: globe surrounded by aircraft (20p)
Liberation By Bike: woman on bicycle (26p)
Linking The Nation: railway station (43p)
Cook's Endeavour: Captain Cook and man (63p)

■ 1999, February 2. The Travellers' Tale
Des: G. Hardie (20p), Sara Fanelli (26p), J. Lawrence (43p), A. Klimowski (63p). Printed in photogravure by Enschedé (20p and 63p), by De La Rue (26p), or litho by Enschedé (43p). One phosphor band (20p), two phosphor bands (others).

Set	3.00	3.00
Gutter pairs	7.50	
First day cover		3.75
Stamp cards	2.00	6.50

Jenner's Vaccination: cow with markings of vaccinated child (20p)
Nursing Care: patient on trolley (26p)
Fleming's Penicillin: penicillin mould (43p)
Test Tube Baby: sculpture of baby (63p)

■ 1999, March 2. The Patients' Tale

Des: P. Brookes (20p), Susan Macfarlane (26p), M. Dempsey (43p), A. Gormley (63p. Printed in photogravure by Questa. One phosphor band (20p), two phosphor bands (others).

Set	3.00	3.00
Gutter pairs	7.50	
First day cover		3.75
Stamp cards	2.00	6.50

(*The 20p also appears in the World Changers prestige stamp book issued on September 21, 1999.)

Migration To Scotland: Norman settler and dove (20p)
Pilgrim Fathers: settlers and Red Indian (26p)
Destination Australia: sailing ship and aspects of settlement (43p)
Migration To UK: face superimposed on hummingbird (63p)

■ 1999, April 6. The Settlers' Tale

Des: J. Byrne (20p), W. McLean (26p), J. Fisher (43p), G. Powell (63p). Printed in litho (20p) or photogravure (others) by Walsall. One phosphor band (20p), two phosphor bands (others).

Set	3.00	3.00
Gutter pairs	7.50	
First day cover		3.75
Stamp cards	2.00	6.50

(*The 26p also appears in a booklet issued on May 12, 1999.)

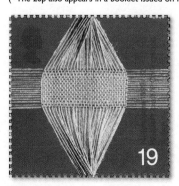

Weaver's Craft: woven threads (19p)
Mill Towns: Salts Mill, Saltaire (26p)
Shipbuilding: hull on slipway (44p)
City Finance: Lloyd's Building (64p)

■ 1999, May 4. The Workers' Tale

Des: P. Collingwood (19p), D. Hockney (26p), R. Sanderson (44p), B. Neiland (64p). Printed in litho (19p) or photogravure (others) by De La Rue. One phosphor band (19p), two phosphor bands (others).

Set	3.00	3.00
Gutter pairs	7.50	
First day cover		3.75
Stamp cards	2.00	6.50

(*The 26p from this set also appears in a booklet issued on May 12, 1999, printed in photogravure by Walsall; priced at £1.75 mint or used.)

Mercury's Magic: Freddie Mercury of Queen on stage (19p)
World Cup: Bobby Moore holding the trophy (26p)
Doctor Who: dalek (44p)
Chaplin's Genius: Charlie Chaplin (64p)

■ 1999, June 1. The Entertainers' Tale

Des: P. Blake (19p), M. White (26p), Lord Snowdon (44p), R. Steadman (64p). Printed in photogravure by Enschedé. One phosphor band (19p), two phosphor bands (others).

Set	3.00	3.00
Gutter pairs	7.50	
First day cover		3.75
Stamp cards	5.00	6.50

Prince Edward and Miss Sophie Rhys-Jones facing front (26p)
Prince Edward and Miss Sophie Rhys-Jones facing sideways (64p)

■ 1999, June 15. Royal Wedding

Des: J. Gibbs from photographs by John Swannell. Printed in photogravure by De La Rue.

Set	1.50	1.50
Gutter pairs	4.00	
First day cover		2.50
Stamp cards	2.00	3.50

Equal Rights: suffragette behind bars (19p)
Right To Health: tap (26p)
Right To Learn: children at school (44p)
First Rights: Magna Carta (64p)

■ 1999, July 6. The Citizens' Tale
Des: Natasha Kerr (19p), M. Craig-Martin (26p), A. Drummond (44p), A. Kitching (64p). Printed in photogravure by De La Rue. One phosphor band (19p), two phosphor bands (others).

Set	3.00	3.00
Gutter pairs	7.50	
First day cover		3.75
Stamp cards	2.00	6.50

Decoding DNA: molecular structures (19p)
Darwin's Theory: Galapagos finch and skeleton (26p)
Faraday's Electricity: light polarised by magnetism (44p)
Newton: Saturn, from Hubble Space Telescope (64p)

■ 1999, August 3. The Scientists' Tale
Des: M. Curtis (19p), R. Harris Ching (26p), C. Gray (44p), photograph (64p). Printed in photogravure (19p, 64p) or litho (others) by Questa. One phosphor band (19p), two phosphor bands (others).

Set	3.00	3.00
Gutter pairs	7.50	
First day cover		3.75
Stamp cards	2.00	6.50

(* The 26p and 44p also appear in the World Changers prestige stamp book of September 21, 1999; priced at £3.50 for the pair. The 64p also appears on a miniature sheet of August 11.)

Saturn, from Hubble Space Telescope (64p)

■ 1999, August 11. Solar Eclipse
Printed in photogravure by De La Rue. Miniature sheet, comprising four 64p values from issue of August 3.

Miniature sheet	12.00	12.00
First day cover		12.50

Strip Farming: upland landscape (19p)
Mechanical Farming: horse-drawn seed drill (26p)
Food From Afar: peeling potato (44p)
Satellite Agriculture: combine harvester in field (64p)

■ 1999, September 7. The Farmers' Tale
Des: D. Tress (19p), C. Wormell (26p), Tessa Traeger (44p), R. Cooke (64p). Printed in photogravure by De La Rue. One phosphor band (19p), two phosphor bands (others).

Set	3.00	3.00
Gutter pairs	7.50	
First day cover		3.75
Stamp cards	2.00	6.50

(* The 26p also appears in a booklet issued on September 21, 1999, printed in gravure by Walsall; priced at £2.00 mint or used.)

Bannockburn: Robert the Bruce (19p)
Civil War: Cavalier and horse (26p)
World Wars: war graves (44p)
Peace Keeping: soldiers with boy (64p)

■ 1999, October 5. The Soldiers' Tale
Des: A. Davidson (19p), R. Kelly (26p), D. McCullin (44p), C. Corr (64p). Printed in litho (19p) or photogravure (others) by Walsall. One phosphor band (19p), two phosphor bands (others).

Set	3.00	3.00
Gutter pairs	7.50	
First day cover		3.75
Stamp cards	2.00	6.50

Wesley: Hark the Herald Angels Sing (19p)
King James Bible: James I and Authorised Version of Bible (26p)
St. Andrews Pilgrimage: St. Andrews Cathedral, Fife (44p)
First Christmas: Nativity (64p)

■ 1999, November 2. The Christians' Tale
Des: B. Neuenschwander (19p), Claire Melinsky (26p), Catherine Yass (44p), C. Aitchison (64p). Printed in photogravure by De La Rue. One phosphor band (19p), two phosphor bands (others).

Set	3.00	3.00
Gutter pairs	7.50	
First day cover		3.75
Stamp cards	2.00	6.50

(* The 19p and 26p were also sold in booklets.)

World Of The Stage: dancers behind curtain (19p)
World Of Music: coloured stripes (26p)
World Of Literature: untitled book (44p)
New Worlds: rainbow abstract (64p)

■ 1999, December 7. The Artists' Tale
Des: Allen Jones (19p), Bridget Riley (26p), Lisa Milroy (44p), Sir Howard Hodgkin (64p). Printed in photogravure by Walsall. One phosphor band (19p), two phosphor bands (others).

Set	3.00	3.00
Gutter pairs	7.00	
First day cover		3.75
Stamp cards	2.00	6.50

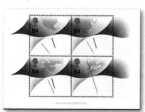

Globe showing North America (64p)
Globe showing Asia (64p)
Globe showing Middle East (64p)
Globe showing Europe (64p)

■ 1999, December 14. Millennium Timekeeper
Des: David Gentleman. Printed in gravure by De La Rue.

Miniature sheet	12.00	12.00
First day cover		11.50
Stamp cards	9.00	18.50

(* The miniature sheet also exists with the margin overprinted 'Earls Court, London 22-28 May 2000 The Stamp Show 2000', sold at £10 with tickets to the exhibition from March 1, 2000; price £18.00 mint.)

Third Millennium, Muncaster: barn owl (19p)
National Space Centre, Leicester: night sky (26p)
Torrs Walkway, New Mills: River Goyt and textile mills (44p)
Seabird Centre, North Berwick: cape gannets (64p)

■ 2000, January 18. Above and Beyond
Printed in litho (44p) and gravure (others) by Questa. One phosphor band (19p), two phosphor bands (others).

Set	3.50	3.50
Gutter pairs	9.50	
First day cover		4.00
Stamp cards	2.25	6.50

(* The 26p also appears as a 1st class value in a £2.70 stamp booklet issued on May 26, 2000, printed in gravure by Walsall. Price: £2.50 mint.)

Beacons Across The Land: millennium beacon (19p)
Rheilffordd Eryri, Snowdonia: Garratt locomotive and train (26p)
Dynamic Earth Centre, Edinburgh: lightning (44p)
Lighting Croydon's Skyline: floodlighting (64p)

■ 2000, February 1. Fire and Light
Printed in gravure by De La Rue. One phosphor band (19p), two phosphor bands (others).

Set	3.50	3.50
Gutter pairs	9.50	
First day cover		4.00
Stamp cards	2.25	6.50

Turning The Tide, Durham: beach pebbles (19p)
National Pondlife Centre, Merseyside: frog's legs and lilies (26p)
Parc Arfordirol, Llanelli: cliff boardwalk (44p)
Portsmouth Harbour: reflections in water (64p)

■ 2000, March 7. Water and Coast
Printed in litho (44p) or gravure (others) by Walsall. One phosphor band (19p), two phosphor bands (others).

Set	3.50	3.50
Gutter pairs	9.50	
First day cover		4.00
Stamp cards	2.25	6.50

ECOS, Ballymena: River Braid reed beds (2nd)
Web Of Life, London Zoo: South American leaf-cutter ants (1st)
Earth Centre, Doncaster: solar sensors (44p)
Project Suzy, Teesside: hydroponic leaves (64p)

■ 2000, April 4. Life and Earth
Printed in gravure by De La Rue. One phosphor band (2nd), two phosphor bands (others).

Set	3.50	3.50
Gutter pairs	9.50	
First day cover		4.00
Stamp cards	2.25	6.50

(* The 1st also appears in a booklet issued on May 26, 2000.)

Ceramica Museum, Stoke-on-Trent: pottery glaze (2nd)
Tate Modern, London: bankside galleries (1st)
Cycle Network: road marking for bicycle (45p)
Lowry Centre, Salford: people in Salford (65p)

■ 2000, May 2. Art and Craft
Printed in gravure by Enschedé. One phosphor band (2nd), two phosphor bands (others).

Set	3.50	3.50
Gutter pairs	9.50	
First day cover		4.00
Stamp cards	2.25	6.50

Millennium Greens project: children playing (2nd)
Millennium Bridge, Gateshead: bridge (1st)
Mile End Park, London: daisies (45p)
On The Meridian Line: African hut and thatched cottage (65p)

■ 2000, June 6. People and Places
Printed in gravure (2nd, 45p) or litho (others) by Walsall. One phosphor band (2nd), two phosphor bands (others).

Set	3.50	3.50
Gutter pairs	9.50	
First day cover		4.00
Stamp cards	2.25	6.50

Strangford Stone, Killyleagh: raising the stone (2nd)
Trans-Pennine Trail, Derbyshire: horse's hooves (1st)
Kingdom Of Fife Cycle Ways: cyclist and reflection (45p)
Groundwork's Changing Places: bluebell wood (65p)

2000, July 4. Stone and Soil

Printed in gravure in Enschedé. One phosphor band (2nd), two phosphor bands (others).

Set	3.50	3.50
Gutter pairs	9.50	
First day cover		4.00
Stamp cards	2.25	6.50

(* The 1st also appears in a £2.70 stamp booklet issued on September 5, 2000, printed in gravure by Walsall. Priced at 75p mint. The 65p also appears in the Treasury of Trees prestige stamp book issued on September 18, 2000, printed in gravure by Walsall; priced at £1.50 mint.)

Yews For The Millennium: tree roots (2nd)
Eden Project, St. Austell: sunflower (1st)
Millennium Seed Bank, Ardingly: sycamore seeds (45p)
Forest For Scotland: Doire Dach forest (65p)

2000, August 1. Tree and Leaf

Printed in gravure in De La Rue. One phosphor band (2nd), two phosphor bands (others).

Set	3.50	3.50
Gutter pairs	9.50	
First day cover		4.00
Stamp cards	2.25	6.50

(* The 2nd, 45p and 65p also appear in the Treasury of Trees prestige stamp book issued on September 18, 2000, printed in gravure by Walsall; priced at £3 mint.)

Queen Elizabeth II (27p)
Prince William (27p)
The Queen Mother (27p)
Prince Charles (27p)

2000, August 4. 100th birthday of The Queen Mother

Des: J. Gibbs. Photograph by J. Swannell. Printed in gravure by De La Rue.

Miniature sheet	7.50	7.50
First day cover		8.50
Stamp cards	5.50	12.50

(* The 27p design showing the Queen Mother, and the entire miniature sheet but in a slightly larger size, also appeared in the Life of the Century prestige stamp book issued on August 4, 2000, printed in gravure; stamp price £1.50 mint or used.)

Wildscreen At Bristol: head of Gigantiops (2nd)
Norfolk & Norwich Project: gathering water lilies on Broads (1st)
Millennium Point, Birmingham: X-ray of hand on mouse (45p)
Scottish Cultural Resources Network: tartan wool holder (65p)

2000, September 5. Mind and Matter

Printed in litho by Walsall. One phosphor band (2nd), two phosphor bands (others).

Set	3.50	3.50
Gutter pairs	9.50	
First day cover		4.00
Stamp cards	2.25	6.50

Body Zone, Millennium Dome: acrobats (2nd)
Hampden Park, Glasgow: footballers (1st)
Bath Spa Project: bather (45p)
Centre For Life, Newcastle: hen's egg under magnification (65p)

2000, October 3. Body and Bone

Printed in litho (2nd) or gravure by Questa. One phosphor band (2nd), two phosphor bands (others).

Set	3.50	3.50
Gutter pairs	9.50	
First day cover		4.00
Stamp cards	2.25	6.50

St. Edmundsbury Cathedral, Suffolk: stained glass window (2nd)
Church Floodlighting: St. Peter and St. Paul, Overstowey (1st)
St. Patrick Centre, Downpatrick: Latin gradual (45p)
Mystery Plays, York Minster: Chapter House ceiling (65p)

2000, November 7. Spirit and Faith

Printed in gravure by De La Rue. One phosphor band (2nd),
two phosphor bands (others).

Set	3.50	3.50
Gutter pairs	9.50	
First day cover		4.00
Stamp cards	2.25	6.50

(*The 2nd class and 1st class were also sold in booklets.)

Ringing In The Millennium: church bells (2nd)
Year Of The Artist: eye (1st)
Canolfan Mileniwm, Cardiff: top of a harp (45p)
Talent & Skills 2000: figure in latticework (65p)

2000, December 5. Sound and Vision

Printed in gravure by De La Rue. One phosphor band (2nd),
two phosphor bands (others).

Set	3.50	3.50
Gutter pairs	9.50	
First day cover		4.00
Stamp cards	2.25	6.50

Children's face painting: Flower (2nd)
Children's face painting: Tiger (1st)
Children's face painting: Owl (45p)
Children's face painting: Butterfly (65p)

2001, January 16. Rights of the Child

Des: Why Not Associates. Printed in gravure by De La Rue. One
phosphor band (2nd), two phosphor bands (others).

Set	3.00	3.00
Gutter pairs	7.50	
First day cover		3.25
Stamp cards	3.25	6.50

Hallmarks: Love (1st)
Thanks (1st)
abc (1st)
Welcome (1st)
Cheers (1st)

2001, February 6. Occasions

Des: Springpoint Design. Printed in gravure by Enschedé.

Set	4.25	4.25
Gutter pairs	11.00	
First day cover		4.00
Stamp cards	4.50	7.50

(*These designs were also used for Smilers sheets in 2001.)

Dog in bath (1st)
Dog and man sitting on bench (1st)
Boxer (1st)
Cat handbag (1st)
Cat on gate (1st)
Dog in car (1st)
Cat at window (1st)
Dog looking over fence (1st)
Cat watching bird (1st)
Cat in wash basin (1st)

2001, February 13. Cats and Dogs

Des: Johnson Banks. Printed in gravure by Walsall. Issued as a
self-adhesive sheetlet, which could be folded to form a booklet,
containing one of each of the ten designs.

Sheetlet	7.50	8.00
First day cover		7.50
Stamp cards	5.00	15.50

(*The ten designs, along with two 1st class definitives, were also
issued in a retail booklet on February 13, 2001.)

Sections of a barometer:
Rain (19p)
Fair (27p)
Stormy (45p)
Very dry (65p)

■ 2001, March 13. The Weather

Des: H. Brown and T. Meeuwissen. Printed in gravure by De La Rue. One phosphor band (19p), two phosphor bands (others).

Set	3.50	3.50
Gutter pairs	10.00	
First day cover		3.50
Stamp cards	3.50	9.00
Miniature sheet (one of each value)	11.00	11.00
Miniature sheet first day cover		11.00

Vanguard Class submarine (2nd)
Swiftsure Class submarine (1st)
Unity Class submarine (45p)
Holland type submarine (65p)

■ 2001, April 10. Centenary of Royal Navy Submarine Service

Des: D. Davis. Printed in gravure by Questa. One phosphor band (2nd), two phosphor bands (others). Perf: 15 × 14. PVA gum.

Set	3.25	3.25
Gutter pairs	9.50	
First day cover		3.50
Stamp cards	3.50	6.50

(* The four stamps are also in the Unseen & Unheard prestige stamp book issued on October 22, 2001. Perf: 15 × 15; priced at £10.00 mint or used. The 1st class design also appears twice in self-adhesive form, together with four 1st class definitives, in a £1.62 stamp booklet issued on April 17, 2001; priced at £35 mint or used. See also the issue of October 22)

Leyland X2, B Type, Leyland Titan TD1, AEC Regent I (1st)
AEC Regent I, Daimler COG5, Guy Arab II, AEC Regent III (1st)
AEC Regent III, Bristol K, AEC Routemaster, Bristol Lodekka FSF (1st)
Bristol Lodekka FSF, Leyland PD3, Leyland Atlantean, Daimler Fleetline (1st)
Daimler Fleetline, MCW Metrobus, Leyland Olympian, Dennis Trident (1st)

■ 2001, May 15. Double-deck Buses

Des: M. English. Printed in gravure by Questa. The illustrations extend into the sheet margins, and across the sheet, so that some of the illustrations span two stamps.

Set of five in se-tenant strip	3.75	3.75
Gutter pairs	10.00	
First day cover		3.75
Miniature sheet (one of each value)	6.50	6.50
Miniature sheet first day cover		8.00
Stamp cards	6.00	15.50

Toque hat (1st)
Butterfly hat (E)
Top hat (45p)
Spiral hat (65p)

■ 2001, June 19. Hats

Des: Rose Design, from photographs by N. Knight. Printed in litho by Enschedé.

Set	3.50	3.50
Gutter pairs	9.00	
First day cover		3.75
Stamp cards	3.00	6.50

Common frog (1st)
Great diving beetle (E)
Three-spined stickleback (45p)
Southern Hawker Dragonfly (65p)

■ 2001, July 10. Pond Life. Europa

Des: J. Gibbs. Printed in gravure by De La Rue.

Set	3.75	3.75
Gutter pairs	9.50	
First day cover		4.00
Stamp cards	2.50	6.50

Policeman (1st)
Mr Punch (1st)
Clown (1st)
Judy (1st)
Beadle (1st)
Crocodile (1st)

■ 2001, September 4. Punch and Judy

Des: K. Bernstein, from puppets made by Bryan Clarkez. Printed in gravure by Walsall. PVA gum. Perf: 14 x 15.

Set (in se-tenant strip of six)	3.75	3.75
Gutter pairs	9.50	
First day cover		3.75
Stamp cards	4.50	8.50

(* The Mr Punch and Judy designs also appear in self-adhesive form with four 1st class definitives in a £1.62 stamp booklet issued on September 4, 2001, printed in gravure by Questa. Perf: 14 x 15; priced at £15 mint, £15 used per pair.)

Carbon molecule, printed in litho and silk screen (2nd)
Globe, printed in litho and recess (1st)
Dove, printed in litho and embossing (E)
Crosses, printed in litho (40p)
'The Ad-dressing of Cats' by T. S. Eliot, printed in litho (45p)
Boron molecule, printed in litho with hologram (65p)

■ 2001, October 2. Nobel Prizes

Des: P.Vermier; engraved by Inge Madle (1st). Printed by Enschedé. One phosphor band (2nd), phosphor band around stamp (others).

Set	8.50	6.00
Gutter pairs	22.00	
First day cover		5.00
Stamp cards	5.00	8.50

White Ensign (1st)
Union Jack (1st)
Jolly Roger (1st)
Flag of Chief of Defence Staff (1st)

■ 2001, October 22. Centenary of Royal Navy Submarine Service. Flags

Printed in gravure by Questa. PVA gum.

Miniature sheet	6.00	6.00
First day cover		5.50
Stamp cards	6.00	14.00

(* The White Ensign and Jolly Roger designs also appear in self adhesive form with four 1st class definitives in a £1.62 stamp booklet issued on October 22, 2001; priced at £16 mint or used per pair. The Union Jack and White Ensign designs have been used for Smilers sheets from 2005, and also appear in the Ian Fleming's James Bond prestige stamp book issued on January 8, 2008. See also the issue of April 10.)

Robins with snowman (2nd)
Robins on bird table (1st)
Robins skating on bird bath (E)
Robins with Christmas pudding hanging from tree (45p)
Robins in nest made of paper chains (65p)

■ **2001, November 6. Christmas. Robins**
Des: A. Robins and H. Brown. Printed in gravure by De La Rue.
Self-adhesive.

Set	4.00	4.00
First day cover		4.00
Stamp cards	2.50	7.50

(* The 2nd and 1st class values were also issued in booklets, and were used for Smilers stamps in 2003 and 2005.)

The Elephant's Child (1st)
How the Whale got his Throat (1st)
How the Camel got his Hump (1st)
How the Rhinoceros got his Skin (1st)
How the Leopard got his Spots (1st)
The Sing Song of Old Man Kangaroo (1st)
The Beginning of the Armadillos (1st)
The Crab that played with the Sea (1st)
The Cat that walked by Himself (1st)
The Butterfly that stamped (1st)

■ **2002, January 15. Centenary of the Just So Stories by Rudyard Kipling**
Des: I. Cohen. Printed in gravure by Walsall. Issued as a self-adhesive sheetlet, which could be folded to form a booklet, containing one of each of the ten designs.

Sheetlet	6.50	6.50
First day cover		6.50
Stamp cards	4.50	21.00

Queen Elizabeth II in 1952, by Dorothy Wilding (2nd)
In 1968, by Cecil Beaton (1st)
In 1978, by Lord Snowdon (E)
In 1984, by Yousef Karsh (45p)
In 1996, by Tim Graham (65p)

■ **2002, February 6. Golden Jubilee**
Des: Kate Stephens. Printed in gravure by De La Rue. One phos band (2nd), two phos bands (others). Wmk: 50 (sideways).

Set	4.50	4.50
Gutter pairs	12.00	
First day cover		4.75
Stamp cards	2.50	7.00

(* The stamps are also in the Gracious Accession prestige book, but with the Wmk upright; price £12 mint, £12 used.)

Wilding design (1st)
Wilding design (2nd)

■ **2002, February 6. Wilding Design Decimal Definitives**
Des: M. Farrar-Bell (2nd), Enid Marx (1st). Printed in gravure by Enschedé. Wmk: 50. One phosphor band (2nd) or two phosphor bands (1st). Issued only in the £7.29 A Gracious Accession prestige stamp book issued on February 6, 2002. One pane had a tilted 2nd, resulting in a diagonal watermark.

2nd carmine-red	0.90	1.00
2nd carmine-red (Wmk diagonal)	2.50	2.50
1st green	0.90	1.00

Love (1st)
Rabbits, inscribed 'a new baby' (1st)
'Hello' written in sky (1st)
Bear pulling topiary tree in shape of house (1st)
Flowers inscribed 'best wishes' (1st)

■ **2002, March 5. Occasions**
Des: I. Bilbey (Rabbits and Flowers), A. Kitching (Love), Hoop Associates (Hello), G. Percy (Bear). Printed in litho by Questa.

Set	3.50	3.50
Gutter pairs	10.00	
First day cover		3.50
Stamp cards	3.25	7.00

(* The Hello design also appears in a booklet of 1st gold definitives issued on March 4, 2003, self-adhesive; price £3.50 mint or used. All designs were used for Smilers sheets in 2002.)

Studland Bay (27p)
Luskentyre (27p)
Cliffs of Dover (27p)
Padstow Harbour (27p)
Broadstairs (27p)
St Abb's Head (27p)
Dunster Beach (27p)
Newquay (27p)
Portrush (27p)
Conwy (27p)

■ 2002, March 19. British Coastlines
Des: R. Cooke. Printed in litho by Walsall.

Set of ten in se-tenant block	4.75	5.00
Gutter pairs	13.00	
First day cover		5.25
Stamp cards	4.00	13.50

Slack wire act (2nd)
Lion tamer (1st)
Trick tri-cyclists (E)
Krazy kar (45p)
Equestrienne (65p)

■ 2002, April 10. Circus. Europa
Des: R. Fuller. Printed in gravure by Questa. One phosphor band (2nd), two phosphor bands (others).

Set	3.75	3.75
Gutter pairs	10.00	
First day cover		4.25
Stamp cards	2.50	7.00

20p design from the Queen Mother issue of 1990 (1st)
29p design (E)
34p design (45p)
37p design (65p)

■ 2002, April 25. Queen Mother Memorial
Des: J. Gorham. Printed in gravure by De La Rue.

Set	3.50	3.50
Gutter pairs	9.00	
First day cover		4.00

Airbus A340-600 (2nd)
Concorde (1st)
Trident (E)
VC 10 (45p)
Comet (65p)

■ 2002, May 2. Airliners
Des: Roundel. Printed in gravure by De La Rue. One phosphor band (2nd), two phosphor bands (others).

Set	6.25	6.25
Gutter pairs	16.00	
First day cover		4.25
Miniature sheet (one of each value)	7.50	7.50
Miniature sheet first day cover		8.00
Stamp cards	3.00	14.00

(*The 1st class design also appears in self-adhesive form in a £1.62 booklet issued on May 2, 2002, printed in gravure; price £3.50 mint or used. It also appears in the British Design Classics prestige stamp book issued on January 13, 2009)

Lion with shield of St. George (1st)
Football with quarters: top left (1st)
Football with quarters: top right (1st)
Football with quarters: bottom left (1st)
Football with quarters: bottom right (1st)

■ **2002, May 21. World Cup Football Championships**
Des: Sedley Place (Lion), H. Brown (flag). Printed in gravure by Walsall.

1st (St George design)	1.25	1.25
Gutter pair	3.00	
First day cover		2.75
Miniature sheet	4.50	4.50
Miniature sheet first day cover		5.00
Stamp cards	3.50	11.00

(*The 1st class designs showing the top left and top right of the English flag also appear in self-adhesive form in a £1.62 booklet issued on May 21, 2002; price £5.50 per pair. The design showing the bottom right of the flag also appeared on Smilers sheets.)

Swimming (2nd)
Running (1st)
Cycling (E)
Long jump (47p)
Wheelchair racing (68p)

■ **2002, July 16. 17th Commonwealth Games, Manchester**
Des: Madeleine Bennett. Printed in gravure by Enschedé. One phosphor band (2nd), two phosphor bands (others).

Set	4.25	4.25
Gutter pairs	11.00	
First day cover		4.00
Stamp cards	2.50	10.00

Tinkerbell (2nd)
Wendy, John and Michael Darling flying past Big Ben (1st)
Crocodile and the alarm clock (E)
Captain Hook (47p)
Peter Pan (68p)

■ **2002, August 20. Peter Pan**
Des: Tutsells. Printed in gravure by De La Rue. One phosphor band (2nd), two phosphor bands (others).

Set	4.25	4.25
Gutter pairs	11.00	
First day cover		4.50
Stamp cards	3.50	8.00

Millennium Bridge (2nd)
Tower Bridge (1st)
Westminster Bridge (E)
Blackfriars Bridge (47p)
London Bridge (68p)

■ **2002, September 10. Bridges of London**
Des: Sarah Davies and Robert Maude. Printed in litho by Questa. One phosphor band (2nd), two phosphor bands (others).

Set	6.50	6.50
Gutter pairs	17.00	
First day cover		5.50
Stamp cards	3.00	10.00

(*The 1st class design also appears in self-adhesive form in a £1.62 booklet issued on September 10, 2002, printed in gravure by Questa; price £3.50 mint or used.)

Planetary nebula in Aquila (1st)
Seyfert 2 galaxy in Pegasus (1st)
Planetary nebula in Norma (1st)
Seyfert 2 galaxy in Circinus (1st)

■ **2002, September 24. Astronomy**
Des: Rose. Printed in gravure by Questa.

Miniature sheet	3.50	3.50
First day cover		4.50
Stamp cards	4.00	10.00

(*The design of the miniature sheet also appears in a larger size in the Across The Universe prestige stamp book issued on September 21, 2002.)

Pillar box of 1857 in green (2nd)
Pillar box of 1874 (1st)
Air mail box of 1934 (E)
Pillar box of 1939 (47p)
Pillar box of 1980 (68p)

■ 2002, October 8. 150th Anniversary of the First Pillar Box

Des: Silk Pearce; engraved by C. Slania. Printed in recess and litho by Enschedé. One phosphor band (2nd), two phosphor bands (others).

Set	4.50	4.50
Gutter pairs	12.00	
First day cover		4.50
Stamp cards	4.00	7.50

Blue spruce (2nd)
Holly (1st)
Ivy (E)
Mistletoe (47p)
Pine cone (68p)

■ 2002, November 5. Christmas. Christmas Flowers

Des: Rose. Printed in gravure by De La Rue. One phosphor band (2nd), two phosphor bands (others). Self-adhesive.

Set	4.50	4.50
First day cover		4.50
Stamp cards	2.50	7.50

(*The 2nd and 1st class stamps also appear in booklets.)

The Wilding definitives collection 1 ~ 1952 ~ 1953

Wilding designs (1p, 2p, 5p, 2nd, 1st, 33p, 37p, 47p, 50p)

■ 2002, December 5. 50th Anniversary of the Wilding Definitives, 1st issue

Des: Rose (based on the original designs of 1952). Printed in gravure by De La Rue. Wmk: 50. One phosphor band (2nd), two phosphor bands (others).

Miniature sheet	5.50	5.50
First day cover		5.00
Stamp cards	5.50	15.50

Barn Owl about to land, five different views (1st)
Kestrel in flight, five different views (1st)

■ 2003, January 14. Birds of Prey

Des: J. Gibbs from photographs by S. Dakon. Printed in litho by Walsall.

Set (in se-tenant block of ten)	7.00	7.00
Gutter pairs	17.50	
First day cover		7.00
Stamp cards	5.00	15.00

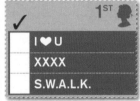

Gold star, See me, Playtime (1st)
I 'love' U, XXXX, SWALK (1st)
Angel, Poppet, Little terror (1st)
Yes, No, Maybe (1st)
Oops! Sorry, Will try harder (1st)
I did it! You did it! We did it! (1st)

2003, February 4. Occasions

Des: UNA, Sarah Wiegand and M. Exon. Printed in litho by Questa.

Set (in se-tenant block of six)	5.00	5.00
Gutter pairs	13.00	
First day cover		5.00
Stamp cards	2.50	8.75

(* These designs also appeared as Smilers sheets.)

Genome **The End of the Beginning**

The genetic jigsaw (2nd)
Ape looking at scientist behind bars (1st)
DNA snakes and ladders (E)
Animals dressed as scientists (47p)
Looking into a DNA crystal ball (68p)

2003, February 25. 50th Anniversary of the Discovery of DNA

Des: William Murray Hamm and P. Brookes. Printed in litho by Enschedé. One phosphor band (2nd), two phosphor bands (others).

Set	4.25	4.25
Gutter pairs	11.00	
First day cover		5.00
Stamp cards	2.50	8.50

(* The 2nd and E designs also appear in the Microcosmos prestige stamp book issued on February 25, 2003.)

Red Pepper (1st)
Strawberry (1st)
Potato (1st)
Apple (1st)
Pear (1st)
Orange (1st)
Tomato (1st)
Lemon (1st)
Brussels sprout (1st)
Aubergine (1st)

2003, March 25. Fruit and Vegetables

Des: Johnson Banks. Printed in gravure by Walsall. Issued as a self-adhesive sheetlet containing one each of the ten designs.

Sheetlet	6.50	6.50
First day cover		7.00
Stamp cards	7.50	22.00

(* This sheetlet came with a pane of self-adhesive stickers, such as of eyes, ears and mouths, so that the fruit and vegetables could be customised to resemble faces. These designs were also used for a Smilers sheet in 2006.)

Amy Johnson with biplane (2nd)
1953 Everest team (1st)
Freya Stark in the desert (E)
Ernest Shackleton (42p)
Francis Chichester with Gipsy Moth IV (47p)
Robert Falcon Scott at the South Pole (68p)

2003, April 29. Extreme Endeavours

Des: H. Brown. Printed in gravure by Questa. One phosphor band (2nd), two phosphor bands (others). Perf: 15 x 14½.

Set	4.75	4.75
Gutter pairs	13.00	
First day cover		5.00
Stamp cards	3.00	9.50

(* The 1st class design also appears twice, in self adhesive form, with four 1st class definitives in a £1.62 stamp booklet issued on April 29, 2003. Printed in gravure by De La Rue. Perf: 14½; priced at £3.50 mint, £3.50 used.)

Wilding designs (4p, 8p, 10p, 20p, 28p, 34p, E, 42p, 68p)

2003, May 20. 50th Anniversary of the Wilding Definitives, 2nd issue

Des: Rose (based on the original designs of 1952). Printed in gravure by De La Rue. Wmk: 50. One phosphor band (20p), two phosphor bands (others).

Miniature sheet	5.00	5.25
First day cover		6.50

Coronation procession (1st)
Children reading poster (1st)
The Queen seated in the Coronation Chair (1st)
Children producing Royal montage (1st)
The Queen in Coronation robes, by Cecil Beaton (1st)
Children racing during street party (1st)
Coronation Coach passing through Admiralty Arch (1st)
Children in fancy dress (1st)
Coronation Coach outside Buckingham Palace (1st)
Children at street party (1st)

■ 2003, June 2. 50th Anniversary of the Coronation
Des: Kate Stephens. Printed in gravure by De La Rue.

Set of ten in se-tenant block	6.00	6.00
Gutter pairs	16.00	
First day cover		5.25
Stamp cards	5.00	20.00

(* Eight of these designs also appear in the A Perfect
Coronation prestige stamp book issued on June 2, 2003.)

■ 2003, June 2. Wilding design decimal definitives
Des: as issue of March 10, 1998. Printed in gravure by Walsall.
Wmk: 50. Issued only in the £7.46 A Perfect Coronation
prestige stamp book.

47p bistre-brown	3.00	3.25
68p grey-blue	3.00	3.25

(* The booklet pane comprised two of each value, plus the 1953
Coronation design by Edmund Dulac with face value £1. The
latter stamp with Wmk 50 priced at £28.00 mint, £28.00 used.)

Photograph of Prince William by Brendan Beirne (28p)
Photograph of Prince William by Tim Graham (E)
Photograph of Prince William by Camera Press (47p)
Photograph of Prince William by Tim Graham (68p)

■ 2003, June 17. 21st Birthday of Prince William
Des: Madeleine Bennett. Printed in gravure by Walsall.

Set	6.50	6.50
Gutter pairs	20.00	
First day cover		4.50
Stamp cards	6.50	20.00

Loch Assynt, Sutherland (2nd)
Ben More, Isle of Mull (1st)
Rothiemurchus, Cairngorms (E)
Dalveen Pass, Lowther Hills (42p)
Glenfinnan Viaduct, Lochaber (47p)
Papa Little, Shetland Islands (68p)

■ 2003, July 15. A British Journey: Scotland
Des: Phelan Barker. Printed in gravure by De La Rue. One
phosphor band (2nd), two phosphor bands (others).

Set	4.50	4.50
Gutter pairs	12.00	
First day cover		5.00
Stamp cards	2.50	9.00

(* The 1st class design also appears twice, in self adhesive form,
with four 1st class definitives in a £1.68 stamp booklet issued
on July 15, 2003; price £3.25 mint, £3.25 used.)

The Station (1st)
Black Swan (E)
The Cross Keys (42p)
The Mayflower (47p)
The Barley Sheaf (68p)

■ 2003, August 12. Pub Signs. Europa
Des: Elmwood. Printed in gravure by De La Rue.

Set	5.00	5.00
Gutter pairs	12.50	
First day cover		5.00
Stamp cards	2.50	7.50

(* The 1st class design also appears in a Letters by Night
prestige stamp book issued on March 16, 2004.)

MECCANO
Constructor Biplane c1931

Meccano Constructor Biplane (1st)
Wells-Brimtoy bus (E)
Hornby M1 locomotive (42p)
Dinky Toys Ford Zephyr (47p)
Mettoy Space Ship Eagle (68p)

■ 2003, September 18. Toys
Des: Trickett and Webb. Printed in gravure by Enschedé.

Set	4.75	4.75
Gutter pairs	12.00	
First day cover		4.75
Stamp cards	3.50	13.50
Miniature sheet (one of each value)	4.50	4.50
Miniature sheet first day cover		7.50

(*The 1st class design also appears in self-adhesive form, in a £1.68 booklet issued on September 18, 2003, printed in gravure by De La Rue; price £3.25 mint or used.)

Coffin of Denytenamun (2nd)
Alexander the Great (1st)
Sutton Hoo helmet (E)
Sculpture of Parvati (42p)
Mask of Xiuhtecuhtli (47p)
Hoa Hakananai'a (68p)

■ 2003, October 7. 250th Anniversary of the British Museum
Des: Rose. Printed in gravure by Walsall. One phosphor band (2nd), band at right (42p, 68p), two phosphor bands (others).

Set	5.50	5.50
Gutter pairs	14.00	
First day cover		5.50
Stamp cards	3.00	9.00

Spiral (2nd)
Star (1st)
Wall (E)
Ball (42p)
Hole (47p)
Pyramids (68p)

■ 2003, November 4. Christmas. Ice Sculptures
Des: D. Davis, from ice Sculptures by Andy Goldsworthy. Printed in gravure by De La Rue. One phosphor band (2nd), two phosphor bands (others). Self-adhesive.

Set	6.00	6.00
First day cover		6.50
Stamp cards	4.00	12.00

(*The 1st class and 2nd class designs also appear in booklets, and in Smilers sheets.)

England fans and England flag (1st)
England team standing in a circle (1st)
The Rugby World Cup (1st)
The England team after winning the Rugby World Cup (1st)

■ 2003, December 19. England's Victory in the Rugby World Cup
Des: Why Not Associates. Printed in litho by Walsall.

Miniature sheet	10.00	10.00
First day cover		10.00

'Dolgoch' on the Rheilffordd Tayllyn Railway (20p)
CR 439 on the Bo'ness and Kinneil Railway (28p)
GCR 8K on the Grand Central Railway (E)
GWR Manor on the Severn Valley Railway (42p)
SR West Country on the Bluebell Railway (47p)
BR Standard on the Keighley and Worth Valley Railway (68p)

■ 2004, January 13. Classic Locomotives

Des: Roundel. Printed in litho by De La Rue. One phosphor band (2nd), two phosphor bands (others).

Set	5.50	5.50
Gutter pairs	14.00	
First day cover		6.00
Stamp cards	5.00	25.00
Miniature sheet (one of each value)	15.00	15.00
Miniature sheet first day cover		16.00

(* The 28p, E and 42p designs also appear in the Letters by Night prestige stamp book issued on March 16, 2004.)

Postman (1st)
Face (1st)
Duck (1st)
Baby (1st)
Aircraft (1st)

■ 2004, February 3. Occasions.

Des: S. Kambayashi. Printed in litho by De La Rue.

Set (in se-tenant strip of five)	3.75	3.75
Gutter pairs	8.50	
First day cover		4.50
Stamp cards	2.75	7.50

(* These designs also appear as a Smilers sheet.)

J.R.R. TOLKIEN · THE LORD OF THE RINGS

Middle Earth (1st)
Forest of Lothlórien (1st)
The Fellowship of the Ring (1st)
Rivendell (1st)
The Hall at Bag End (1st)
Orthanc (1st)
Doors of Durin (1st)
Barad-dûr (1st)
Minas Tirth (1st)
Fangorn Forest (1st)

■ 2004, February 26. The Lord of The Rings by J. R. R. Tolkien

Des: HGV Design. Printed in litho by Walsall.

Set (in se-tenant block of ten)	6.50	6.50
Gutter pairs	17.00	
First day cover		6.50
Stamp cards	5.00	15.00

Ely Island, Lower Lough Erne (2nd)
Giant's Causeway, Antrim coast (1st)
Slemish, Antrim Mountains (E)
Banns Road, Mourne Mountains (42p)
Glenelly Valley, Sperrins (47p)
Islandmore, Strangford Lough (68p)

■ 2004, March 16. A British Journey: Northern Ireland

Des: Phelan Barker. Printed in gravure by Enschedé. One phosphor band (2nd), two phosphor bands (others).

Set	4.50	4.50
Gutter pairs	12.00	
First day cover		6.00
Stamp cards	2.50	9.50

(* The 28p design also appears in self-adhesive form in a £1.68 booklet issued on March 16, 2004; price £3.50 mint or used.)

'Lace 1 (trial proof) 1968' by Sir Terry Frost (28p)
'Coccinelle' by Sonia Delaunay (57p)

■ **2004, April 6. Entente Cordiale**

Des: Rose. Printed in gravure by Walsall.

Set	2.00	2.00
Gutter pairs	5.00	
Traffic light gutter pairs	11.00	
First day cover		2.50
Stamp cards	3.00	4.00

(*This was a joint issue with La Poste of France.)

RMS Queen Mary 2 (1st)
SS Canberra (E)
RMS Queen Mary (42p)
RMS Mauretania (47p)
SS City of New York (57p)
PS Great Western (68p)

■ **2004, April 13. Ocean Liners**

Des: J. Gibbs. Printed in gravure by De La Rue.

Set	4.75	4.75
Gutter pairs	12.50	
First day cover		5.75
Stamp cards	3.50	20.00
Miniature sheet (one of each value)	8.00	8.00
Miniature sheet first day cover		10.00

(*The 1st class design also appears in self-adhesive form, in a £1.68 booklet issued on April 13, 2004; price £3.50 mint or used.)

Dianthus Allwoodii group (2nd)
Dahlia Garden Princess (1st)
Clematis Arabella (E)
Miltonia French Lake (42p)
Lilium Lemon Pride (47p)
Delphinium Clifford Sky (68p)

■ **2004, May 25. Bicentenary of the Royal Horticultural Society**

Des: Rose. Printed in gravure by Enschedé. One phosphor band (2nd), two phosphor bands (others).

Set	5.50	5.50
Gutter pairs	14.00	
First day cover		5.75
Stamp cards	4.00	20.00
Miniature sheet (one of each value)	7.00	7.00
Miniature sheet first day cover		8.00

(*All values also appear in the Glory of the Garden prestige book of May 25, 2004, and the 1st class on Smilers sheets.)

Barmouth Bridge (2nd)
Hyddgen, Plynlimon (1st)
Brecon Beacons (40p)
Pen-pych, Rhondda Valley (43p)
Rhewl, Dee Valley (47p)
Marloes Sands (68p)

■ **2004, June 15. A British Journey: Wales. Europa**

Des: Phelan Barker. Printed in gravure by De La Rue. One phosphor band (2nd), two phosphor bands (others).

Set	4.25	4.50
Gutter pairs	12.00	
First day cover		5.50
Stamp cards	2.25	9.00

(*The 1st class design also appears in self-adhesive form in a £1.68 booklet of June 15, 2004; price £4.50.)

Penny Black with citation to Sir Rowland Hill (1st)
William Shipley (40p)
R, S and A as typewriter keys (43p)
Brush for sweeping chimneys (47p)
Typeface by Eric Gill (57p)
Zero Waste (68p)

■ **2004, August 10. 250th Anniversary of the Royal Society of Arts**

Des: D. Birdsall. Printed in litho by Walsall.

Set	6.00	6.00
Gutter pairs	15.00	
First day cover		6.00
Stamp cards	2.75	9.50

Pine Marten (1st)
Roe Deer (1st)
Badger (1st)
Yellow-necked mouse (1st)
Wild Cat (1st)
Red Squirrel (1st)
Stoat (1st)
Natterer's Bat (1st)
Mole (1st)
Fox (1st)

■ 2004, September 16. Woodland Animals

Des: Kate Stephens. Printed in gravure by Enschedé.

Set (in se-tenant block of ten)	7.00	6.25
Gutter pairs	18.00	
Traffic light gutter blocks	45.00	
First day cover		6.00
Stamp cards	5.00	15.00

Scotland definitives (40p, 1st, 2nd, 1st, 40p)

■ 2004, October 5. Opening of the Scottish Parliament Building

Des: H. Brown. Printed in gravure by De La Rue.

Miniature sheet	4.50	4.50
First day cover		4.00

Pte McNamara (2nd)
Piper Muir (1st)
Sgt Major Edwards (40p)
Sgt Powell (57p)
Sgt Major Poole (68p)
Sgt Glasgow (£1.12)

■ 2004, October 12. The Crimean War

Des: Atelier Works, from photographs taken during The Crimean War. Printed in litho by Walsall. One phosphor band (2nd), two phosphor bands (others).

Set	6.50	6.50
Gutter pairs	17.00	
Traffic light gutter pairs	40.00	
First day cover		6.00
Stamp cards	3.00	9.00

Father Christmas on roof (2nd)
Father Christmas welcoming the sunrise (1st)
Father Christmas battling against the wind (40p)
Father Christmas holding umbrella (57p)
Father Christmas holding torch (68p)
Father Christmas sheltering by a chimney (£1.12)

■ 2004, November 2. Christmas

Des: R. Briggs. Printed in gravure by De La Rue. One phosphor band (2nd), two phosphor bands (others). Counter stamps self-adhesive, miniature sheet gummed.

Set	5.50	5.50
First day cover		7.50
Stamp cards	4.50	15.00
Miniature sheet (one of each value)	6.50	6.50
First day cover		8.00

(* The 1st class and 2nd class designs also appear in booklets, and in Smilers sheets.)

Embden geese (1st)
British Saddleback pigs (1st)
Khaki Campbell ducks (1st)
Clydeside mare with foal (1st)
Dairy Shorthorn cattle (1st)
Border Collie (1st)
Light Sussex chickens (1st)
Suffolk sheep (1st)
Bagot goat (1st)
Norfolk Black turkeys (1st)

■ 2005, January 11. Farm Animals
Des: Rose, from illustrations by C. Wormell. Printed in gravure by Enschedé.

Set of ten in se-tenant block	6.50	6.50
Gutter pairs	17.00	
Traffic light gutter blocks	30.00	
First day cover		7.00
Stamp cards	5.00	15.50

Old Harry Rocks, Studland Bay (2nd)
Wheal Coates, St Agnes (1st)
Start Point, Start Bay (40p)
Horton Down, Wiltshire (43p)
Chiselcombe, Exmoor (57p)
St James's Stone, Lundy (68p)

■ 2005, February 8. A British Journey: South-West England
Des: J. Phelan and Lissa Barker. Printed in gravure by De La Rue. One phosphor band (2nd), two phosphor bands (others).

Set	4.75	4.75
Gutter pairs	12.50	
First day cover		5.50
Stamp cards	2.50	9.00

Mr Rochester (2nd)
Come to me (1st)
In the comfort of her bonnet (40p)
La Ligne des Rats (57p)
Refectory (68p)
Inspection (£1.12)

■ 2005, February 24. 150th Anniversary of the Death of Charlotte Brontë
Des: P. Willberg, from illustrations by Paula Rego. Printed in litho by Walsall. One phosphor band (2nd), two phosphor bands (others).

Set	6.25	6.25
Gutter pairs	17.00	
Traffic light gutter blocks	50.00	
First day cover		6.00
Stamp cards	4.00	15.00
Miniature sheet (one of each value)	6.25	6.25
First day cover		6.00

(* All designs also appear in the Brontë Sisters prestige stamp book issued on February 24, 2005.)

Heads or tails (1st)
Rabbit and top hat (40p)
Coloured scarves and tube (47p)
Ace of hearts (68p)
Three fezzes and pyramids (£1.12)

■ 2005, March 15. Magic
Des: Tatham Design; illustration by George Hardie. Printed in gravure by Walsall. Rubbing the 1st class stamp with a coin reveals either the head or tail of a coin; parts of the 47p and £1.12 designs fade temporarily when exposed to heat.

Set	5.75	5.75
Gutter pairs	15.00	
First day cover		5.00
Stamp cards	3.00	7.50

(* The 1st class design is also found in a Smilers sheet issued on March 15, 2005.)

Carrickfergus Castle (50p)
Caernarvon Castle (£1)
Edinburgh Castle (£1)
Windsor Castle (50p)

■ 2005, March 22. The Castles Definitives of 1955
Des: Sedley Place (original illustrations by Lynton Lamb). Printed by intaglio and litho by Enschedé.

Miniature sheet	4.75	5.00
First day cover		6.50
Stamp cards	5.00	16.00

(* The 50p design also appears in the First UK Aerial Post prestige stamp book issued on September 9, 2011.)

At the Mey Games in the Scottish Highlands (30p)
At Birkhall (68p)

▪ 2005, April 8. The Wedding of Prince Charles and Mrs Camilla Parker Bowles

Des: Rose, from photographs by Christopher Furlong (30p) and Carolyn Robb (68p). Printed in litho by Enschedé.

Miniature sheet	5.00	5.00
First day cover		6.00

(*Whilst the first day handstamps and the miniature sheet are dated April 8, the wedding took place on April 9.)

Hadrian's Wall (2nd)
Uluru Kata Tjuta National Park (2nd)
Stonehenge (1st)
Wet Tropics of Queensland (1st)
Blenheim Palace (47p)
Greater Blue Mountains Area (47p)
Heart of Neolithic Orkney (68p)
Pumululu National Park (68p)

▪ 2005, April 21. World Heritage Sites

Des: Jason Godfrey from photographs by Peter Marlow. Litho printed by Enschedé. One phosphor band (2nd), two phosphor bands (others).

Set of four se-tenant pairs	5.25	5.50
Gutter pairs	13.50	
Traffic light gutter blocks	35.00	
First day cover		7.00
Stamp cards	3.00	12.50

(*This was a joint issue with Australia Post.)

Ensign of the Scots Guards (2nd)
The Queen taking the salute (1st)
Trumpeter of the Household Cavalry (42p)
Welsh Guardsman (60p)
The Queen on horseback (68p)
The Queen with Duke of Edinburgh in an open carriage (£1.12)

▪ 2005, June 7. Trooping the Colour

Des: Why Not Associates. Printed in litho by Walsall. One phosphor band (2nd), two phosphor bands (others).

Set	5.75	5.75
Gutter pairs	17.00	
First day cover		7.00
Stamp cards	2.50	17.50
Miniature sheet (one of each value)	6.00	6.00
Miniature sheet first day cover		6.50

Searchlights in a 'V' over St Paul's Cathedral (1st)
Definitives (1st, 1st, 1st, 1st, 1st)

2005, July 5. End of the War
Des: Jeffery Matthews, using a stamp designed by J. Gorham and originally issued on May 2, 1995. Printed in gravure by Enschedé.

Miniature sheet	3.75	3.75
First day cover		5.00

1991 **Norton F.1** road version of a race winner

Norton F.1 (1st)
BSA Rocket 3 (40p)
Vincent Black Shadow (42p)
Triumph Speed Twin (47p)
Brough Superior (60p)
Royal Enfield (68p)

2005, July 19. Motorcycles
Des: Atelier Works, with illustrations by Michael English. Printed in litho by Walsall.

Set	5.00	5.00
Gutter pairs	12.50	
First day cover		6.50
Stamp cards	4.00	9.50

Athletes (1st, 1st, 1st, 1st, 1st, 1st, 1st)

2005, August 12. London 2012
Des: one of each of the five designs issued for the Olympic and Paralympic Games stamps of 1996, plus a second of one design, but with Olympic rings omitted and new values. Printed in litho by Walsall.

Miniature sheet	4.50	4.50
First day cover		4.50

Eating rice (2nd)
Drinking tea (1st)
Eating sushi (42p)
Eating pasta (47p)
Eating chips (60p)
Eating an apple (68p)

2005, August 23. Changing Tastes in Britain. Europa
Des: Rose, with illustrations by Catell Ronca. Printed in gravure by Enschedé. One phosphor band (2nd), two phosphor bands (others).

Set	4.75	4.75
Gutter pairs	12.00	
First day cover		5.75
Stamp cards	2.50	9.50

Inspector Morse (2nd)
Emmerdale (1st)
Rising Damp (42p)
The Avengers (47p)
The South Bank Show (60p)
Who Wants To Be A Millionaire? (68p)

2005, September 15. Classic ITV
Des: Kate Stephens. Printed in litho by De La Rue. One phosphor band (2nd), two phosphor bands (others).

Set	4.75	4.75
Gutter pairs	12.00	
First day cover		5.75
Stamp cards	4.00	9.00

(*The 1st class design is also found on a Smilers sheet.)

Gazania splendens (1st)
Hello (1st)
Love (1st)
Union flag (1st)
Teddy bear (1st)
Robin looking through pillar box slit (1st)

■ 2005, October 4. Smilers stamps

Printed by litho by Walsall. Self-adhesive. Issued in booklets containing one of each of the six designs.

Booklet	10.00	
Booklet (with PiP information)	6.00	
First day cover		10.00

(* These designs were made available in a Smilers generic sheet on July 4, 2006. For the same designs with elliptical perforations, see the issues of January 16, 2007, and February 28, 2008.)

England team celebrating (two 1st designs)
England team in action (two 68p designs)

■ 2005, October 6. The Ashes

Des: Why Not Associates. Printed in litho by Cartor.

Miniature sheet	4.50	4.50
First day cover		5.50

The Entrepreante with British Belle Isle (1st)
Nelson wounded (1st)
Entrepreante and the French Achille (42p)
The schooner Pickle (42p)
Nelson attacking in two columns (68p)
Putting to sea from Cadiz (68p)

■ 2005, October 18. Battle of Trafalgar

Des: Dick Davis from a painting by William Heath. Printed in litho by Walsall.

Set (of three se-tenant pairs)	5.25	5.50
Gutter pairs	14.00	
First day cover		6.00

Stamp cards	6.00	25.00
Miniature sheet (1 x each value)	5.50	5.50
Miniature sheet first day cover		6.00

(* The stamps also appear in a Battle of Trafalgar prestige stamp book issued on October 18, 2005.)

Haitian (2nd)
European (1st)
European (42p)
North American Indian (60p)
Indian (68p)
Australian Aboriginal (£1.12)

■ 2005, November 1. Christmas. Madonna and Child

Des: Irene von Treskow. Printed in gravure by De La Rue. One phosphor band (2nd), two phoshor bands (others). Counter stamps self-adhesive, miniature sheet gummed.

Set	6.00	6.00
First day cover		7.00
Stamp cards	5.00	18.50
Miniature sheet (one of each value)	6.00	6.00
First day cover		7.00

(* The 2nd class and 1st class stamps also appear in booklets.)

The Tale of Mr Jeremy Fisher (2nd)
Kipper (2nd)
The Enormous Crocodile (1st)
More About Paddington (1st)
Comic Adventures of Boots (42p)
Alice's Adventures in Wonderland (42p)
The Very Hungry Caterpillar (68p)
Maisy's ABC (68p)

■ 2006. January 10. Animal Tales

Des: Rose. Printed in litho by De La Rue.

Set	6.00	6.00
Gutter pairs	15.00	
Traffic light gutter blocks	55.00	
First day cover		7.00
Stamp cards	4.00	12.50

Carding Mill Valley, Shropshire (1st)
Beachey Head, Sussex (1st)
St Paul's Cathedral (1st)
Brancaster, Norfolk (1st)
Derwent Edge, Peak District (1st)
Robin's Hood Bay, Yorkshire (1st)
Buttermere, Lake District (1st)
Chipping Campden, Cotswolds (1st)
St Boniface Down, Isle of Wight (1st)
Chamberlain Square, Birmingham (1st)

■ 2006, February 7. A British Journey: England
Des: Phelan Parker Design Consultants. Printed in gravure by De La Rue.

Set (in se-tenant block of 10)	7.00	6.50
Gutter pairs	17.00	
First day cover		7.00
Stamp cards	4.00	15.00

Royal Albert Bridge (1st)
Box Tunnel (40p)
Paddington Station (42p)
PSS Great Britain (47p)
Clifton Suspension Bridge (60p)
Maidenhead Bridge (68p)

■ 2006, February 23. Bicentenary of the Birth of Isambard Kingdom Brunel
Des: Hat-Trick Design. Printed in litho by Enschedé.

Set	5.00	5.00
Gutter pairs	12.50	
First day cover		6.00
Stamp cards	3.50	25.00
Miniature sheet (one of each value)	5.50	5.50
Miniature sheet first day cover		6.00

Wales definitives (68p, 1st, 2nd, 1st, 68p)

■ 2006, March 1. Welsh Assembly
Des: Silk Pearce. Printed in gravure by De La Rue.

Miniature sheet	4.50	4.50
First day cover		5.00

Sabre-tooth cat (1st)
Giant deer (42p)
Woolly rhino (47p)
Woolly mammoth (68p)
Cave bear (£1.12)

■ 2006, March 21. Ice Age Animals
Des: Howard Brown (illustrations by Andrew Davidson). Printed in litho by Enschedé.

Set	5.25	5.25
Gutter pairs	14.00	
First day cover		6.00
Stamp cards	4.00	8.50

The Queen in 1972 (2nd)
The Queen in 1985 (2nd)
The Queen in 1931 (1st)
The Queen in 2001 (1st)
The Queen in 1951 (44p)
The Queen in 1960 (44p)
The Queen in 1940 (72p)
The Queen in 1950 (72p)

■ 2006, April 18. The Queen's 80th Birthday
Des: Sedley Place. Printed in gravure by Enschedé.

Set	6.50	6.50
Gutter pairs	17.00	
First day cover		7.50
Stamp cards	6.50	16.00

42

England (1st)
Italy (42p)
Argentina (44p)
Germany (50p)
France (64p)
Brazil (72p)

■ 2006, June 6. World Cup Winners
Des: Getty Images. Printed in litho by Walsall.

Set	6.00	6.00
Gutter pairs	15.00	
First day cover		6.50
Stamp cards	4.00	11.00

30 St Mary Axe, London (1st)
Maggie's Centre, Dundee (42p)
Selfridges, Birmingham (44p)
Downland Gridshell, Chichester (50p)
An Turas Isle of Tiree (64p)
The Deep, Hull (72p)

■ 2006, June 20. Modern Architecture
Des: Roundel. Printed in gravure by Walsall.

Set	5.50	5.50
Gutter pairs	14.00	
First day cover		6.25
Stamp cards	2.75	10.00

T. S. Eliot (1st)
Sir Winston Churchill (1st)
Sir Joshua Reynolds (1st)
Emmeline Pankhurst (1st)
Virginia Woolf (1st)
Sir Walter Scott (1st)
Mary Seacole (1st)
William Shakespeare (1st)
Dame Cicely Saunders (1st)
Charles Darwin (1st)

■ 2006, July 18. 150th Anniversary of the National Portrait Gallery
Des: Peter Willberg. Printed in gravure by De La Rue.

Set (in se-tenant block of 10)	6.50	6.75
Gutter pairs	17.00	
Traffic light gutter blocks	35.00	
First day cover		7.00
Stamp cards	4.00	15.00

Definitive (£3)

■ 2006, August 31. The Year of the Three Kings
Des: Together Design. Printed in gravure by De La Rue.

Miniature sheet	5.75	5.75
First day cover		6.50

(* The border illustrates the 1d stamps of the reigns of King George V, King Edward VIII and King George VI.)

Agansing Rai, a Gurkha (1st)
Boy Seaman First Class Jack Cornwell (1st)
Midshipman Charles Lucas (64p)
Captain Noel Chavasse (64p)
Captain Alan Ball (72p)
Captain Charles Upham (72p)

■ 2006, September 21. Victoria Cross
Des: Atelier Works. Printed in litho by Enschedé.

Set	6.75	6.75
Gutter pairs	17.00	
First day cover		7.00
Stamp cards	3.00	20.00
Miniature sheet (one of each value, plus the		
20p Victoria Cross from September 1990)	7.00	7.00
Miniature sheet first day cover		7.25
Press sheet	75.00	

Asian sitar (1st)
Caribbean base player (42p)
Latin American maracas (44p)
Irish fiddle (50p)
Black American blues (72p)

■ 2006, October 3. Sounds of Britain
Des: CDT. Printed in litho by Cartor.

Set	5.75	5.75
Gutter pairs	15.00	
Traffic light gutter blocks	30.00	
First day cover		6.50
Stamp cards	3.50	8.00

New baby (1st)
Best wishes (1st)
Thank you (1st)
Balloons (1st)
Firework (1st)
Champagne, flowers and butterflies (1st)

■ 2006, October 17. Smilers stamps
Printed by litho by Walsall. Self-adhesive. Issued in booklets containing one of each of the six designs.

Booklet	4.50	
First day cover		5.50
Stamp cards	7.00	21.00

(*These designs were also available in a generic Smilers sheet. For the same designs with elliptical perforations, see the issue of February 28, 2008.)

Poppies (1st)
Country definitives (72p, 72p, 72p, 72p)

■ 2006, November 6. Lest We Forget
Des: Hat-Trick Design. Printed in gravure by De La Rue.

Miniature sheet	6.00	6.00
First day cover		6.50

(* The 1st class design was also available in Smilers sheets.)

Snowman (2nd and 2nd Large)
Father Christmas sitting on chimney (1st and 1st Large)
Reindeer (72p)
Christmas tree (£1.19)

■ 2006, November 7. Christmas
Des: CDT. Printed in litho by De La Rue. Counter sheets self-adhesive, miniature sheet gummed.

Set	5.75	5.75
Gutter pairs	15.00	
First day cover		7.00
Stamp cards	4.00	18.00
Miniature sheet (one of each value)	6.00	6.00
Miniature sheet first day cover		6.75

(* The 2nd class and 1st class were also sold in booklets.)

Scottish flag (1st)
St Andrew (72p)
Edinburgh Castle (72p)
Scotland definitive (1st)

■ 2006, November 30. Celebrating Scotland
Des: P. Crowther, Claire Melinsky, Silk Pearce. Printed in gravure by De La Rue.

Miniature sheet	4.25	4.25
First day cover		5.00
Stamp cards	3.00	15.00

With The Beatles (1st)
Sgt Pepper's Lonely Hearts Club Band (1st)
Help! (64p)
Abbey Road (64p)
Revolver (72p)
Let It Be (72p)

■ **2007, January 9. The Beatles**
Des: Johnson Banks, from album sleeve covers. Printed in gravure by Walsall. Self-adhesive. Available in horizontal pairs.

Set	6.50	7.00
First day cover		7.50
Stamp cards (set & miniature sheet)	5.50	25.00

Guitar (1st)
Yellow Submarine lunch box (1st)
Love Me Do (1st)
Tea Tray (1st)

■ **2007, January 9. The Beatles**
Printed in litho by Walsall. Miniature sheet.

Miniature sheet	3.00	3.00
First day cover		4.00

■ **2007, January 16. Smilers stamp**
Printed in litho by Walsall. Self-adhesive. Design as the 'Love' 1st class stamp of October 4, 2005, but with elliptical perforations along vertical sides. Issued in booklets of six.

Booklet	6.00	6.00

(*This design was also issued in a booklet released on January 15, 2008, and in Smilers sheets.)

Moon Jellyfish (1st)
Common Starfish (1st)
Beadlet Anemone (1st)
Bass (1st)
Thornback Ray (1st)
Lesser Octopus (1st)
Common Mussels (1st)
Grey Seal (1st)
Shore Crab (1st)
Common Sun Star (1st)

■ **2007, February 1. Sea Life**
Des: A. Ross. Printed in litho by Cartor.

Set (in se-tenant block of ten)	7.00	6.75
Gutter pairs	18.00	
First day cover		7.00
Stamp cards	4.50	16.00

Saturn Nebula (1st)
Eskimo Nebula C39 (1st)
Cat's Eye Nebula C6 (50p)
Helix Nebula (50p)
Flaming Star Nebula C31 (72p)
The Spindle (72p)

■ **2007, February 13. The Sky at Night**
Des: D. Davis, Printed in gravure by Walsall. Self-adhesive. Issued in se-tenant pairs. Stamps have description of designs on the backing paper.

Set	6.75	6.75
First day cover		7.00
Stamp cards	4.00	13.00

Railway bridge (1st)
Locomotive with railway track as 'steam' (1st)
Map of British Isles and Australia (64p)
Television and camera (64p)
Globe (72p)
Carrying suitcases on the Moon (72p)

■ 2007, March 1. World of Invention
Des: P. Willberg. Printed in gravure by De La Rue. Counter stamps self-adhesive, with description of designs on the backing paper. Miniature sheet gummed.

Set	6.50	6.50
Gutter pairs	20.00	
First day cover		7.50
Miniature sheet (one of each value)	12.00	12.00
Miniature sheet first day cover		10.00
Stamp cards	4.00	20.00

(* All designs also appear, gummed, in the World of Invention prestige stamp book issued on March 1, 2007.)

William Wilberforce (1st)
Olaudah Equiano (1st)
Granville Sharp (50p)
Thomas Clarkson (50p)
Hannah More (72p)
Ignatius Sancho (72p)

■ 2007, March 22. Abolition of the Slave Trade
Des: Howard Brown. Printed in litho by Cartor. Issued in se-tenant pairs.

Set	5.50	5.50
Gutter pairs	15.50	
Traffic light gutter blocks	50.00	
First day cover		6.75
Stamp cards	4.00	13.00

England definitive (1st)
Flag of England (1st)
St George (78p)
Houses of Parliament (78p)

■ 2007, April 23. Celebrating England
Des: P. Crowther, Claire Melinsky, Silk Pearce. Printed in gravure by De La Rue.

Miniature sheet	4.50	4.75
First day cover		5.00
Stamp cards	3.00	14.00

Ice cream cone (1st)
Sand castle (46p)
Merry-go-round (48p)
Beach huts (54p)
Deckchairs (69p)
Donkeys (78p)

■ 2007, May 15. Beside the Seaside
Des: Phelan Barker Design Consultants. Printed in gravure by De La Rue.

Set	5.50	5.50
Gutter pairs	14.00	
First day cover		7.00
Stamp cards	3.50	11.00

(* The 1st class design also appears, as a self-adhesive, in a booklet issued on May 13, 2008: price £2.00 mint.)

Lion with shield of St George (1st)
England definitives (2nd, 2nd, 78p, 78p)

■ 2007, May 17. Opening of the New Wembley Stadium
Des: Roundel. Printed in gravure by De La Rue.

Miniature sheet	5.25	5.25
First day cover		6.00

(* The 1st Lion design was previously issued on May 21, 2002 with an inscription, and also appears in a Smilers sheet.)

Arnold Machin (1st)
4d Machin olive sepia-brown (1st)
Definitive (£1 bluish-violet)
Definitive (£1 ruby)

■ 2007, June 5. 40th Anniversary of the Machin Definitives

Des: J. Matthews and Together Design. Printed in gravure by De La Rue.

Miniature sheet	5.00	5.00
Press sheet	75.00	
First day cover		6.00
Stamp cards	4.00	16.00

(*The 1st Arnold Machin design also appears on a generic Smilers sheet. The two 1st class designs also appear in The Making of a Masterpiece prestige stamp book.)

Graham Hill (1st)
Stirling Moss (1st)
Jackie Stewart (54p)
Jim Clark (54p)
James Hunt (78p)
Nigel Mansell (78p)

■ 2007, July 3. Grand Prix

Des: True North, from photographs by James Callaghan. Printed in litho by Cartor.

Set	5.50	5.50
Gutter pairs	14.00	
First day cover		7.00
Stamp cards	4.00	11.00

Harry Potter and the Philosopher's Stone (1st)
Harry Potter and the Chamber of Secrets (1st)
Harry Potter and the Prisoner of Azkaban (1st)
Harry Potter and the Goblet of Fire (1st)
Harry Potter and the Order of the Phoenix (1st)
Harry Potter and the Half-blood Prince (1st)
Harry Potter and the Deathly Hallows (1st)

■ 2007, July 17. Harry Potter

Des: from book covers. Printed in litho by Walsall.

Set	4.75	4.50
Gutter pairs	12.00	
Traffic light gutter pairs	35.00	
First day cover		6.50
Stamp cards	7.50	28.00

Symbol of Gryffindor (1st)
Symbol of Hufflepuff (1st)
Crest of Hogwarts (1st)
Symbol of Ravenclaw (1st)
Symbol of Slytherin (1st)

■ 2007, July 17. Harry Potter

Printed in litho by Walsall.

Miniature sheet	4.25	4.25
First day cover		5.50

(*These designs also appear on a generic Smilers sheet.)

Scout looking at the Moon (1st)
Scouts conquering a mountain (46p)
Scout planting a tree (48p)
Scout practising archery (54p)
Scout piloting an aircraft (69p)
Group of Scouts (78p)

■ 2007, July 26. Scouts. Europa

Des: The Workroom. Printed in litho by Enschedé.

Set	5.50	6.00
Gutter pairs	14.00	
First day cover		7.00
Stamp cards	3.50	11.00

(* These designs were also issued as a set of six stamped postcards, imprinted with either the 1st class or 54p on the address side: priced at £7.50 mint.)

White-tailed eagle (1st)
Bearded tit (1st)
Red kite (1st)
Cirl bunting (1st)
Marsh harrier (1st)
Avocet (1st)
Bittern (1st)
Dartford warbler (1st)
Corncrake (1st)
Peregrine (1st)

■ 2007, September 4. Endangered Species. Birds

Des: Kate Stephens. Printed in litho by De La Rue. Issued in a se-tenant block.

Set (in block)	7.00	7.00
Gutter pairs	18.00	
First day cover		7.00
Stamp cards	5.00	16.00

NCO British Military Police, 1999 (1st)
Tank Commander 5th Royal Tank Regiment, 1944 (1st)
Observer Royal Field Artillery, 1917 (1st)
Rifleman, 95th Rifles (78p)
Grenadier Royal Regiment of Foot of Ireland, 1704 (78p)
Trooper Earl of Oxford's Horse, 1661 (78p)

■ 2007, September 23. British Army Uniforms

Des: Atelier Works and Graham Turner. Printed in litho by Enschedé. Issued in se-tenant strips of three.

Set	5.50	5.75
Gutter pairs	14.00	
Traffic light gutter pairs	35.00	
First day cover		7.50
Stamp cards	3.50	11.00

(*These stamps are also available in a prestige stamp book.)

The Queen and Prince Philip in 2006 (1st)
The Queen and Prince Philip in 1997 (1st)
The Queen and Prince Philip in 1980 (54p)
The Queen and Prince Philip in 1969 (54p)
The Queen and Prince Philip in 1961 (78p)
The Queen and Prince Philip in 1947 (78p)

■ 2007, October 16. Royal Diamond Wedding Anniversary

Des: Pentagram. Printed in gravure by Walsall. Normal gum. Issued in se-tenant pairs.

Set	5.75	5.75
Gutter pairs	15.00	
First day cover		7.00

Photographs of the Royal Family (1st, 1st, 69p, 78p)

■ 2007, October 16. Royal Diamond Wedding Anniversary

Des: Pentagram. Printed in gravure by Walsall. Self-adhesive. The reverse of the sheet shows photographs of the Royal couple leading up to their marriage.

Miniature sheet	4.00	4.50
Press sheet	60.00	
First day cover		6.50
Stamp cards	6.50	28.00

Angels playing musical instruments
(2nd, 2nd Large, 1st, 1st Large, 78p, £1.24)

2007, November 6. Christmas
Des: Rose, with illustrations by Marco Ventura. Printed in gravure by De La Rue. Counter stamps self-adhesive, miniature sheet gummed.

Set	7.00	7.00
Gutter pairs	18.00	
First day cover		7.50
Miniature sheet (one of each value)	7.00	7.00
Miniature sheet first day cover		7.50
Stamp cards	5.00	17.50

(* The 2nd class and 1st class designs also appear in booklets, and the 2nd, 1st and 78p in Smilers sheets.)

'Madonna & Child' by William Dyce (2nd)
'The Madonna of Humility' by Lippo di Dalmasio (1st)

2007, November 6. Christmas. Madonna and Child
Des: Peter Willberg, from paintings. Printed in gravure by De La Rue.

Set	1.50	1.50
Gutter pairs	5.00	
First day cover		3.00

(* These stamps were re-issued at Christmas in 2008-2011.)

Part of poppy (1st)
Country definitives (78p, 78p, 78p, 78p)

2007, November 8. Lest We Forget
Des: Hat-Trick Design. Printed in gravure by De La Rue.

Miniature sheet	6.50	6.50
First day cover		7.00

(* The 1st class design also appeared in a generic Smilers sheet.)

Book cover of Casino Royale (1st)
Book cover of Dr No (1st)
Book cover of Goldfinger (54p)
Book cover of Diamonds Are Forever (54p)
Book cover of For Your Eyes Only (78p)
Book cover of From Russia With Love (78p)

2008, January 8. Centenary of the Birth of Ian Fleming
Des: A2. Prined in litho by De La Rue.

Set	5.50	5.75
Gutter pairs	14.00	
First day cover		7.00
Miniature sheet	10,00	10,00
Miniature sheet first day cover		7.50
Press sheet	75.00	
Stamp cards (set and miniature sheet)	4.00	25.00

(* These stamps are also found in the Ian Fleming's James Bond prestige stamp book, issued on January 8, 2008.)

Assistance dog with letter (1st)
Mountain rescue dog (46p)
Police dog (48p)
Customs dog (54p)
Sheepdog (69p)
Guide dog (78p)

2008, February 5. Working Dogs
Des: Redpath Design. Printed in litho by Cartor.

Set	5.50	5.50
Gutter pairs	14.00	
First day cover		7.00
Stamp cards	5.00	14.00

Henry IV (1st)
Henry V (1st)
Henry VI (54p)
Edward IV (54p)
Edward V (69p)
Richard III (69p)

■ 2008, February 28. Kings and Queens. Houses of Lancaster and York

Des: Ian Chilvers, Atelier Works. Printed in litho by Walsall.

Set	5.25	5.50
Gutter pairs	14.00	
Traffic light gutter blocks	35.00	
First day cover		7.00
Stamp cards (set and miniature sheet)	5.50	26.00

Owain Glyndwr (1st)
Battle of Agincourt (1st)
Battle of Tewkesbury (78p)
William Caxton (78p)

■ 2008, February 28. Kings and Queens. The Age of Lancaster and York

Des: Ian Chilvers. Printed in litho by Walsall.

Miniature sheet	3.75	3.75
First day cover		5.25
Press sheet	90.00	

■ 2008, February 28. Smilers stamps

Printed in litho by Walsall. Self-adhesive. As design of Hello, Gazania splendens and Union flag 1st class of October 4, 2005, and Firework and Champagne, Flowers and butterfly and New baby 1st class of October 17, 2006, but with elliptical perforations on vertical sides. Issued in booklets of six.

Booklet	4.25	4.50
First day cover		5.00

(* These designs have also been issued in Smilers sheets.)

Carrickfergus Castle (1st)
St Patrick (78p)
The Queen's Bridge, Belfast (78p)
The Giant's Causeway (1st)

■ 2008, March 11. Celebrating Northern Ireland

Des: Silk Pearce (sheet) and David Lyons, Clare Melinsky, Tony Pleavin and Ric Ergenbright (stamps). Printed in litho by De La Rue.

Miniature sheet	4.25	4.50
First day cover		5.00
Stamp cards (stamps and miniature sheet) 3.00		15.00

Lifeboat at Barra (1st)
Lifeboat and dinghy at Appledore (46p)
Helicopter rescue at Portland (48p)
Lifeboat at St Ives (54p)
Rescue helicopter at Lee-on-Solent (69p)
Lifeboat at Dinbych-y-Pysgod, Tenby (78p)

■ 2008, March 13. Rescue at Sea

Des: Hat Trick Design. Printed in litho by Walsall. 'Dot' and 'dash' shaped perforations at top and bottom.

Set	5.50	5.50
Gutter pairs	14.00	
First day cover		7.00
Stamp cards	3.50	13.00

Adonis blue butterfly (1st)
Southern damselfly (1st)
Red-barded ant (1st)
Barberry carpet moth (1st)
Stag beetle (1st)
Hazel pot beetle (1st)
Field cricket (1st)
Silver-spotted skipper (1st)
Purbeck mason wasp (1st)
Noble chafer beetle (1st)

■ 2008, April 15. Endangered Species: Insects.
Des: Andrew Ross. Printed in litho by De La Rue. Issued in se-tenant blocks of ten.

Set	7.00	6.75
Gutter pairs	18.00	
First day cover		7.00
Stamp cards	6.00	22.00

LICHFIELD CATHEDRAL

Lichfield Cathedral (1st)
Belfast Cathedral (48p)
Gloucester Cathedral (50p)
St Davids Cathedral (56p)
Westminster Cathedral (72p)
St Magnus Cathedral, Kirkwall, Orkney (81p)

■ 2008, May 13. Cathedrals
Des: Howard Brown. Printed in litho by Enschedé.

Set	6.25	6.25
Gutter pairs	17.00	
Traffic light gutter pairs	35.00	
First day cover		7.50
Stamp cards (set and miniature sheet)	6.50	27.50

Composite view inside St Paul's Cathedral (1st, 1st, 81p, 81p)

■ 2008, May 13. St. Paul's Cathedral
Des: Howard Brown. Printed in litho by Enschedé.

Miniature sheet	4.50	4.50
First day cover		5.00
Press sheet	70.00	

Carry On Sergeant (1st)
Dracula (48p)
Carry on Cleo (50p)
The Curse of Frankenstein (56p)
Carry On Screaming (72p)
The Mummy (81p)

■ 2008, June 10. Classic Carry On and Hammer Films
Des: Elmwood Design Group, from film posters. Printed in litho by Walsall.

Set	5.50	5.75
Gutter pairs	14.00	
First day cover		7.50
Stamp cards	4.00	14.00
Postcards and stamp set	8.00	

(*The postcard and stamp set comprised six cards showing the stamp designs against a brick background, together with a folder containing three 1st class and three 56p values; priced at £7.)

Red Arrows (1st)
FAF Falcons parachute display (48p)
Watching the Red Arrows (50p)
Avro Vulcan prototype and Avro 707S (56p)
Robert Wyndham, one-armed parachutist (72p)
WB Moorhouse at Hendon air race (81p)

■ 2008, July 17. Air Displays

Des: Roundel. Printed in litho by Cartor.

Set	5.50	5.50
Gutter pairs	15.00	
First day cover		7.00
Stamp cards	4.00	14.00

(*The 1st class design also appeared in the Pilot To Plane: RAF Uniforms prestige stamp book of September 18, 2008, and on a Smilers sheet.)

Beijing National Stadium (1st)
The London Eye (1st)
The Tower of London (1st)
Corner Tower the Forbidden City, Beijing (1st)

■ 2008, August 22. Olympics Handover

Des: Why Not Associates. Printed in litho by Walsall, with the Olympic rings in a silk screen varnish.

Miniature sheet	3.00	3.00
First day cover		5.00
Stamp cards	3.50	15.00

Drum Major, RAF Central Band (1st)
Helicopter rescue winchman, 1984 (1st)
Hawker Hunter pilot, 1951 (1st)
Lancaster air gunner, 1944 (81p)
WAAF plotter, World War II (81p)
Pilot, 1918 (81p)

■ 2008, September 18. RAF Uniforms

Des: Quentin Newark of Atelier Works and Graham Turner. Printed in litho by Walsall. Issued in se-tenant strips of three.

Set	5.50	5.75
Gutter pairs	15.00	
Traffic light gutter pairs	27.50	
First day cover		6.50
Stamp cards	4.00	14.00

(* The same stamps are also found in the Pilot To Plane: RAF Uniforms prestige stamp book issued on September 18, 2008.)

1958 Northern Ireland 3d design (1st)
1958 Northern Ireland 6d design (1st)
1958 Northern Ireland 1s 3d design (1st)
1958 Scotland 3d design (1st)
1958 Scotland 6d design (1st)
1958 Scotland 1s 3d design (1st)
1958 Wales 3d design (1st)
1958 Wales 6d design (1st)
1958 Wales 1s 3d design (1st)

■ 2008, September 29. 50th anniversary of the Country Definitives

As the 1958 regional stamps of Northern Ireland, Scotland and Wales, with changed values. Printed in gravure by De La Rue.

Miniature sheet	6.00	6.00
Press sheet	80.00	
First day cover		7.00
Stamp cards	6.00	35.00

(* These stamps are also found in the Heraldry and Symbol prestige stamp book issued on September 29, 2008.)

Poppy (1st)
Country definitives (four at 81p)

Millicent Garrett Fawcett (Votes for Women) (1st)
Elizabeth Garrett Anderson (Women's Health) (48p)
Marie Stopes (Family Planning) (50p)
Eleanor Rathbone (Family Allowance) (56p)
Claudia Jones (Civil Rights) (72p)
Barbara Castle (Equal Pay Act) (81p)

■ 2008, October 14. Women of Distinction
Des: Together Design. Printed in gravure by Walsall.

Set	5.50	5.50
Gutter pairs	14.00	
First day cover		7.00
Stamp cards	4.00	14.00

■ 2008, November 6. Lest We Forget
Des: Hat-Trick Design. Printed in litho by De La Rue.

Miniature sheet	6.00	6.00
First day cover		7.00

(*The 1st class design also appeared in a generic Smilers sheet.)

■ 2008, November 6. Lest We Forget
The Poppy designs of November 6, 2006, November 8, 2007,
and November 6, 2008, but in se-tenant strips in counter sheets.
Printed in litho by De La Rue.

Set	2.50	2.50
Gutter pairs	10.00	
Traffic light gutter pairs	17.00	
First day cover		3.00
Stamp cards (3 stamps, 3 mini sheets)	12.00	27.00

The Ugly Sisters from Cinderella (2nd, 2nd Large)
The Genie from Aladdin (1st, 1st Large)
Captain Hook from Peter Pan (50p)
The Wicked Queen from Snow White (81p)

■ 2008, November 4. Christmas
Des: Steve Haskins, using photographs by Peter Thorpe.
Printed in gravure by De La Rue. Counter stamps self-adhesive,
miniature sheet gummed.

Set	5.50	5.50
Gutter pairs	14.00	
First day cover		6.00
Miniature sheet (one of each value)	5.50	5.50
Miniature sheet first day cover		6.00
Stamp cards	4.00	19.00

(*The 1st class and 2nd class designs also appear in booklets, and
the 2nd, 1st and 81p designs in a Smilers sheet.)

Supermarine Spitfire (1st)
Mini skirt (1st)
Mini (1st)
Anglepoise lamp (1st)
Concorde (1st)
K2 Telephone Kiosk (1st)
Polypropylene Chair (1st)
Penguin books (1st)
London Underground Map (1st)
Routemaster bus (1st)

■ 2009, January 13. Design Classics

Des: HGV Design. Printed in litho by Cartor. Issued in se-tenant blocks of 10.

Set	10.00	10.00
Gutter pairs	25.00	
First day cover		10.00
Stamp cards	6.00	22.00
Postcards and stamp set	9.00	

(*The postcard and stamp set comprises 10 cards reproducing the stamp designs against a Union Flag background, and a set of the stamps; price 10.00 mint. The stamps also appear in the British Design Classics prestige stamp book of January 13, 2009. The Routemaster, Telephone kiosk, Mini, Concorde, Spitfire and Mini Skirt designs also appear in self-adhesive form in booklets; price £1.55 each mint. The Mini and Concorde designs also appear in generic Smilers sheets.)

'A Man's a Man for a' That' (1st)
Portrait of Burns by Alexander Nasmyth (1st)
Scotland definitives (2nd, 1st, 50p, 81p)

■ 2009, January 22. 250th anniversary of the Birth of Robert Burns

Des: Tayburn. Printed in gravure by Enschedé.

Miniature sheet	5.25	5.25
First day cover		6.00
Press sheet	90.00	
Stamp cards	2.00	12.50

Charles Darwin (1st)
Marine iguana (48p)
Finches (50p)
Atoll (56p)
Bee orchid (72p)
Orang-utan (81p)

■ 2009, February 12. Bicentenary of the Birth of Charles Darwin

Des: Hat-Trick Design. Printed in gravure by De La Rue. Self-adhesive, to resemble jigsaw piece.

Set	5.75	6.00
Gutter pairs	15.00	
First day cover		8.00
Stamp cards	7.00	28.00

(*The stamps also appear in the Charles Darwin prestige stamp book issued on February 12, 2009, but with PVA gum.)

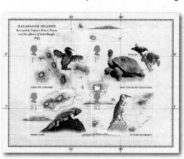

Flightless cormorant (1st)
Giant tortoise and cactus finch (1st)
Marine iguana (81p)
Floreana mockingbird (81p)

■ 2009, February 12. Bicentenary of the Birth of Charles Darwin

Des: Howard Brown. Printed in litho by De La Rue.

Miniature sheet	4.25	4.50
First day cover		6.00
Press sheet	55.00	

(*The miniature sheet also appears as a pane in the Charles Darwin prestige stamp book issued on February 12, 2009.)

Red Dragon (1st)
St David (81p)
National Assembly for Wales building, Cardiff (81p)
Welsh Dragon (1st)

■ 2009, February 26. Celebrating Wales

Des: Silk Pearce. Printed in litho by De La Rue.

Miniature sheet	4.50	4.50
First day cover		6.00
Stamp cards	3.00	15.00

MATTHEW BOULTON MANUFACTURING

Matthew Boulton, manufacturing (1st)
James Watt, engineering (1st)
Richard Arkwright, textiles (50p)
Josiah Wedgwood, ceramics (50p)
George Stephenson, railways (56p)
Henry Maudslay, machine making (56p)
James Brindley, canal engineering (72p)
John McAdam, road building (72p)

■ 2009, March 17. Pioneers of the Industrial Revolution

Des: Webb & Webb. Printed in litho by Enschedé. Issued in se-tenant pairs for each denomination.

Set	7.00	7.00
Gutter pairs	18.00	
First day cover		9.00
Stamp cards	5.00	20.00

HENRY VII
1485-1509

Henry VII (1st)
Henry VIII (1st)
Edward VI (62p)
Lady Jane Grey (62p)
Mary I (81p)
Elizabeth I (81p)

■ 2009, April 21. Kings and Queens. The House of Tudor

Des: Ian Chilvers, Atelier Works. Printed in litho by Walsall. Issued in separate sheets for each denomination.

Set	6.25	6.75
Gutter pairs	15.00	
Traffic light gutter pairs	32.50	
First day cover		7.50
Stamp cards	7.00	30.00

THE AGE OF THE TUDORS

Mary Rose (1st)
Field of Cloth of Gold (1st)
Royal Exchange (90p)
Francis Drake (90p)

■ 2009, April 21. The Age of the Tudors

Des: Ian Chilvers, Atelier Works. Printed in litho by Walsall.

Miniature sheet	4.25	4.25
First day cover		6.00
Press sheet	90.00	

ENDANGERED PLANTS
Dwarf Milkwort *Polygala amarella*

Round-headed leek (1st)
Floating water-plantain (1st)
Lady's slipper orchid (1st)
Dwarf milkwort (1st)
Marsh saxifrage (1st)
Downy woundwort (1st)
Upright spurge (1st)
Plymouth pear (1st)
Sea knotgrass (1st)
Deptford pink (1st)

■ 2009, May 19. Endangered Species: Plants

Des: Studio Dempsey. Printed in litho by Cartor. Issued in se-tenant blocks of ten.

Set	7.00	6.75
Gutter pairs	18.00	
First day cover		7.50
Stamp cards	7.00	35.00

Palm House, Kew Gardens (1st)
Millennium Seed Bank, Wakehurst Place (1st)
Pagoda, Kew Gardens (90p)
Sackler Crossing, Kew Gardens (90p)

■ 2009, May 19. 250th Anniversary of the Royal Botanic Gardens, Kew

Des: Studio Dempsey. Printed in litho by Cartor.

Miniature sheet	4.25	4.25
First day cover		6.00
Maximum cards set	12.00	
Press sheet	70.00	

(* The maximum cards set comprises four postcards each with one stamp from the miniature sheet affixed and cancelled on the picture side, sold in a pack with a mint miniature sheet.)

Dragons (1st)
Unicorns (1st)
Giants (62p)
Pixies (62p)
Mermaids (90p)
Fairies (90p)

■ 2009, June 16. Mythical Creatures

Des: Morgan Radcliffe, from illustrations by Dave McKean. Printed in gravure by De La Rue.

Set	6.25	6.75
Gutter pairs	16.00	
First day cover		8.00
Stamp cards	4.00	17.00

George V type B wall box at Cookham Rise (1st)
Edward VII Ludlow box at Bodiam post office (56p)
Victorian lamp box at Burmarsh Road, Hythe, Kent (81p)
Elizabeth II type A box at Slaithwaite sorting office (90p)

■ 2009, August 18. Post Boxes

Des: Elmwood Design Group from photographs by Peter Marlow. Printed in litho by Cartor.

Miniature sheet	4.25	4.25
First day cover		6.00
Stamp cards	3.50	17.50
Press sheet	70.00	

(* The four designs also appear in the Treasures of the Archive prestige stamp book of August 18, 2009, and the 1st class design in a generic Smilers sheet.)

Firefighting (1st)
Chemical fire (54p)
Emergency rescue (56p)
Flood rescue (62p)
Search and rescue (81p)
Fire safety (90p)

■ 2009, September 1. Fire and Rescue Services

Des: Rose. Printed in gravure by De La Rue.

Set	6.50	6.50
Gutter pairs	16.00	
First day cover		8.00
Stamp cards	4.00	17.00

Flight Deck Officer 2009 (1st)
Captain 1941 (1st)
Second Officer WRNS 1918 (1st)
Able Seaman 1880 (90p)
Royal Marine 1805 (90p)
Admiral 1795 (90p)

■ 2009, September 17. Navy Uniforms

Des: Atelier Works, with illustrations by Graham Turner. Printed in litho by Cartor. Issued in se-tenant strips of three.

Set	6.00	6.00
Gutter pairs	15.00	
Traffic light gutter pairs	32.50	
First day cover		7.50
Stamp cards	4.00	17.00

(* These stamps also appear in the Royal Navy Uniforms prestige stamp book.)

Sir Matt Busby 1909–1994
Footballer and football manager

Fred Perry (1st)
Henry Purcell (1st)
Sir Matt Busby (1st)
William Gladstone (1st)
Mary Wollstonecraft (1st)
Sir Arthur Conan Doyle (1st)
Donald Campbell (1st)
Judy Fryd (1st)
Samuel Johnston (1st)
Sir Martin Ryle (1st)

■ 2009, October 8. Eminent Britons

Des: Together Design. Printed in litho by Cartor. Issued in strips of five se-tenant designs, in two different sheets.

Set	7.00	6.50
Gutter pairs	18.00	
First day cover		7.50
Stamp cards	6.50	26.00

Canoe Slalom (1st)
Paralympic Archery (1st)
Track Athletics (1st)
Aquatics (1st)
Paralympic Boccia (1st)
Judo (1st)
Paralympic Equestrianism (1st)
Badminton (1st)
Weightlifting (1st)
Basketball (1st)

■ 2009, October 22. London 2012 Olympic and Paralympic Games (part I)

Des: John Royle (Canoe), George Hardie (Archery), Nathalie Guinamard (Athletics), Julian Opie (Aquatics), David Doyle (Boccia), Paul Slater (Judo), Andrew Davidson (Equestrian), David Holmes (Badminton), Guy Billout (Weightlifting), Huntley Muir (Basketball), Studio David Hillman (set). Printed in litho by Cartor. Issued in strips of five se-tenant designs in two different sheets.

Set	7.00	6.50
Gutter pairs	18.00	
First day cover		8.00
Stamp cards	6.00	26.00
Postcard and stamp set (Athletics)	9.00	
Postcard and stamp set (Badminton)	9.00	
Postcard and stamp set (Equestrian)	9.00	
Postcard and stamp set (Judo)	9.00	

(* All values also appear in a commemorative sheet. The Judo, Archery, Track Athletics and Basketball designs also appear as self-adhesives in stamp booklets; price £1.50 each mint.)

Angel by William Morris (2nd, 2nd large)
Madonna and Child by Henry Holiday (1st, 1st Large)
Joseph by Henry Holiday (56p)
Wise Man by Sir Edward Burne-Jones (90p)
Shepherd by Henry Holiday (£1.35)

■ 2009, November 3. Christmas
Des: Andrew Ross, from stained glass windows. Printed in gravure by De La Rue. Counter stamps self-adhesive, miniature sheet gummed.

Set	7.00	7.50
Gutter pairs	17.50	
First day cover		8.50
Miniature sheet (one of each value)	7.50	7.50
Miniature sheet first day cover		8.50
Stamp cards	4.75	30.00

(* The 1st and 2nd class designs also appear in booklets, and the 2nd, 1st, 56p and 90p designs in a Smilers sheet.)

The Division Bell by Pink Floyd, 1994 (1st)
A Rush of Blood to the Head by Coldplay, 2002 (1st)
Parklife by Blur, 1994 (1st)
Power, Corruption and Lies by New Order, 1983 (1st)
Let It Bleed by The Rolling Stones, 1969 (1st)
London Calling by The Clash, 1979 (1st)
Tubular Bells by Mike Oldfield 1973 (1st)
IV by Led Zepplin, 1971 (1st)
Screamadelica by Primal Scream, 1991 (1st)
The Rise and Fall of Ziggy Stardust by David Bowie, 1972 (1st)

■ 2010, January 7. Classic Album Covers
Des: Studio Dempsey. Counter sheets printed in gravure by De La Rue, in strips of five se-tenant designs in two different sheets, self-adhesive. Miniature sheet printed in litho by Cartor, gummed.

Set	7.50	7.50
Gutter pairs	20.00	
First day cover		8.00
Miniature sheet (one of each value)	25.00	25.00
Miniature sheet first day cover		30.00
Stamp cards	6.50	26.00

(* The litho-printed stamps also appear in a prestige stamp book. A souvenir sheet bearing 10 of the Division Bell designs was issued on March 6, 2010 and sold at £4.75, but was not available from post offices; price £6.50)

Aircraft (1st)
Front of sports car (1st)
Seal and Crown (1st)
'Happy birthday' birthday cake (1st)
Bird with envelope (Europe up to 20g)
Front of steam locomotive (1st)
Bow of ship (1st)
Poppies and barbed wire (1st)
Wrapped present (1st)
Aircraft with 'Hello' message (Worldwide up to 20g)

■ 2010, January 26. Business Customised and Smilers Stamps
Des: Hat-Trick (Seal and Crown, Poppy); Lucy Davey (Europe, Worldwide); Annabel Wright (Cake, Present); Andrew Davidson (others). Printed in litho by Cartor.

Miniature sheet	10.00	10.00
First day cover		11.00
Stamp cards	6.50	30.00

(* These designs were issues primarily for use on Smilers sheets, where they are self-adhesive.)

Rainbows against background of activities (1st)
Brownies against background of activities (56p)
Guides against background of activities (81p)
Senior Section against background of activities (90p)

■ 2010, February 2. Centenary of Girlguiding
Des: Together Design. Printed in litho by Cartor.

Miniature sheet	4.50	4.50
First day cover		6.00
Stamp cards	3.00	22.00

Robert Boyle, chemistry (1st)
Isaac Newton, optics (1st)
Benjamin Franklin, electricity (1st)
Edward Jenner, vaccination (1st)
Charles Babbage, computing (1st)
Alfred Russel Wallace, evolution (1st)
Joseph Lister, antiseptic surgery (1st)
Ernest Rutherford, atomic structure (1st)
Dorothy Hodgkin, crystallography (1st)
Nicholas Shackleton, earth science (1st)

■ 2010, February 25. 350th anniversary of The Royal Society

Des: Hat-Trick Design. Printed in litho by Cartor. Issued in se-tenant blocks of ten.

Set	7.00	6.75
Gutter pairs	18.00	
First day cover		8.00
Stamp cards	4.00	25.00

(* The above designs are also available in The Royal Society prestige stamp book.)

Pixie (1st)
Button (1st)
Herbie (1st)
Mr Tumnus (1st)
Talka (1st)
Boris (1st)
Casey (1st)
Tigger (1st)
Leonard (1st)
Tia (1st)

■ 2010, March 11. 150th anniversary of Battersea Dogs & Cats Home

Des: CDT Design Ltd. Printed in litho by Cartor. Issued in se-tenant blocks of ten.

Set	7.00	6.25
Gutter pairs	18.00	
First day cover		9.00
Stamp cards	6.50	25.00

James I (1st)
James II (1st)
James III (1st)
James IV (62p)
James V (62p)
Mary (81p)
James VI (81p)

■ 2010, March 23. Kings and Queens. The House of Stewart

Des: Atelier Works. Printed in litho by Cartor.

Set	6.25	6.50
Gutter pairs	16.00	
Traffic light gutter pairs	35.00	
First day cover		9.00
Stamp cards	7.00	35.00

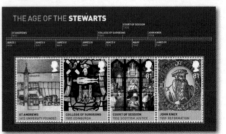

St Andrews University (1st)
College of Surgeons (1st)
Court of Session (81p)
John Knox (81p)

■ 2010, March 23. The Age of the Stewarts

Des: Atelier Works. Printed in litho by Cartor.

Miniature sheet	4.25	4.25
First day cover		6.00
Press sheet	75.00	

Humpback Whale (1st)
Wildcat (1st)
Brown Long-eared Bat (1st)
Polecat (1st)
Sperm Whale (1st)
Water Vole (1st)
Greater Horseshoe Bat (1st)
Otter (1st)
Dormouse (1st)
Hedgehog (1st)

■ 2010, April 13. Endangered Species: Mammals

Des: Jason Godfrey. Printed in litho by Cartor. Issued in se-tenant blocks of ten.

Set	7.00	7.00
Gutter pairs	18.00	
First day cover		8.00
Stamp cards	6.00	25.00

(* The Otter and Hedgehog designs also exist as self-adhesives from stamp booklets; price £1.25 each mint or used.)

Machin portrait of Queen Elizabeth II superimposed on Mackennal portrait of King George V (1st)
Mackennal and Downey portraits of King George V (£1)

■ 2010, May 6. Centenary of the Accession of King George V

Des: Sedley Place. Printed in litho by Cartor. 1st class design printed in sheets; 1st and £1 designs issued in miniature sheets.

1st class	1.50	1.50
Gutter pair of 1st class	4.50	
First day cover		3.50
Miniature sheet	3.50	3.50
Miniature sheet first day cover		12.50
Press sheet	45.00	

(* These stamps also appear in the King George V prestige stamp book. The miniature sheet was also issued on May 8, 2010, with an additional overprint in the margin reading 'BUSINESS DESIGN

CENTRE, LONDON, 8-15 May 2010'; price £11.00 mint, £13.00 on first day cover. Stamp cards showing the stamps and miniature sheets of this issue were included in the issue of May 8.)

British Empire Exhibition 1924 1d stamp (1st)
British Empire Exhibition 1924 1½d stamp (1st)
1913-34 'Seahorses' £1 stamp (£1)
1913-34 'Seahorses' 10/- stamp (£1)

■ 2010, May 8. The King's Stamps

Des: Sedley Place. Printed in intaglio and litho by Enschedé.

Miniature sheet	4.50	4.50
First day cover		6.50
Press sheet	40.00	
Stamp cards (issues of May 6 and May 8)	5.50	28.00

(* These stamps also appear in the King George V prestige stamp book.)

Churchill (1st)
Land Girls (1st)
Home Guard (60p)
Evacuees (60p)
Air Raid Wardens (67p)
Women in Factories (67p)
Royal Broadcast (97p)
Fire Service (97p)

■ 2010, May 13. Britain Alone

Des: Why Not Associates. Printed in litho by Cartor.

Set	8.00	8.00
Gutter pairs	22.50	
First day cover		9.50
Stamp cards	7.75	37.50

(* These stamps also appear in the Britain Alone prestige stamp book.)

William Harvey (1st)
Civil War (60p)
John Milton (88p)
John Vanbrugh (97p)

Evacuation of British soldiers from Dunkirk (1st)
Vessels involved in 'Operation Dynamo' (60p)
British soldiers on board a Royal Navy destroyer (88p)
Two boats from the Dunkirk evacuation (97p)

■ 2010, May 13. Evacuation of Dunkirk
Des: Why Not Associates. Printed in litho by Cartor.

Miniature sheet	5.00	5.00
First day cover		6.50

(* These stamps also appear in the Britain Alone prestige stamp book.)

James I (1st)
Charles I (1st)
Charles II (60p)
James II (60p)
William III (67p)
Mary II (67p)
Anne (88p)

■ 2010, June 15. Kings and Queens. The House of Stuart
Des: Atelier Works. Printed in litho by Cartor.

Set	6.50	6.75
Gutter pairs	15.00	
Traffic light gutter pairs	35.00	
First day cover		8.50
Stamp cards	7.00	35.00

■ 2010, June 15. The Age of the Stuarts
Des: Atelier Works. Printed in litho by Cartor.

Miniature sheet	4.75	4.75
First day cover		6.50
Press sheet	85.00	

Paralympic Rowing (1st)
Shooting (1st)
Modern Pentathlon (1st)
Taekwondo (1st)
Cycling (1st)
Paralympic Table Tennis (1st)
Hockey (1st)
Football (1st)
Paralympic Goalball (1st)
Boxing (1st)

■ 2010, July 27. London 2012 Olympic and Paralympic Games (part II)
Des: Marian Hill (Rowing), David Hillman (Shooting), Katherine Baxter (Modern Pentathlon), James Fryer (Taekwondo), Matthew Dennis (Cycling), Michael Craig-Martin (Table Tennis), Darren Hopes (Hockey), Alex Williamson (Football), Tobatron (Goalball), Stephen Ledwidge (Boxing), Studio David Hillman (set). Printed in litho by Cartor. Issued in strips of five se-tenant designs in two different sheets.

Set	7.00	6.75
Gutter pairs	18.00	
First day cover		8.00
Stamp cards	6.00	25.00
Postcard and stamp set (Boxing)	9.00	
Postcard and stamp set (Rowing)	9.00	

(* All values also appear in a commemorative sheet. The Paralympic Rowing, Table Tennis, Football and Cycling designs also exist as self-adhesives in booklets; price £1.50 each mint or used.)

LMS Coronation Class locomotive (1st)
BR Class 9F locomotive (1st)
GWR King Class locomotive (67p)
LNER Class A1 locomotive (67p)
SR King Arthur Class locomotive (97p)
LMS NCC Class WT locomotive (97p)

■ 2010, August 19. Great British Railways
Des: Delaney Design Consultants. Printed in gravure by De La Rue.

Set	6.25	6.50
Gutter pairs	16.00	
First day cover		8.00
Stamp cards	4.00	17.50

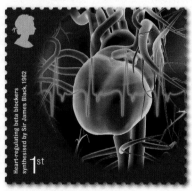

Heart-regulating beta-blockers (1st)
Antibiotic properties of penicillin (58p)
Total hip replacement (60p)
Artificial lens implant surgery (67p)
Malaria parasite (88p)
Computed tomography scanner (97p)

■ 2010, September 16. Medical Breakthroughs
Des: Howard Brown. Printed in litho by Cartor.

Set	6.25	6.50
Gutter pairs	16.00	
First day cover		7.50
Stamp cards	4.00	17.50

(*The Beta-Blockers design also exists as a self-adhesive from stamp booklets; price £1.50 each mint or used.)

Winnie-the-Pooh, Piglet and Christopher Robin (1st)
Winnie-the-Pooh and Piglet (58p)
Winnie-the-Pooh and Rabbit (60p)
Winnie-the-Pooh and Eeyore (67p)
Winnie-the-Pooh and Friends (88p)
Winnie-the-Pooh and Tigger (97p)

■ 2010, October 12. Winnie-the-Pooh
Des: Magpie Studio, using the illustrations of E. H. Shepard. Printed in litho by Cartor.

Set	6.00	6.00
Gutter pairs	16.00	
First day cover		9.00
Stamp cards	7.00	36.00

Winnie-the-Pooh and Christopher Robin (1st)
Christopher Robin reads to Winnie-the-Pooh (60p)
Winnie-the-Pooh and Christopher Robin set sail (88p)
Christopher Robin pulls on his Wellingtons (97p)

■ 2010, October 12. Winnie-the-Pooh
Des: Magpie Studio, using the illustrations of E. H. Shepard. Printed in litho by Cartor.

Miniature sheet	4.50	4.75
First day cover		6.50

Wallace and Gromit singing carols (2nd, 2nd Large)
Gromit posting Christmas cards (1st, 1st Large)
Wallace and Gromit decorating a Christmas tree (60p)
Gromit carrying a Christmas pudding (97p)
Gromit wearing a sweater (£1.46)

■ 2010, November 2. Christmas
Des: Aardman Animations and Nick Park. Printed in gravure by De La Rue. Counter stamps self-adhesive; miniature sheet gummed.

Set	7.50	7.50
Gutter pairs	19.00	
First day cover		10.00
Miniature sheet (1 x each design)	7.50	7.50
Miniature sheet first day cover		10.00
Stamp cards	5.00	27.00

(*The 2nd and 1st class designs also appear in booklets, and the 2nd, 1st, 60p and 97p designs in a Smilers sheet.)

Joe 90 (1st)
Captain Scarlet (1st)
Thunderbird 2 (1st)
Stingray (97p)
Fireball XL5 (97p)
Supercar (97p)

■ 2011, January 11. FAB. The Genius of Gerry Anderson
Des: GBH. Printed in litho by Cartor. Issued in se-tenant strips for each denomination.

Set	6.50	6.50
Gutter pairs	18.00	
First day cover		8.00
Stamp cards	7.50	35.00

(*The Thunderbirds 2 design also exists in self-adhesive format from a stamp booklet: price £1.50 mint or used.)

Thunderbird 4 (41p)
Thunderbird 3 (60p)
Thunderbird 2 (88p)
Thunderbird 1 (97p)

■ 2011, January 11. Thunderbirds
Des: GBH. Printed in microlenticular by Cartor and Outer Aspect, New Zealand.

Miniature sheet	4.50	4.50
First day cover		5.00

BR Dean Goods (1st)
Peckett R2 Thor (60p)
Lancashire and Yorkshire Railway 1093 (88p)
BR WD (97p)

■ 2011, February 1. Classic Locomotives of England
Des: Delaney Design Consultants. Printed in litho by Cartor.

Miniature sheet	4.50	4.50
First day cover		5.50
Stamp cards	3.50	22.00

(*The BR Dean Goods design also exists in self-adhesive format from a booklet: price 90p mint)

Oliver (1st)
Blood Brothers (1st)
We Will Rock You (1st)
Spamalot (1st)
Rocky Horror Show (97p)
Me and My Girl (97p)
Return to the Forbidden Planet (97p)
Billy Elliot (97p)

■ 2011, February 24. Musicals
Des: Webb and Webb. Printed in litho by Cartor.

Set	8.50	8.50
Gutter pairs	22.00	
Traffic light gutter pairs	27.00	
First day cover		10.00
Stamp cards	5.50	22.00

Rincewind from Terry Pratchett's Discworld (1st)
Nanny Ogg from Terry Pratchett's Discworld (1st)
Dumbledore from J. K. Rowling's Harry Potter (1st)
Lord Voldemort from J. K. Rowling's Harry Potter (1st)
Merlin from Arthurian Legend (60p)
Morgan Le Fay from Arthurian Legend (60p)
Aslan from C. S. Lewis's Narnia (97p)
The White Witch from C. S. Lewis's Narnia (97p)

■ 2011, March 8. Magical Realms
Des: So Design Consultants. Printed in gravure by De La Rue.
Issued in vertical se-tenant pairs.

Set	7.50	7.50
Gutter pairs	18.00	
First day cover		8.50
Stamp cards	5.50	22.00

African Elephant (1st)
Mountain Gorilla (1st)
Siberian Tiger (1st)
Polar Bear (1st)
Amur Leopard (1st)
Iberian Lynx (1st)
Red Panda (1st)
Black Rhinoceros (1st)
African Wild Dog (1st)
Golden Lion Tamarin (1st)

■ 2011, March 22. WWF
Des: Rose Design Consultants. Printed in litho by Cartor. Issued
in strips of five se-tenant designs, in two different sheets.

Set	7.00	6.50
Gutter pairs	16.00	
First day cover		7.50
Stamp cards	8.50	36.00

(*These stamps were also available in a prestige stamp book.)

The Amazon Rainforest (1st, 60p, 88p, 97p)

■ 2011, March 22. Amazon Alive. Europa
Des: Janice Nicholson and Rose Design Consultants. Printed in
litho by Cartor.

Miniature sheet	4.50	4.50
First day cover		5.00

(*This miniature sheet is also found in a prestige stamp book.)

Hamlet (1st)
The Tempest (66p)
Henry VI (68p)
King Lear (76p)
A Midsummer's Night Dream (£1)
Romeo and Juliet (£1.10)

■ 2011, April 12. 50th anniversary of the Royal Shakespeare Company
Des: Hat-Trick Design. Printed in gravure by Walsall.

Set	7.00	7.00
Gutter pairs	18.00	
First day cover		9.00
Stamp cards	7.50	35.00

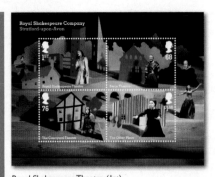

Royal Shakespeare Theatre (1st)
Swan Theatre (68p)
The Courtyard Theatre (76p)
The Other Place (£1)

■ 2011, April 12. 50th anniversary of the Royal Shakespeare Company

Des: Hat-Trick Design. Printed in litho by Cartor.

Miniature sheet	4.50	4.50
First day cover		5.50

HRH Prince William of Wales and Catherine Middleton (1st)
HRH Prince William of Wales and Catherine Middleton (£1.10)

■ 2011, April 21. Royal Wedding of Prince William and Catherine Middleton

Des: Atelier Works, from portraits by Mario Testino. Printed in gravure by Walsall.

Miniature sheet	5.00	5.00
First day cover		7.00

Cray by William Morris, 1884 (1st)
Cherries by Philip Webb, 1867 (1st)
Seaweed by John Henry Dearle, 1901 (76p)
Peony by Kate Faulkner, 1877 (76p)
Acanthus by William Morris and William De Morgan, 1876 (£1.10)
The Merchant's Daughter by Edward Burne-Jones, c1864 (£1.10)

■ 2011, May 5. Morris and Co

Des: Kate Stevens. Printed in litho by Cartor.

Set	7.00	7.00
Gutter pairs	18.00	
First day cover		9.00
Stamp cards	4.50	20.00

(* These stamps were also available in a prestige stamp book.)

Thomas (1st)
James (66p)
Percy (68p)
Daisy (76p)
Toby (£1)
Gordon (£1.10)

■ 2011, June 14. Thomas the Tank Engine

Des: Elmwood, from stills from the television series. Printed in litho by Cartor.

Set	7.00	7.00
Gutter pairs	18.00	
First day cover		8.50
Stamp cards	7.00	30.00

Thomas racing Bertie the Bus (1st)
James has a crash (68p)
Percy ends up in the sea (76p)
Henry walled up in a tunnel (£1)

■ 2011, June 14. Thomas the Tank Engine

Des: Elmwood, from book illustrations by Reginald Dalby and John Kenney. Printed in litho by Cartor.

Miniature sheet	4.50	4.50
First day cover		5.50

(*The 1st class design also exists in self-adhesive format from a booklet: price 90p mint)

Paralympic Sailing (1st)
Field Events (1st)
Volleyball (1st)
Wheelchair Rugby (1st)
Wrestling (1st)
Wheelchair Tennis (1st)
Fencing (1st)
Gymnastics (1st)
Triathlon (1st)
Handball (1st)

■ 2011, July 27. London 2012 Olympic and Paralympic Games (part III)

Des: Lara Harwood (Sailing), Anthony Pike (Field), Ben Dalling (Volleyball), Matthew Hollings (Wheelchair Rugby), Daniel Stolle (Wrestling), David McConochie (Wheelchair Tennis), Lyndon Hayes (Fencing), Kathy Wyatt (Gymnastics), Adam Simpson (Triathlon), David Cutter (Handball), Studio David Hillman (set). Printed in litho by Cartor. Issued in strips of five se-tenant designs in two different sheets.

Set	7.00	6.50
Gutter pairs	18.00	
First day cover		8.50
Stamp cards	6.00	25.00
Postcard and stamp set (Sailing)		9.00
Postcard and stamp set (Gymnastics)		9.00
Composite sheet (entire series of 30)	22.50	

(*All values also appear in a commemorative sheet. The Wheelchair Rugby, Paralympic Sailing, Gymnastics and Fencing designs also appear as self-adhesives in booklets: price £1.50 each mint. The composite sheet comprises one of each design from Series I, II and III of the Olympic and Paralympic Games sets.)

Sovereign's Sceptre with Cross (1st)
St. Edward's Crown (1st)
Rod and Sceptre with Doves (68p)
Queen Mary's Crown (68p)
The Sovereign's Orb (76p)
Jewelled Sword of Offering (76p)
Imperial State Crown (£1.10)
Coronation Spoon (£1.10)

■ 2011, August 23. The Crown Jewels

Des: Purpose. Printed in litho by Cartor.

Set	9.00	9.00
Gutter pairs	22.50	
First day cover		11.00
Stamp cards	5.00	25.00

Gustav Hamel receives first mailbag (1st)
Hamel ready to leave Hendon (68p)
Greswell's Blériot at Windsor (£1)
Airmail delivered at Windsor (£1.10)

■ 2011, September 9. Centenary of the First UK Aerial Post

Des: Robert Maude and Sarah Davies, from photography by Geoff Dann. Printed in litho by Cartor.

Miniature sheet	5.00	5.00
Miniature sheet first day cover		7.00
Press sheet	£100	
Stamp cards	3.50	22.00

(*The £1 and £1.10 designs also appear in a prestige stamp book.)

GEORGE I
1714-1727

George I (1st)
George II (1st)
George III (76p)
George IV (76p)
William IV (£1.10)
Victoria (£1.10)

■ 2011, September 15. Kings and Queens. The House of Hanover

Des: Ian Chilvers, Atelier Works. Printed in litho by Cartor.

Set	7.00	7.50
Gutter pairs	17.00	
Traffic light gutter pairs	32.00	
First day cover		9.00
Stamp cards	7.00	34.00

THE AGE OF THE HANOVERIANS

Robert Walpole (1st)
Ceiling by Robert Adam (68p)
Penny Black (76p)
Queen Victoria (£1)

■ 2011, September 15. The Age of the Hanoverians

Des: Ian Chilvers, Atelier Works. Printed in litho by Cartor.

Miniature sheet	4.50	5.00
First day cover		6.50
Press sheet	90.00	

Angel of the North

Angel of the North (1st)
Blackpool Tower (1st)
Carrick-a-Rede (1st)
Downing Street (1st)
Edinburgh Castle (1st)
Forth Railway Bridge (1st)
Glastonbury Tor (1st)
Harlech Castle (1st)
Ironbridge (1st)
Jodrell Bank (1st)
Kursaal, Southend (1st)
Lindisfarne Priory (1st)

■ 2011, October 13. UK A-Z (part 1)

Des: Robert Maude and Sarah Davies. Printed in litho by Cartor. Issued in se-tenant strips of six in two different sheets.

Set	8.00	8.50
Gutter pairs	20.00	
Traffic light gutter pairs	36.00	
First day cover		10.00
Stamp cards	8.00	26.00

MATTHEW 1:21

The angel visits Joseph, Matthew 1:21 (2nd)
The angel visits Joseph, Matthew 1:21 (2nd Large)
Madonna and child, Matthew 1:23 (1st)
Madonna and child, Matthew 1:23 (1st Large)
Jesus in the manger, Luke 2:7 (68p)
The angel visits the shepherds, Luke 2:10 (£1.10)
The wise men and the star, Matthew 2:10 (£1.65)

■ 2011, November 8. Christmas: 400th anniversary of the King James Bible

Des: Peter Malone, The Artworks and Together Design. Printed in gravure by De La Rue. Counter stamps self-adhesive; miniature sheet gummed.

Set	8.25	8.50
First day cover		10.00
Miniature sheet (one of each design)	8.25	8.50
Miniature sheet first day cover		10.00
Stamp cards	5.50	30.00

(*The 2nd and 1st class also appear in booklets, the 2nd, 1st, 68p, £1.10 and £1.50 in a generic Smilers sheet, and the 2nd, 1st, 68p and £1.10 in customised Smilers sheets.)

Olympic Games logo (1st and Worldwide up to 20g)
Paralympic Games logo (1st and Worldwide up to 20g)

■ 2012, January 5. Olympic and Paralympic Games definitives

Des: Studio Dempsey. Printed in gravure by De La Rue. Self-adhesive. The two designs for each value are arranged in a checkerboard fashion in sheets, with the order alternating.

Set	5.00	5.50
Gutter pairs (1st class only)	12.00	
First day cover		6.50
Stamp cards	3.00	12.00

(*The 1st class values also exist from booklets printed by Walsall.)

Charlie and The Chocolate Factory (1st)
Fantastic Mr Fox (66p)
James and The Giant Peach (68p)
Matilda (76p)
The Twits (£1)
The Witches (£1.10)

■ 2012, January 10. Roald Dahl

Des: Magpie Studios. Printed in litho by Cartor.

Set	7.00	7.50
Gutter pairs	17.00	
First day cover		8.50
Stamp cards	7.50	33.00

(*The six designs were also issued in the Roald Dahl prestige stamp book.)

The BFG carrying Sophie (1st)
The BFG and the giants (68p)
Sophie sitting on the Queen's window-sill (76p)
The BFG and Sophie at the writing desk (£1)

■ 2012, January 10. Roald Dahl's The BFG

Des: Magpie Studios. Printed in litho by Cartor.

Miniature sheet	4.50	5.00
Miniature sheet first day cover		6.00

(*The four designs were also issued in the Roald Dahl prestige stamp book.)

Edward VII (1st)
George V (68p)
Edward VIII (76p)
George VI (£1)
Elizabeth II (£1.10)

■ 2012, February 2. Kings and Queens. The House of Windsor

Des: Ian Chilvers, Atelier Works. Printed in litho by Cartor.

Set	6.50	7.00
Gutter pairs	16.00	
Traffic light gutter pairs	27.00	
First day cover		8.00
Stamp cards	7.00	32.00

Scott Expedition to South Pole (1st)
World War II: King and Queen visiting bombed London (68p)
England 1966 World Cup winning team (76p)
Channel Tunnel (£1)

■ 2012, February 2. The Age of the Windsors and Saxe-Coburg-Gotha

Des: Ian Chilvers, Atelier Works. Printed in litho by Cartor.

Miniature sheet	4.50	5.00
First day cover		6.00
Press sheet	90.00	

Dorothy Wilding stamp portrait (1st)
Robert Austin banknote portrait (1st)
Harry Eccleston banknote portrait (1st)
Mary Gillick coinage portrait (1st)
Arnold Machin coinage portrait (1st)
Arnold Machin stamp portrait (1st)

■ 2012, February 6. Diamond Jubilee

Printed in gravure by Walsall. The Arnold Machin stamp portrait design has overlay text reading 'Diamond Jubilee' and source code 'MMND'.

Miniature sheet	5.00	5.00
First day cover		6.00
Press sheet	55.00	

(*The Arnold Machin stamp portrait design also exists as a self-adhesive definitive, from counter sheets, business sheets and booklets. The Dorothy Wilding and Arnold Machin stamp portrait designs also appear in the Diamond Jubilee prestige stamp book.)

Coventry Cathedral by Sir Basil Spence (1st)
Frederick Delius (1st)
Orange Tree embroidery by Mary 'May' Morris (1st)
Odette Hallowes (1st)
Atmospheric steam engine by Thomas Newcomen (1st)
Kathleen Ferrier (1st)
Interior of Palace of Westminster by Augustus Pugin (1st)
Montague Rhodes James (1st)
Bombe code-breaking machine by Alan Turing (1st)
Joan Mary Fry (1st)

■ 2012, February 23. Britons of Distinction

Des: Purpose. Printed in litho by Cartor. Issued in se-tenant strips of five in two separate sheets.

Set	7.00	7.50
Gutter pairs	17.00	
First day cover		8.50
Stamp cards	7.00	22.00

BR Class D34 locomotive (1st)
BR Class D40 locomotive (68p)
Andrew Barclay No.807 locomotive (£1)
BR Class 4P locomotive (£1.10)

■ 2012, March 8. Classic Locomotives of Scotland

Des: Delaney Design Consultants. Printed in litho by Cartor.

Miniature sheet	5.00	5.50
Miniature sheet first day cover		6.50
Stamp cards	3.75	18.00

The Dandy and Desperate Dan (1st)
The Beano and Dennis the Menace (1st)
Eagle and Dan Dare(1st)
The Topper and Beryl the Peril (1st)
Tiger and Roy of the Rovers (1st)
Bunty and The Four Marys (1st)
Buster and Buster(1st)
Valiant and The Steel Claw (1st)
Twinkle and Nurse Nancy (1st)
2000AD and Judge Dredd (1st)

■ 2012, March 20. Comics
Des: The Chase. Printed in litho by Cartor. Issued in se-tenant strips of five in two separate sheets.

Set	7.00	7.50
Gutter pairs	17.00	
First day cover		8.50
Stamp cards	7.00	27.00

Manchester Town Hall (1st)
Narrow Water Castle (1st)
Old Bailey (1st)
Portmeirion (1st)
The Queen's College, Oxford (1st)
Roman Baths (1st)
Stirling Castle (1st)
Tyne Bridge (1st)
Urquhart Castle (1st)
Victoria and Albert museum (1st)
White Cliffs of Dover (1st)
Station X, Bletchley Park (1st)
York Minster (1st)
ZSL London Zoo (1st)

■ 2012, April 10. UK A-Z (part 2). Europa
Des: Robert Maude and Sarah Davies. Printed in litho by Cartor. Issued in se-tenant strips of six (M-R and S-X),and in se-tenant pairs (Y-Z), in three different sheets.

Set	9.00	9.50
Gutter pairs	22.00	
Traffic light gutter pairs	27.00	
First day cover		10.50
Stamp cards	10.00	30.00
Composite sheet (entire series of 26)	22.00	

Hardy Ames (1st)
Norman Hartnell (1st)
Granny Takes A Trip (1st)
Ossie Clark (1st)
Tommy Nutter (1st)
Jean Muir (1st)
Zandra Rhodes (1st)
Vivienne Westwood (1st)
Paul Smith (1st)
Alexander McQueen (1st)

■ 2012, May 15. Great British Fashion
Des: Johnson Banks. Printed in litho by Cartor. Printed in se-tenant strips of five in two separate sheets.

Set	7.00	7.50
Gutter pairs	17.00	
First day cover		8.50
Stamp cards	7.00	24.00

Golden Jubilee 2002 (1st)
Trooping the Colour 1967 (1st)
The Royal Welsh 2007 (77p)
First Christmas TV Broadcast 1957 (77p)
Silver Jubilee Walkabout 1977 (87p)
Garter Ceremony 1997 (87p)
United Nations Address 1957 (£1.28)
Commonwealth Games 1982 (£1.28)

■ 2012, May 31. Diamond Jubilee
Des: Kate Stephens. Printed in litho by Cartor. Issued in se-tenant pairs of each denomination.

Set	9.00	9.50
Gutter pairs	22.00	
Traffic light gutter pairs	29.00	
First day cover		10.50
Stamp cards	6.00	24.00

(* All designs also appear in the Diamond Jubilee prestige stamp book. The Golden Jubilee design also exists as a self-adhesive from a booklet: price £1 mint or used.)

Mr Bumble, from Oliver Twist (2nd)
Mr Pickwick, from The Pickwick Papers (1st)
The Marchioness, from The Old Curiosity Shop (77p)
Mrs Gamp, from Martin Chuzzlewit (87p)
Captain Cuttle, from Dombey and Son (£1.28)
Mr Micawber, from David Copperfield (£1.90)

■ **2012, June 19. Bicentenary of the Birth of Charles Dickens**
Des: Howard Brown, from illustrations by 'Kyd' (Joseph Clayton Clarke). Printed in litho by Cartor.

Set	8.00	8.50
Gutter pairs	20.00	
Traffic light gutter pairs	27.00	
First day cover		9.50
Stamp cards	8.00	30.00

Nicholas Nickleby (1st)
Bleak House (1st)
Little Dorrit (1st)
A Tale of Two Cities (1st)

■ **2012, June 19. Bicentenary of the Birth of Charles Dickens**
Des: Howard Brown, from illustrations by 'Phiz' (Hablot Knight Brown). Printed in litho by Cartor.

Miniature sheet	3.50	4.00
Miniature sheet first day cover		5.00

Fencer and Tower Bridge (1st)
Track athletes and Olympic Stadium (1st)
Diver and Tate Modern (£1.28)
Track cyclist and London Eye (£1.28)

■ **2012, July 27. Welcome to the London 2012 Olympic Games**
Des: Hat-Trick. Printed in litho by Cartor.

Miniature sheet	6.00	7.00
Miniature sheet first day cover		8.00
Stamp cards	4.00	20.00

Gold medal winner, to be confirmed (1st x 6)

■ **2012, July 27-August 12. London 2012 Olympic Games Gold Medal Winners**
Royal Mail planned to issue a miniature sheet comprising six 1st class stamps for each gold medal winner from Team GB at the Olympic Games. Printed in gravure by Walsall (base design) and digitally overprinted by six different printers (main image and event-specific inscriptions). Details of any issued stamps were unknown as this publication went to press.

Amputee athlete and Olympic Stadium (1st)
Wheelchair basketball player and Houses of Parliament (1st)
Weightlifter and St Paul's Cathedral (£1.28)
Cyclist and London Eye (£1.28)

■ **2012, August 29. Welcome to the London 2012 Paralympic Games**
Des: Hat-Trick. Printed in litho by Cartor.

Miniature sheet	6.00	7.00
Miniature sheet first day cover		8.00
Stamp cards	4.00	20.00

DO YOU COLLECT GREAT BRITAIN STAMPS?

Our printed monthly retail list covers
all issues from 1840 to date
(with many new issues offered at face value!)

**JUST COMPLETE THE COUPON BELOW TO
RECEIVE YOUR FREE COPY - NO STAMP REQUIRED
- OR VISIT OUR USER FRIENDLY WEBSITE
www.gbstamps.co.uk**

GREAT BRITAIN COLLECTORS ON THE INTERNET

The world's largest selection of Great Britain stamps is just one
click away. Our profusely illustrated private treaty catalogues are
issued twice monthly and contain a wide selection of better
singles, rarities, proofs, colour trials, high values, multiples,
Cinderella material and much more other specialist material
seldom offered elsewhere. Up to £500,000 of fine GB material
can be viewed on-line at

www.gbstamps.co.uk

**YOU CAN ORDER BY
MAIL, PHONE, FAX
OR ON-LINE
24 HOURS A DAY,
7 DAYS A WEEK.
CREDIT CARDS
ACCEPTED.**

Please tick boxes of interest:

❑ Pre stamp/postal history ❑ QV Line engraved
❑ QV Surface printed   ❑ QV High values
❑ King Edward VII   ❑ King George V
❑ Essays/proofs/colour trials ❑ General Great Britain
❑ Specialised shades   ❑ Cinderella

Arthur Ryan & Co.
OF RICHMOND

FREEPOST, Dept. SM, RICHMOND, SURREY TW9 1DY

Please send me a **FREE** copy of your Retail List

NAME ....

ADDRESS ....

....

.... POST CODE ....

OR TELEPHONE: 020 8940 7777   FAX: 020 8940 7755

SELLING? WE BUY STAMPS

Enfield Stamp Centre (Est. 1977). A small family business, we have produced a Newsletter listing all the collections we have acquired over our shop counter, for many years. We do not buy at auctions. We buy from the public: Collectors, Solicitor's Probate lots, Banks, Charities, Attic finds etc. Many of the thousands, who have bought from us, return to sell their treasures, for all manner of reasons, eg. moving, changing interests, retirement. We make a free market valuation of the stamps. We offer to buy them there and then or invite you to get another offer if you wish. It's as simple as that! No auctions with unpredictable results and exorbitant commission charges. No waiting months whilst the auctioneer catalogues your collection, only to sell it to a dealer like us. No waiting 45 working days (or more) for payment after the sale. Instant, friendly, face to face dealing. As they say "Life's complicated enough". Why complicate it more sending your life's work by some freight company to a faceless valuer. We buy direct. No hassle. No charges, no waiting. Got something to sell? Try us. What have you got to lose? Come to our shop, no appointment required (open Wed, Fri and Sat - 9.00 a.m. - 4 p.m.) for a free, no obligation, offer.

35 years of experience, valuing stamps every day, will ensure you have made the right move.

HOW TO GET TO THE SHOP

Enfield Stamp Centre is located in Lancaster Road, three doors down from the Holly Bush pub. Two buses pass our door from the town - 191 & W8

NEAREST TUBE
Oakwood. Then take a cab (15 minutes)

NEAREST TRAIN STATION
Gordon Hill (Hertford Line from Finsbury Park)

BY CAR
Turn off the M25 at junction 24 then take the A1005 signposted Enfield and follow for three miles. At mini roundabout (just past Chase Farm Hospital) turn left. At the next mini roundabout bear left and follow this road past Gordon Hill Station. This will lead you to another mini roundabout. Cross this and our shop is thirty yards along the right. We can also be found if you take junction 25, down the A10 and turn right at the traffic lights for Carterhatch Lane.

Enfield Stamp Centre, 192-194 Lancaster Road, Enfield, Middx. EN2 0JH

Tel: 020 8367 2653 Fax: 020 8342 0007 Email: enfieldstamp@btconnect.com

YOUR LOCAL STAMP SHOP JUST A PHONE CALL OR EMAIL AWAY!

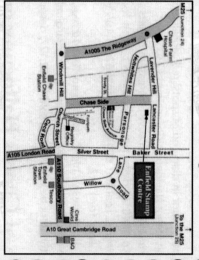

PHILANGLES LTD

International postage stamp & postal history auctioneers

ESTABLISHED 1990

AUCTIONEERS OF QUALITY POSTAGE STAMPS
POSTAL HISTORY AND COLLECTIONS OF THE WORLD

Our monthly auctions always contains fine and interesting Great Britain with
single stamps, collections, postal history & specialist material.

OUR SERVICES

Monthly auctions & Specialist sales
Advice on buying & selling
Valuations including probate & insurance

If you have a collection to sell please contact Simon Carson for your free home visit.
We travel throughout the UK.

WWW.PHILANGLES.CO.UK

Carson House, 44 Legh Street
Warrington, Cheshire, WA1 1UJ

Telephone: 01925 231151   Facsimile: 01925 232204
Email: philangles@btinternet.com

REGIONAL ISSUES

Prices in this section are quoted in two columns: mint (left) and fine used (right).

The definitive issues for Guernsey, the Isle of Man and Jersey which pre-date their postal independence are listed first, followed by those for the four countries that comprise the United Kingdom.

CHANNEL ISLANDS

Gathering seaweed (1d)

Islanders gathering seaweed (2½d)

■ 1948, May 10. Third Anniversary of Liberation

Des: J.R.R. Stobie (1d), E. Blampied (2½d). Printed in photogravure by Harrison. Multiple GVIR watermark. Perf: 15 x 14.

Set	0.15	0.20
First day cover		17.50

GUERNSEY

2½d

3d, 4d, 5d

■ 1958-69

Des: E.A. Piprell. Printed in photogravure by Harrison. Perf: 15 x 14.

A) Wmk: Multiple St Edward's Crown. Non phosphor (except where stated).

2½d red (June 8, 1964)	0.30	0.35
3d lilac (August 18, 1958)	0.30	0.30
one centre phos band (May 24, 1967)	0.10	0.15
4d ultramarine (February 7, 1966)	0.20	0.25
two phos bands (October 24, 1967)	0.10	0.15
First day cover (2½d)		25.00
First day cover (3d)		20.00
First day cover (4d)		10.00

B) No watermark. Chalky paper. Two phosphor bands (except where stated).

4d ultramarine (April 16, 1968)	0.10	0.15
4d sepia (September 4, 1968)		
one centre phosphor band	0.10	0.15
4d red (February 26, 1969)		
one centre phosphor band	0.10	0.20
5d deep blue (September 4, 1968)	0.10	0.20
First day cover (4d sepia, 5d)		2.00
First day cover (4d red)		1.50

JERSEY

2½d

3d, 4d, 5d

3d, 4d, 5d

■ **1958-69**
Des: J. Nicholson. Printed in photogravure by Harrison.
Perf: 15 x 14.

A) Wmk: Multiple St Edward's Crown. Non phosphor (except where stated).

2½d carmine-red (June 8, 1964)		0.20	0.35
3d lilac (August 18, 1958)		0.15	0.20
chalky paper (May 17, 1964)		4.50	4.00
one centre phos band (June 27, 1968)		0.10	0.15
4d ultramarine (February 7, 1966)		0.75	0.75
a) two phosphor bands (July 5, 1967)		0.10	0.15
First day cover (2½d)			25.00
First day cover (3d)			30.00
First day cover (4d)			10.00

B) No watermark. Chalky paper. Two phosphor bands (except where stated).

4d ultramarine (June 24, 1968)		0.10	0.15
4d sepia (September 4, 1968)			
one centre phosphor band		0.10	0.15
4d red (February 26, 1969)			
one centre phosphor band		0.20	0.30
5d deep blue (September 4, 1968)		0.20	0.30
First day cover (4d sepia, 5d)			2.00
First day cover (4d red)			1.50

■ **1958-69**
Des: E. Blampied (2½d), W.M. Gardner (others). Printed in photogravure by Harrison. Perf: 15 x 14.

A) Wmk: Multiple St. Edward's Crown. Non phosphor (except where stated).

2½d carmine-red (June 8, 1964)		0.20	0.25
3d lilac (August 18, 1958)		0.25	0.25
one centre phos band (June 9, 1967)		0.10	0.15
4d ultramarine (February 7, 1966)		0.20	0.25
two phos bands (September 5, 1967)		0.10	0.15
First day cover (2½d)			25.00
First day cover (3d)			20.00
First day cover (4d)			10.00

B) No watermark. Chalky paper, PVA gum. One centre phosphor band (4d), two phosphor bands (5d).

4d sepia (September 4, 1968)		0.10	0.15
4d red (February 26, 1969)		0.10	0.20
5d deep blue (September 4, 1968)		0.10	0.20
First day cover (4d sepia, 5d)			2.00
First day cover (4d red)			1.50

ISLE OF MAN

2½d

■ **1971, July 7**

Des: J. Matthews. Printed in photogravure by Harrison.

2½p magenta		0.20	0.20
3p ultramarine		0.20	0.20
5p violet		0.60	0.60
7½p pale brown		0.75	0.75
First day cover			2.50

(*The 2½p and 3p exist on either ordinary coated paper or fluorescent-coated paper.)

COUNTRY ISSUES

Prices in this section are quoted in two columns: mint (left) and fine used (right).

Country definitives are listed by country in alphabetical order, although those representing England were introduced long after those for Northern Ireland, Scotland and Wales.

Except where otherwise stated, all the stamps in this section are printed in photogravure by Harrisons and perf 15 x 14.

ENGLAND

Three lions (2nd)
Crowned lion and shield of St George (1st)
Oak tree (E)
Tudor rose (65p, 68p)

■ 2001, April 23. Designs without white borders

Des: Sedley Place, from sculptures by D. Dathan. Printed in gravure by De La Rue. One phosphor band (2nd), two phosphor bands (others).

2nd slate blue and silver	0.90	0.70
1st red-brown and silver	1.20	0.90
E olive-green and silver	1.50	1.00
65p deep lilac and silver	1.75	1.50
68p deep lilac and silver (July 4, 2002)	1.75	1.60
First day cover (2nd, 1st, E, 65p)		3.00
First day cover (68p)		3.00
Stamp cards	6.00	14.00

(*The 2nd and 1st class also appear printed in gravure by Questa in the Across the Universe prestige stamp book of September 24, 2002.)

Three lions (2nd)
Crowned lion and shield of St George (1st)
Oak tree (E, 40p, 42p, 44p, 48p, 50p, 56p, 60p, 87p)
Tudor rose (68p, 72p, 78p, 81p, 90p, 97p, £1.10, £1.28)

■ 2003, October 14. Designs with white borders

Designs as for April 23, 2001, but with a white border. Printed in gravure by De La Rue (2nd, 1st, E, 40p, 42p, 44p, 48p, 50p, 56p, 60p, 68p, 72p, 78p, 81p, 90p, 97p), in gravure by Walsall (2nd, 42p), in litho by De La Rue (1st, 78p, 81p), in litho by Enschedé (1st) or in litho by Cartor (68p, 87p, £1.10, £1.28). One phosphor band (2nd) or two phosphor bands (others).

2nd slate blue and silver	0.80	0.70
1st red-brown and silver	1.00	0.85
E olive-green and silver	1.50	1.25
40p olive-green and silver (May 11, 2004)	1.00	1.25
42p olive-green and silver		
(Apr 5, 2005, printed by Walsall)	1.25	1.25
(May 10, 2005, printed by De La Rue)	1.25	1.25
44p olive-green and silver (May 28, 2006)	1.25	1.25
48p olive-green and silver (Mar 27, 2007)	1.25	1.25
50p olive green and silver (Apr 1, 2008)	1.25	1.25
56p olive green and silver (Mar 31, 2009)	1.25	1.25
60p olive green and silver (Mar 30, 2010)	1.00	1.00
68p deep lilac and silver		
(Oct 14, 2003, printed by De La Rue)	1.50	1.80
(Mar 29, 2011, printed by Cartor)	1.00	1.00
72p deep lilac and silver (Mar 28, 2006)	1.50	1.50
78p deep lilac and silver (Mar 27, 2007)	1.60	1.60
81p deep lilac and silver (Apr 1, 2008)	1.70	1.70
87p olive green and silver (Apr 25, 2012)	1.50	1.50
90p deep lilac and silver (Mar 31, 2009)	1.70	1.70
97p deep lilac and silver (Mar 30, 2010)	1.50	1.50
£1.10 deep lilac and silver (Mar 29, 2011)	1.50	1.50
£1.28 deep lilac and silver (Apr 25, 2012)	2.50	2.50
First day cover (2nd, 1st, E, 68p)		6.50
First day cover (40p)		2.50
First day cover (42p)		2.50
First day cover (44p, 72p)		2.50
First day cover (48p, 78p)		3.50
First day cover (50p, 81p)		3.50
First day cover (56p, 90p)		3.00
First day cover (60p, 97p)		3.50
First day cover (68p, £1.10)		4.00
First day cover (87p, £1.28)		5.00
Stamp cards	2.00	10.00

(*Values in this series have also appeared in miniature sheets and prestige stamp books. The 1st class also exists, self-adhesive, in generic Smilers sheets.)

NORTHERN IRELAND

3d lilac
6d purple
1/3 green

3p blue

1958-1968
Des: W. Hollywood (3d, 4d, 5d), L. Philton (6d, 9d), T. Collins (1/3, 1/6).

A) Wmk: Multiple St Edward's Crown. Non phosphor except where stated.

3d lilac (August 18, 1958)	0.15	0.15
one centre band	0.15	0.20
4d blue (February 7, 1966)	0.15	0.15
two phosphor bands	0.15	0.15
6d purple (September 29, 1958)	0.20	0.20
9d green (March 1, 1967)		
two phosphor bands	0.35	0.40
1/3 green (September 29, 1958)	0.35	0.40
1/6 grey-blue (March 1, 1967)		
two phosphor bands	0.40	0.40
First day cover (3d)		25.00
First day cover (6d, 1/3)		30.00
First day cover (4d)		7.50
First day cover (9d, 1/6)		4.00

B) No wmk. Two phosphor bands and PVA gum except where stated.

4d blue, gum Arabic	0.15	0.15
4d sepia (September 4, 1968)		
one centre band	0.15	0.25
4d red (February 26, 1969)	0.20	0.30
5d blue (September 4, 1968)	0.20	0.20
1/6 grey-blue	1.50	1.40
First day cover (4d sepia, 5d)		2.50
First day cover (4d red)		1.00

(*The 4d blue exists with gum arabic or PVA gum. The latter was not placed on sale in Northern Ireland; priced £8.50 mint.)

1971, July 7. Decimal Currency
Des: J. Matthews. The symbol was redrawn and moved less close to the top of the design, creating type II.

A) Two phosphor bands except where stated.
i) PVA gum. Original coated paper.

2½p pink, one centre band	0.50	0.50
3p blue	0.25	0.25
5p violet	0.75	0.75
7½p brown	0.80	0.80

ii) PVA gum. Fluorescent coated paper.

2½p pink, one centre band	5.25	4.00
3p blue	7.50	7.00
one centre band	0.35	0.30

iii) PVAD gum.

3p blue, one centre band	0.90	0.85
3½p green (January 23, 1974)	0.25	0.20
one centre band	0.25	0.20
4½p grey-blue (November 6, 1974)	0.25	0.20
5½p deep violet (January 23, 1974)	0.25	0.25
one centre band	0.25	0.25
6½p green-blue (January 14, 1976)		
one centre band	0.35	0.30
7p red-brown (January 18, 1978)		
one centre band	0.30	0.30
8p red (January 23, 1974)	0.35	0.35
8½p green (January 14, 1976)	0.35	0.35
9p violet-blue (January 18, 1978)	0.35	0.30
10p orange (October 20, 1976)	0.35	0.35
one centre band	0.35	0.30
10½p grey-blue (January 18, 1978)	0.40	0.30
11p red (October 20, 1976)	0.40	0.30

B) Phosphor coated paper. PVAD gum. Issued on July 23, 1980.

12p yellow-green	0.50	0.40
13½p red-brown	0.50	0.50
15p blue	0.50	0.45

C) Printed in litho by Questa. Perf: 13½ x 14. Phosphor coated paper, except 11½p and 12½p (left side band). PVAD gum (11½p, 14p, 18p, 22p), PVAD gum (others).

11½p mushroom (April 8, 1981)	0.70	0.65
12½p light green (February 24, 1982)	0.35	0.30
14p steel-blue (April 8, 1981)	0.60	0.50
15½p pale violet (February 24, 1982)	0.70	0.60
16p light mushroom (April 27, 1983)	0.85	0.70
18p mauve (April 8, 1981)	0.70	0.70
19½p grey-green (February 24, 1982)	1.50	1.50
20½p bright blue (April 27, 1983)	2.00	2.00
22p deep blue (April 8, 1981)	1.00	1.00
26p red, type I (February 24, 1982)	1.00	1.00
28p blue, type I (April 27, 1983)	1.00	1.00

D) Printed in litho by Questa. Perf: 15 x 14. One phosphor band (12p, 12½p, 13p); phosphor coated paper (16p, 17p, 31p); advanced coated paper (22p, 26p, 28p), or as indicated. PVAD gum.

12p emerald green (January 7, 1986)	1.00	0.80
12½p light green (February 28, 1984)	3.00	3.00
PVA gum	4.00	-
13p reddish-brown, (October 23, 1984)		
type I	0.60	0.60
deep brown, type II	0.80	0.75
13p deep brown, type II (April 14, 1987) printed on paper supplied by Coated Papers Ltd. PVA gum	0.80	0.75
14p deep blue (November 8, 1988) one centre band	0.50	0.55
15p bright blue (November 28, 1989) one centre band	0.55	0.60
16p light mushroom (February 28, 1984)	5.00	4.50
17p steel blue (October 23, 1984)		
type I	1.00	0.80
type I, advanced coated paper	0.70	0.80
type II, advanced coated paper	£125	£100
18p deep green (Janary 6, 1987)	0.90	0.80
18p bright green (December 3, 1991) one centre band	0.60	0.60
18p bright green (December 31, 1992) perf: 14	5.00	5.00
18p bright green (August 10, 1993) left band	2.00	1.80
19p orange-red (November 8, 1988) phosphor paper	0.40	0.40
20p brownish-black (November 28, 1989) phosphor paper	0.60	0.60
22p yellowish-green (October 23, 1984)	0.80	0.70
22p orange-red (December 4, 1990) phosphor paper	1.00	0.70
23p bright green (November 8, 1988) phosphor paper	0.70	0.85
24p deep red (November 28, 1989) phosphor paper	1.00	1.00
24p chestnut (August 10, 1993) two bands	2.00	2.00
26p red, type II (January 27, 1987)	2.00	2.00
26p drab (December 4, 1990) phosphor paper	0.90	0.90
28p blue, type II (January 27, 1987)	1.00	0.90
28p bluish grey (December 3, 1991) phosphor paper	1.10	1.10

31p purple, type I (October 23, 1984)	1.00	1.00
31p purple, type II (April 14, 1987)	1.80	1.50
32p greenish blue (November 8, 1988) phosphor paper	1.25	1.00
34p bluish grey (November 28, 1989) phosphor paper	0.90	0.90
37p rosine (December 4, 1990) phosphor paper	1.20	1.20
39p mauve) (December 3, 1991) phosphor paper	1.50	1.30

(* The 18p with side phosphor band and 24p chestnut with two phosphor bands come from prestige stamp books.)

E) Stamps with an elliptical perforation along each vertical side. Printed in litho by Questa. One phosphor band (19p and 20p), or two phosphor bands (others).

19p bistre (December 7, 1993)	0.60	0.65
band at left	1.00	1.00
band at right	2.00	2.00
20p bright green (July 23, 1996)	1.50	1.50
25p red (December 7, 1993)	0.80	0.75
26p red-brown (July 23, 1996)	1.00	1.00
30p olive-grey (December 7, 1993)	1.50	1.50
37p mauve (July 23, 1996)	2.00	2.00
41p grey-brown (December 7, 1993)	1.00	1.00
63p emerald (July 23, 1996)	2.75	2.50

(* Some of these stamps are also found in prestige stamp books, including the 19p with the phosphor band to the left or right.)

F) Stamps with an elliptical perforation along each vertical side. Printed in gravure by Walsall. One phosphor band (19p and 20p), two phosphor bands (others).

19p bistre (June 8, 1999)	2.25	2.00
20p bright green (July 1, 1997)	0.90	0.90
20p bright green, band at right	3.00	2.00
26p chestnut (July 1, 1997)	0.90	0.90
26p chestnut, perf: 14	2.25	2.25
26p chestnut, printed by Harrison	2.00	2.00
37p mauve (July 1, 1887)	1.10	1.10
37p mauve, printed by Harrison	1.20	1.20
38p ultramarine (June 8, 1999)	5.50	5.50
40p azure (April 25, 2000)	3.00	3.00
63p emerald (July 1, 1997)	4.00	4.00
64p turquoise (June 8, 1999)	6.00	6.00
65p greenish blue (April 25, 2000)	3.00	3.00

(* The 20p with one band at right and 26p with perf: 14 are printed by Harrison. As with the 26p and 37p printed by Harrison, they come from prestige stamp books.)

G) Printed in gravure by Walsall. One phosphor band.

1st orange-red (February 15, 2000) perf: 14	2.25	2.20
1st orange-red (April 25, 2000) perf: 15x14	6.50	6.50

(* The perf: 14 stamp also comes from a prestige stamp book.)

First day cover (2½p, 3p, 5p, 7½p)	1.70
First day cover (3½p, 5½p, 8p)	1.40
First day cover (4½p)	0.80
First day cover (6½p, 8½p)	0.80

First day cover (10p, 11p)	0.90
First day cover (7p, 9p, 10½p)	0.90
First day cover (12p, 13½p, 15p)	1.70
First day cover (11½p, 14p, 18p, 22p)	1.40
First day cover (12½p, 15½p, 19½p, 26p)	2.00
First day cover (16p, 20½p, 28p)	2.00
First day cover (13p, 17p, 22p, 31p)	1.00
First day cover (12p)	1.00
First day cover (18p)	2.90
First day cover (14p, 19p, 23p, 32p)	2.90
First day cover (15p, 20p, 24p, 34p)	2.90
First day cover (17p, 22p, 26p, 37p)	2.90
First day cover (18p, 24p, 28p, 39p)	2.90
First day cover (19p, 25p, 30p, 41p)	3.50
First day cover (20p, 26p, 37p, 63p)	5.00
First day cover (19p, 38p, 64p)	5.00
First day cover (1st, 40p, 65p)	6.00

Basalt columns (2nd)
Patchwork fields (1st)
Linen (E, 40p, 42p, 44p, 48p, 50p, 56p, 60p, 87p)
Pattern on vase (68p, 72p, 78p, 81p, 90p, 97p, £1.10, £1.28)

■ 2003, October 14. Designs with white borders

Designs as for March 6, 2001, but with a white border. Printed in litho by De La Rue (2nd, 1st, E, 40p, 42p, 44p, 68p, 72p, 78p, 81p), in litho by Walsall (42p), in gravure by De La Rue (2nd, 1st, 48p, 50p, 56p, 60p, 72p, 78p, 81p, 90p, 97p), in litho by Enschedé (1st) or in litho by Cartor (68p, 87p, £1.10, £1.28). One phosphor band (2nd) or two phosphor bands (others).

2nd multicoloured	1.20	0.90
1st multicoloured	1.15	0.90
E multicoloured	2.00	2.00
40p multicoloured (May 11, 2004)	1.00	0.75
42p multicoloured (Walsall, Apr 5, 2005)	1.20	1.00
42p multicoloured (July 26, 2005)	1.20	1.00
44p multicoloured (March 25, 2006)	1.75	1.50
48p multicoloured (March 27, 2007)	1.00	1.00
50p multicoloured (April 1, 2008)	1.00	1.00
56p multicoloured (Mar 31, 2009)	1.00	1.00
60p multicoloured (Mar 30, 2010)	1.50	1.50
68p multicoloured		
(Oct 14, 2003, printed by De La Rue)	1.20	1.10
(Mar 29, 2011, printed by Cartor)	1.00	1.00
72p multicoloured (March 28, 2006)	1.20	1.10
78p multicoloured (March 27, 2007)	1.75	1.75
81p multicoloured (April 1, 2008)	1.75	1.75
87p multicolored (Apr 25, 2012)	1.50	1.50
90p multicoloured (Mar 31, 2009)	1.70	1.70
97p multicoloured (Mar 30, 2010)	1.75	1.75
£1.10 multicoloured (Mar 29, 2011)	1.50	1.50
£1.28 multicoloured (Apr 25, 2012)	2.50	2.50
First day cover (2nd, 1st, E, 68p)		6.50
First day cover (40p)		2.50
First day cover (42p)		1.50
First day cover (44p, 72p)		2.50
First day cover (48p, 78p)		3.00
First day cover (50p, 81p)		3.50
First day cover (56p, 90p)		3.00
First day cover (60p, 97p)		3.50
First day cover (68p, £1.10)		4.00
First day cover (87p, £1.28)		5.00
Stamp cards	2.00	10.00

(*Values in this series have also appeared in miniature sheets and prestige stamp books. The 1st class also exists, self-adhesive, in generic Smilers sheets.)

Basalt columns (2nd)
Patchwork fields (1st)
Linen (E,)
Pattern on vase (65p, 68p)

■ 2001, March 6. Designs without white borders

Des: Rodney Miller Associates. Printed in litho by De La Rue (E and 68p), Walsall (2nd, 1st, E, 65p) or Enschedé (2nd, 1st), One phosphor band (2nd), two phosphor bands (others).

2nd multicoloured	0.90	0.80
(Enschedé, Feb 23, 2003)	1.35	1.20
1st multicoloured	1.20	0.90
(Enschedé, Feb 23, 2003)	1.70	1.50
E multicoloured (Walsall)	1.75	1.75
E multicoloured (De La Rue)	1.75	1.75
65p multicoloured	2.50	2.50
68p multicoloured (July 4, 2002)	2.20	2.20
First day cover (2nd, 1st, E, 65p)	4.50	4.50
First day cover (68p)	2.00	5.00
Stamp cards	6.00	15.00

(* The 2nd and 1st printed by Enschedé come from the £6.99 Microcosmos prestige stamp book.)

SCOTLAND

3d lilac

3½p green

■ 1958-1967

Des: G. F. Huntley (3d, 4d, 5d), J. B. Fleming (6d, 9d), A. B. Imrie (1/3, 1/6).

A) Wmk: Multiple St Edward's Crown. Non phosphor except where stated.

3d lilac (August 18, 1958)	0.15	0.15
two phosphor bands	8.00	2.00
one band at left	0.20	0.35
one band at right	0.20	0.35
one centre band	0.20	0.30
4d blue (February 7, 1966)	0.15	0.15
two phosphor bands	0.15	0.15
6d purple (September 29, 1958)	0.15	0.15
two phosphor bands	0.20	0.25
9d green (March 1, 1967)		
two phosphor bands	0.35	0.40
1/3 green (September 29, 1958)	0.35	0.25
two phosphor bands	0.35	0.40
1/6 grey-blue (March 1, 1967)		
two phosphor bands	0.40	0.50
First day cover (3d)		10.00
First day cover (6d, 1/3)		20.00
First day cover (3d, 6d, 1/3 phosphor)		£100
First day cover (4d)		7.50
First day cover (9d, 1/6)		2.75

B) No watermark. Two phosphor bands except where stated.
i) Gum Arabic.

3d lilac (one centre band)	0.15	—
4d blue	0.15	—
ii) PVA gum.		
3d lilac (one centre band)	0.15	0.20
4d blue	0.15	0.20
4d sepia (September 4, 1968)		
one centre band	0.15	0.20
4d red (February 26, 1969)		
one centre band	0.20	0.20
5d blue (September 4, 1968)	0.20	0.25
9d green	3.25	3.25
1/6 grey-blue	1.25	1.00
First day cover (4d sepia, 5d)		2.50
First day cover (4d red)		1.00

■ 1971, July 7. Decimal Currency

Des: J. Matthews. The lion symbol was re-drawn. On type I the eye appears as a circle, while the tongue and claws are thin; on type II the eye is solid while the tongue and claws are thicker.

A) Two phosphor bands except where stated.
i) Gum Arabic.

2½p pink, one centre band	0.40	—
3p blue	1.00	—
ii) PVA gum. Original coated paper.		
2½p pink, one centre band	0.25	0.25
3p blue	0.25	0.25
5p violet	0.75	0.0
7½p brown	0.80	0.80
iii) PVA gum. Fluorescent coated paper.		
2½p pink, one centre band	5.00	4.00
3p blue	11.00	10.50
one centre band	3.50	3.00
3½p green	10.00	—
5p violet	25.00	21.50
7½p brown	80.00	70.00
iv) PVAD gum.		
3p blue, one centre band	0.75	—
3½p green (January 23, 1974)	0.35	0.30
one centre band	0.35	0.30
4½p grey-blue (November 6, 1974)	0.35	0.30
5½p deep violet (January 23, 1974)	0.25	0.25
one centre band	0.30	0.30
6½p green-blue (January 14, 1976)		
one centre band	0.35	0.30
7p red-brown (January 18, 1974)		
one centre band	0.35	0.30
8p red (January 23, 1974)	0.35	0.30
8½p green (January 14, 1976)	0.35	0.30
9p violet-blue (January 18, 1978)	0.40	0.35
10p orange (October 20, 1976)	0.45	0.40
one centre band	0.45	0.40
10½p grey-blue (January 18, 1978)	0.40	0.35
11p red (October 20, 1976)	0.40	0.35

B) Phosphor coated paper. PVAD gum. Issued July 23, 1980.

12p yellow-green	0.50	0.40
13½p red-brown	0.50	0.50
15p blue	0.50	0.50

C) Printed in litho by Waddington. Perf 13½ x 14. Phosphor coated paper, except 11½p, 12p, 12½p, 13p (left side band), 22p (advanced coated paper). PVAD gum except 11½p, 12½p (PVA).

11½p mushroom (April 8, 1981)	0.60	0.50
12p emerald-green (January7, 1986)	1.80	1.80
12½p light green (February 24, 1982)	0.50	0.50
13p light brown, type I (Oct 23, 1984)	0.70	0.70
type II	8.00	7.90
14p grey-blue (April 8, 1981)	0.60	0.50
15½p pale-violet (February 24, 1982)	0.60	0.60
16p light mushroom (April 27, 1983)	0.75	0.60
printed by Harrison on advanced coated paper (November 2, 1983)	4.00	3.75
17p steel blue, type I (Oct 23, 1984)	3.00	1.50
type II	0.75	0.75
type II, PVA gum (June 25, 1985)	3.00	3.00
18p violet (April 8, 1981)	0.70	0.70
19½p grey-green (February 24, 1982)	1.40	0.90
20½p bright blue (April 27, 1983)	3.00	3.00
22p deep blue (April 8, 1981)	0.70	0.65
22p yellowish green, type I (Oct 23, 1984)	3.00	2.00
type II	25.00	25.00
26p red, type I (February 24, 1982)	0.80	0.80
28p blue, type I (April 27, 1983)	0.80	0.80
31p purple, type I (October 23, 1984)	1.75	1.65
type II	95.00	85.00

D) Printed in litho by Questa. Perf 15 x 14. One phosphor band (12p, 13p), or as indicated. PVAD gum. All Type II.

12p emerald-green (April 29, 1986)	1.50	1.20
13p light brown (November 4, 1986)	0.70	0.70
printed on paper supplied by Coated Paper Ltd, PVA gum (April 14, 1987)	0.70	0.60
14p deep blue (November 8, 1988)		
one centre band	0.50	0.50
one left band (March 21, 1989)	0.45	0.45
15p bright blue (November 28, 1989)		
one left band	0.60	0.60
17p steel blue (April 29, 1986)	3.00	3.00
18p deep green (January 6, 1987)	1.00	1.00
18p bright green (December 3, 1991)		
one centre band	1.00	1.00
perf. 14 (September 26, 1992)	1.00	0.90
one left band (August 10, 1993)	1.80	1.80
19p orange-red (November 8, 1988)		
phosphor paper	0.50	0.50
two bands (March 21, 1989)	1.00	1.00
20p brownish-black (November 28, 1989)		
phosphor paper	0.65	0.60
22p yellowish-green (January 27, 1987)		
advanced coated paper	0.75	0.80
22p orange-red (December 4, 1990)		
phosphor paper	0.60	0.60
23p bright green (November 8, 1988)		
phosphor paper	0.75	0.75
two bands (March 21, 1989)	10.00	10.00
24p deep red (November 28, 1989)		
phosphor paper	0.80	0.80
24p chestnut (December 3, 1991)		
phosphor paper	1.00	1.00

phosphor paper, perf 14 (October 19, 1992)	5.00	5.00
two bands (August 10, 1993)	2.00	2.00
26p red (January 27, 1987)		
advanced coated paper	2.50	2.50
26p drab (December 4, 1990)		
phosphor paper	0.75	0.75
28p blue (January 27, 1987)		
advanced coated paper	0.80	0.80
28p bluish grey (December 3, 1991)		
phosphor paper	1.00	1.00
phosphor paper, perf 14 (February 18, 1993)	7.00	7.00
31p purple (April 29, 1986)	1.25	1.25
32p greenish blue (November 8, 1988)		
phosphor paper	1.00	1.00
34p bluish grey (November 28, 1989)		
phosphor paper	1.20	1.25
37p rosine (December 4, 1990)		
phosphor paper	1.40	1.35
39p mauve (December 3, 1991)		
phosphor paper	1.40	1.35
phosphor paper, perf: 14 (November 1992)	6.00	6.00

(* The 19p and 23p with two bands come from a prestige stamp book.)

E) Stamps with an elliptical perforation along each vertical side, Printed in litho by Questa. One phosphor band (19p and 20p), or two phosphor bands (others).

19p bistre (December 7, 1993)	0.70	0.75
one right band	1.75	1.75
20p bright green (July 23, 1996)	0.90	0.90
25p red (December 7, 1993)	0.80	0.85
26p red-brown (July 23, 1996)	1.00	1.00
30p olive-grey (December 7, 1993)	1.00	0.90
37p mauve (July 23, 1996)	2.00	2.00
41p grey-brown (December 7, 1993)	1.75	1.80
63p emerald (July 23, 1996)	3.00	3.00

(* The 19p with phosphor band on the right comes from a prestige stamp book.)

F) Stamps with an elliptical perforation along each vertical side. Printed in gravure by Walsall except where stated. One phosphor band (19p and 20p), or two phosphor bands (others).

20p bright green (July 1, 1997)	1.25	1.25
one right band	2.00	2.00
26p chestnut (July 1, 1997)	1.00	1.00
perf: 14	2.00	2.00
printed by Harrison	1.50	1.50
37p mauve (July 1, 1997)	2.00	2.00
printed by Harrison	1.60	1.60
63p emerald (July 1, 1997)	2.50	2.50

(* The 20p with one band at right, the 26p perf 14 and the 26p and 37p printed by Harrison come from prestige stamp books.)

G) Printed in gravure by Walsall. One phosphor band. Issued on February 15, 2000, in a prestige stamp book.

1st orange-red	1.35	1.20

First day cover (2½p, 3p, 5p, 7½p)		1.70
First day cover (3½p, 5½p, 8p)		1.40
First day cover (4½p)		0.80

First day cover (6½p, 8½p)	0.80
First day cover (10p, 11p)	0.80
First day cover (7p, 9p, 10½p)	0.90
First day cover (12p, 13½p, 15p)	1.70
First day cover (11½p, 14p, 18p, 22p)	1.70
First day cover (12½p, 15½p, 19½p, 26p)	2.00
First day cover (16p, 20½p, 28p)	2.00
First day cover (13p, 17p, 22p, 31p)	2.00
First day cover (12p)	1.10
First day cover (12p, 17p, 31p)	1.70
First day cover (13p)	1.10
First day cover (18p)	1.00
First day cover (22p, 26p, 28p)	1.70
First day cover (14p, 19p, 23p, 32p)	2.90
First day cover (15p, 20p, 24p, 34p)	2.90
First day cover (17p, 22p, 26p, 37p)	2.90
First day cover (18p, 24p, 28p, 39p)	2.90
First day cover (19p, 25p, 30p, 41p)	3.50
First day cover (20p, 26p, 37p, 63p)	5.00

Scottish flag (2nd)
Scottish lion (1st)
Thistle (E)
Tartan (64p, 65p, 68p)

■ 1999, June 8. Designs without white borders

Des: A. Morris (2nd), F. Pottinger and T. Chalk (1st, E, 40p, 42p), and all adapted by Tayburn. Printed in litho by Walsall (2nd, 1st, E, 64p, 65p), De La Rue (2nd, 1st and 68p) or Questa (2nd, 1st, E and 65p). One phosphor band (2nd), two phosphor bands (others).

2nd multicoloured (Walsall)	0.90	0.75
2nd multicoloured (De La Rue)	0.90	0.75
2nd multicoloured (Questa)	1.15	1.00
1st multicoloured (Walsall)	1.10	0.80
1st multicoloured (De La Rue)	1.10	0.80
1st multicoloured (Questa)	1.35	1.25
E multicoloured (Walsall)	1.50	1.25
E multicoloured (Questa)	2.00	2.00
64p multicoloured	5.00	5.00
65p multicoloured (Walsall, Apr 25, 2000)	1.80	1.80
65p multicoloured (Questa)	4.00	4.00
68p multicoloured (July 4, 2002)	2.00	2.00
First day cover (2nd, 1st E, 64p)	6.50	6.50
First day cover (65p)	4.50	4.50
First day cover (68p)	2.50	2.50
Stamp cards	6.00	12.50

(*The 2nd, 1st, E and 65p printed by Questa come from prestige stamp books.)

Scottish flag (2nd)
Scottish lion (1st)
Thistle (E, 40p, 42p, 44p, 48p, 50p, 56p, 60p, 87p)
Tartan (68p, 72p, 78p, 81p, 90p, 97p, £1.10, £1.28)

■ 2003, October 14. Designs with white borders

Designs as for June 8, 1999, but with a white border. Printed in gravure by De La Rue (2nd, 1st, E, 40p, 42p, 44p, 48p, 50p, 56p, 60p, 68p, 72p, 78p, 81p, 90p, 97p), in gravure by Walsall (42p), in gravure by Enschedé (2nd, 1st, 50p, 81p), in litho by De La Rue (1st, 78p, 81p), in litho by Enschedé (1st) or in litho by Cartor (68p, 87p, £1.10, £1.28). One phosphor band (2nd) or two phosphor bands (others).

2nd multicoloured	0.90	0.75
1st multicoloured	1.10	0.90
E multicoloured	1.70	1.70
40p multicoloured (May 11, 2004)	1.75	1.75
42p multicoloured (Walsall, Apr 5, 2005)	1.20	1.20
42p multicoloured (May 10, 2005)	1.25	1.20
44p multicoloured (March 28, 2006)	1.25	1.20
48p multicoloured (March 27, 2007)	1.25	1.20
50p multicoloured (April 1, 2008)	1.25	1.20
56p multicoloured (Mar 31, 2009)	1.25	1.20
60p multicoloured (Mar 30, 2010)	1.50	1.50
68p multicoloured		
(Oct 14, 2003, printed by De La Rue)	1.50	1.50
(Mar 29, 2011, printed by Cartor)	1.00	1.00
72p multicoloured (March 28, 2006)	2.00	2.00
78p multicoloured (March 27, 2007)	1.70	1.70
81p multicoloured (April 1, 2008)	1.70	1.70
87p multicoloured (Apr 25, 2012)	1.50	1.50
90p multicoloured (Mar 31, 2009)	1.70	1.70
97p multicoloured (Mar 30, 2010)	1.75	1.75
£1.10 multicoloured (Mar 29, 2011)	1.50	1.50
£1.28 multicoloured (Apr 25, 2012)	2.50	2.50
First day cover (2nd, 1st, E, 68p)		6.50
First day cover (40p)		2.50
First day cover (42p)		2.50
First day cover (44p, 72p)		2.50
First day cover (48p, 78p)		3.50
First day cover (50p, 81p)		3.50
First day cover (56p, 90p)		3.00
First day cover (60p, 97p)		3.50
First day cover (68p, £1.10)		4.00
First day cover (87p, £1.28)		5.00
Stamp cards	2.00	10.00

(*Values in this series have also appeared in miniature sheets and prestige stamp books. The 1st class also exists, self-adhesive, in generic Smilers sheets.)

WALES

3d lilac
6d purple
1/3 green

3p blue

■ 1958-1967
Des: Reynolds Stone.
A) Wmk: Multiple St Edward's Crown. Non phosphor except where stated.

3d lilac (August 18, 1958)	0.15	0.15
one centre band	0.15	0.20
4d blue (February 7, 1966)	0.20	0.15
two phosphor bands	0.15	0.15
6d purple (September 29, 1958)	0.30	0.25
9d green (March 1, 1967)		
two phosphor bands	0.35	0.30
1/3 green (September 29, 1958)	0.45	0.40
1/6 grey-blue (March 1, 1967)		
two phosphor bands	0.40	0.30
First day cover (3d)		10.00
First day cover (6d, 1/3)		20.00
First day cover (4d)		7.50
First day cover (9d, 1/6)		2.75

B) No watermark, Two phosphor bands except where stated.
i) Gum Arabic.

3d lilac, one centre band	0.20	0.20
ii) PVA gum		
4d blue	0.20	0.30
4d sepia (September 4, 1968)		
one centre band	0.15	0.15
4d red (February 26, 1969)		
one centre band	0.40	0.15
5d blue (September 4, 1968)	0.30	0.25
1/6 grey-blue	2.00	2.00
First day cover (4d sepia, 5d)		2.50
First day cover (4d red)		1.00

■ 1971, July 7. Decimal Currency
Des: J. Matthews. The dragon symbol was re-drawn. On type I the eye is a circle, while the tongue, claws and tail are thin. On type II the eye is solid, while the tongue, claws and tail are thick.

A) Two phosphor bands except where stated.

i) **2½p** pink, one centre band	0.35	-
3p blue	0.75	-
ii) PVA gum. Original coated paper.		
2½p pink, one centre band	0.25	0.30
3p blue	0.25	0.30
5p violet	1.00	1.00
7½p brown	1.00	1.00
iii) PVA gum. Fluorescent coated paper.		
2½p pink, one centre band	2.25	2.00
3p blue	9.00	7.00
3p blue, one centre band	0.35	0.30
5p violet	18.00	18.00
iv) PVAD gum.		
3½p green (January 23, 1974)	0.30	0.25
one centre band	0.30	0.25
4½p grey-blue (November 6, 1974)	0.35	0.30
5½p deep violet (January 23, 1974)	0.30	0.25
one centre band	0.30	0.30
6½p green-blue (January 14, 1976)		
one centre band	0.35	0.35
7p red-brown (January 18, 1978)		
one centre band	0.35	0.30
8p red (January 23, 1974)	0.40	0.35
8½p green (January 14, 1976)	0.40	0.35
9p violet-blue (January 18, 1978)	0.40	0.35
10p orange (October 20, 1976)	0.40	0.35
one centre band	0.40	0.35
10½p grey-blue (January 18, 1978)	0.45	0.40
11p red (October 20, 1976)	0.45	0.40

B) Phosphor coated paper. PVAD gum. Issued on July 23, 1980.

12p yellow-green	0.50	0.50

13½p red-brown — 0.50 / 0.50
15p blue — 0.50 / 0.50

C) Printed in litho by Questa. Perf 13½ x 14. Phosphor coated paper, except 11½p and 12½p (left side band). PVA gum (11½p, 14p, 18p, 22p). PVAD gum (others).

11½p mushroom (April 8, 1981)	0.60	0.60
12½p light green (February 24, 1982)	0.50	0.40
14p steel-blue (April 8, 1981)	0.50	0.50
15½p pale-violet (February 24, 1982)	0.70	0.60
16p light mushroom (April 27, 1983)	1.00	1.00
18p mauve (April 8, 1981)	0.70	0.75
19½p grey-green (February 24, 1982)	1.00	1.40
20½p bright blue (April 27, 1983)	2.00	2.00
22p deep blue (April 8, 1981)	0.70	0.70
26p red, type I (February 24, 1982	0.80	0.75
28p blue, type I (April 27, 1983)	0.80	0.95

D) Printed in litho by Questa. Perf 15 x 14. One side phosphor band (12p, 12½p, 13p), or as indicated. PVAD gum.

12p emerald-green (January 7, 1986)	1.75	1.75
12½p light green (January 10, 1984)	5.00	5.00
13p reddish-brown (Oct 23, 1984)		
type I	0.65	0.60
deep brown, type II	2.75	2.75
deep brown (April 14, 1987),		
on paper supplied by Coated Papers		
Ltd, PVA gum, type II	2.50	2.50
14p deep blue (November 8, 1988)	0.60	0.60
15p bright blue (November 28, 1989)	0.90	0.90
16p light mushroom (January 10, 1984)		
phosphor coated paper	1.75	1.75
17p steel-blue (October 23, 1984)		
type I, phosphor coated paper	1.00	1.00
type I, fluorescent brightener omitted	0.90	1.90
type I, advanced coated paper	1.25	1.25
type II	40.00	40.00
17p deep blue (December 4, 1990)		
one centre band	0.60	0.90
18p deep green (January 6, 1987)	0.95	0.60
18p bright green (December 3, 1991)		
one centre band	0.90	0.45
left band	2.00	1.50
right band	1.50	1.50
18p bright green (January 12, 1993)		
perf: 14	4.00	4.00
19p orange-red (November 8, 1988)		
phosphor paper	0.95	0.75
20p brownish-black (November 28, 1989)		
phosphor paper	0.90	0.60
22p yellowish-green (Oct 23, 1984)		
advanced coated paper	1.00	0.75
22p orange-red (December 4, 1990)		
phosphor paper	0.95	0.65
23p bright green (November 8, 1988)		
phosphor paper	1.50	0.80
24p deep red (November 28, 1989)		
phosphor paper	1.50	0.90
24p chestnut (December 3, 1991)		
phosphor paper	1.25	0.80

24p chestnut (February 25, 1992)		
two bands	1.25	1.10
24p chestnut (September 14, 1992)		
phosphor paper, perf: 14	3.00	2.00
26p red, type II (January 27, 1987)		
advanced coated paper	4.50	3.50
26p drab (December 4, 1990)		
phosphor paper	1.50	0.95
28p blue, type II (January 27, 1987)		
advanced coated paper	1.50	1.05
28p bluish grey (December 3, 1991)		
phosphor paper	1.50	0.95
31p purple (October 23, 1984)		
phosphor coated paper	1.50	0.95
advanced coated paper (Jan 27, 1987)	2.00	1.00
32p greenish blue (November 8, 1988)		
phosphor paper	1.75	1.20
34p bluish grey (November 28, 1989)		
phosphor paper	1.50	1.20
37p rosine (December 4, 1990)		
phosphor paper	1.75	1.35
39p mauve (December 3, 1991)		
phosphor paper	1.90	1.35

(* The 18p with one band at left or right comes from prestige stamp books.)

E) Stamps with an elliptical perforation along each vertical side. Printed in litho by Questa. One phosphor band (19p and 20p), two phosphor bands (others).

19p bistre (December 7, 1993)	0.75	0.70
19p bistre, right band	2.25	2.25
20p bright green (July 23, 1996)	1.25	1.25
25p red (December 7, 1993)	0.85	0.80
26p red-brown (July 23, 1996)	1.25	1.25
30p olive-grey (December 7, 1993)	1.00	0.95
37p mauve (July 23, 1996)	2.50	2.50
41p grey-brown (December 7, 1993)	1.80	1.80
63p emerald (July 23, 1996)	2.75	2.75

(* The 19p with phosphor band to right comes from a prestige stamp book.)

F) Stamps with an elliptical perforation along each vertical side. Printed in gravure by Walsall. One phosphor band (19p and 20p), two phosphor bands (others). These stamps do not have the 'p' following the denomination.

20p bright green (July 1, 1997)	1.00	1.00
20p bright green, right band	2.50	2.00
26p chestnut (July 1, 1997)	0.90	0.90
26p chestnut, perf: 14	2.50	2.55
26p chestnut, printed by Harrison	2.00	2.00
37p mauve (July 1, 1997)	1.50	1.50
37p mauve, printed by Harrison	1.50	1.50
63p emerald (July 1, 1997)	2.75	2.75

(* The 20p with one band at right and the 26p with perf: 14 come from prestige stamp books. The 26p and 37p printed by Harrison comes from a prestige stamp book.)

G) Printed in gravure by Walsall. One phosphor band. Issued on February 15, 2000, in a prestige stamp book.

1st orange-red — 2.00 / 2.00

First day cover (2½p, 3p, 5p, 7½p)	1.70
First day cover (3½p, 5½p, 8p)	1.40
First day cover (4½p)	0.80
First day cover (6½p, 8½p)	0.80
First day cover (10p, 11p)	0.90
First day cover (7p, 9p, 10½p)	0.90
First day cover (12p 13½p, 15p)	1.70
First day cover (11½p, 14p, 18p, 22p)	1.40
First day cover (12½p, 15½p. 19½p, 26p)	2.00
First day cover (16p, 20½p, 28p)	2.00
First day cover (12p, 17p, 22p, 31p)	2.00
First day cover (12p)	1.00
First day cover (18p)	1.00
First day cover (14p, 19p, 23p, 32p)	2.90
First day cover (15p, 20p, 24p, 34p)	2.90
First day cover (17p, 22p, 26p, 37p)	2.90
First day cover (18p, 24p, 28p, 39p)	3.00
First day cover (19p, 25p, 30p, 41p)	3.50
First day cover (20p, 26p, 37p, 63p)	5.00

Leek (2nd)
Welsh dragon (1st)
Daffodil (E)
Prince of Wales' feathers (64p, 65p, 68p)

■ 1999, June 8. Designs without white borders

Des: D. Petersen (2nd), T. and G. Petersen (1st), I. Rees (E, 40p, 42p), R. Evans (64p, 65p, 68p), and all adapted by Tutssels. Printed in litho by Walsall (2nd, 1st, E, 64p, 65p) or De La Rue (68p). One phosphor band (2nd), two phosphor bands (others).

2nd multicoloured	0.90	0.80
2nd multicoloured, one right band	3.35	3.00
1st multicoloured	1.20	0.95
E multicoloured	1.50	1.20
64p multicoloured	6.00	6.00
65p multicoloured (April 25, 2000)	3.00	3.00
68p multicoloured (July 4, 2002)	3.00	3.00
First day cover (2nd, 1st, E, 64p)		6.50
First day cover (65p)		4.50
First day cover (68p)		2.50

(* The 2nd class with band at right comes from the Treasury of Trees prestige stamp book.)

Leek (2nd)
Welsh dragon (1st)
Daffodil (E, 40p, 42p, 44p, 48p, 50p, 56p, 60p, 87p)
Prince of Wales' feathers (68p, 72p, 78p, 81p, 90p, 97p, £1.10, £1.28)

■ 2003, October 14. Designs with white borders

Designs as for June 8, 1999, but with a white border. Printed in gravure by De La Rue (2nd, 1st, E, 40p, 42p, 44p, 48p, 50p, 56p, 60p, 68p, 72p, 78p, 81p, 90p, 97p), in gravure by Walsall (42p), in litho by De La Rue (1st, 78p, 81p), in litho by Enschedé (1st) or in litho by Cartor (68p, 87p, £1.10, £1.28). One phosphor band (2nd) or two phosphor bands (others).

2nd multicoloured	0.80	0.70
1st multicoloured	1.10	0.90
E multicoloured	1.70	1.70
40p multicoloured (May 11, 2004)	1.70	1.90
42p multicoloured (Walsall, Apr 5, 2005)	1.25	1.25
42p multicoloured (May 10, 2005)	1.25	1.25
44p multicoloured (March 28, 2006)	1.30	1.30
48p multicoloured (March 27, 2007)	1.30	1.30
50p multicoloured (April 1, 2008)	1.30	1.30
56p multicoloured (Mar 31, 2009)	1.30	1.30
60p multicoloured (Mar 30, 2010)	1.50	1.50
68p multicoloured		
(Oct 14, 2003, printed by De La Rue)	1.75	1.75
(Mar 29, 2011, printed by Cartor)	1.00	1.00
72p multicoloured (March 28, 2006)	2.00	2.00
78p multicoloured (March 27, 2007)	1.75	1.75
81p multicoloured (April 1, 2008)	1.75	1.75
87p multicoloured (Apr 25, 2012)	1.50	1.50
90p multicoloured (Mar 31, 2009)	1.75	1.75
97p multicoloured (Mar 30, 2010)	1.75	1.75
£1.10 multicoloured (Mar 29, 2011)	1.50	1.50
£1.28 multicoloured (Apr 25, 2012)	2.50	2.50
First day cover (2nd, 1st, E, 68p)		3.50
First day cover (40p)		2.50
First day cover (42p)		1.40
First day cover (44p, 72p)		2.50
First day cover (48p, 78p)		3.25
First day cover (50p, 81p)		3.50
First day cover (56p, 90p)		3.00
First day cover (60p, 97p)		3.50
First day cover (68p, £1.10)		4.00
First day cover (87p, £1.28)		5.00
Stamp cards	2.00	8.00

(* Values in this series have also appeared in miniature sheets and prestige stamp books. The 1st class also exists, self-adhesive, in generic Smilers sheets.)

Missed an Issue?

Available from myHobbystore.co.uk

Have you missed a copy of your favourite Stamp Magazine? You can now order these online, over the phone or by post!

JUST £3.55 PER COPY*

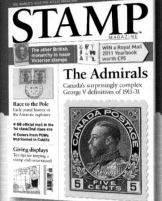

ONLY £8.50!*

ALSO AVAILABLE

You can also get this great **STAMP MAGAZINE** branded binder to keep all of your magazines safe and tidy!

* Plus P&P

Phone: 0844 848 8822

(Phone lines open: Mon-Fri 10am – 4pm)

Order Online: www.myhobbystore.co.uk/stampmags

STITCHED BOOKLETS

In this section, items are priced in mint condition only.

EDWARD VII, 1904-10

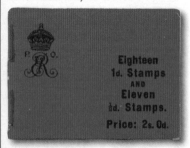

■ 2/- booklets

24 × 1d (sold at 2s ½d). Printed by De La Rue, 1904	£250
12 × 1d, 23 × ½d. Printed by De La Rue, 1906	£1,350
18 × 1d, 11 × ½d. Printed by De La Rue, 1907-09	£1,400
18 × 1d, 11 × ½d. Printed by Harrison, 1911	£1,600

GEORGE V, 1910-35

■ 2/- booklets, Downey head

18 × 1d, 12 × ½d. Wmk: Imperial Crown
printed by Harrison, 1911	£1,000

18 × 1d, 12 × ½d. Wmk: Simple Royal Cypher
printed by Harrison, 1912	£900

■ 2/- booklets, Mackennal head

18 × 1d, 12 × ½d. Wmk: Simple Royal Cypher
printed by Harrison, 1913; stamps of 1911-1913	£800

10 × 1½d, 6 × 1d, 6 × ½d. Wmk: Simple Royal Cypher
printed by Harrison, 1924	£1,750

10 × 1½d, 6 × 1d, 6 × ½d. Wmk: Block GVR
printed by Waterlow, 1924	£650

10 × 1½d, 6 × 1d, 6 × ½d.
printed by Waterlow, 1929; PUC stamps	£400

10 × 1½d, 6 × 1d, 6 × ½d. Wmk: Block GVR
printed by Harrison, 1934	£700

10 × 1½d, 6 × 1d, 6 × ½d. Wmk: Block GVR
printed by Harrison, 1935; photogravure, intermediate	£2,000

10 × 1½d, 6 × 1d, 6 × ½d. Wmk: Block GVR
printed by Harrison, 1935; photogravure, small format	£500

12 × 1½d, 4 × 1d, 4 × ½d
printed by Harrison, 1935; Silver Jubilee stamps	70.00

■ 3/- booklets

12 × 1½d, 12 × 1d, 12 × ½d. Wmk: Simple Royal Cypher
printed by Harrison, 1918	£1,000

18 × 1½d, 6 × 1d, 6 × ½d. Wmk: Simple Royal Cypher
printed by Harrison, 1919	£1,000

18 × 2d
printed by Harrison, 1921	£1,750

24 × 1½d
printed by Harrison, 1922	£1,800

18 × 1½d, 6 × 1d, 6 × ½d. Wmk: Block GVR
printed by Waterlow, 1924	£475

18 × 1½d, 6 × 1d, 6 × ½d
printed by Waterlow, 1929; PUC stamps	£325

18 × 1½d, 6 × 1d, 6 × ½d. Wmk: Block GVR
printed by Harrison, 1934	£525

18 × 1½d, 6 × 1d, 6 × ½d. Wmk: Block GVR
printed by Harrison, 1935; photogravure, intermediate	£1,750

18 × 1½d, 6 × 1d, 6 × ½d. Wmk: Block GVR
printed by Harrison, 1935; photogravure, small format	£425

20 × 1½d, 4 × 1d, 4 × ½d
printed by Harrison, 1935; Silver Jubilee stamps	60.00

■ 3/6 booklets

18 × 2d, 6 × 1d
printed by Harrison, 1920	£1,400

12 × 2d, 6 × 1½d, 6 × 1d, 6 × ½d
printed by Harrison, 1921	£1,400

■ 5/- booklets

34 × 1½d, 6 × 1d, 6 × ½d. Green cover
printed by Waterlow, 1931	£4,600

34 × 1½d, 6 × 1d, 6 × ½d. Buff cover
printed by Waterlow, 1932	£3,600

34 × 1½d, 6 × 1d, 6 × ½d
printed by Harrison, 1934	£1,600

34 × 1½d, 6 × 1d, 6 × ½d
printed by Harrison, 1935; photogravure, intermediate	£4,500

34 × 1½d, 6 × 1d, 6 × ½d
printed by Harrison, 1935; photogravure, small format	£450

EDWARD VIII, 1936

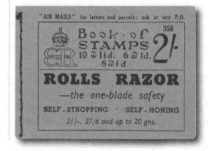

■ 6d booklets
4 x 1½d (plain cover). Printed by Harrison, 1936   30.00

■ 2/- booklets
10 x 1½d, 6 x 1d, 6 x ½d. Printed by Harrison, 1936   90.00

■ 3/- booklets
18 x 1½d, 6 x 1d, 6 x ½d. Printed by Harrison, 1936   80.00

■ 5/- booklets
34 x 1½d, 6 x 1d, 6 x ½d. Printed by Harrison, 1936   £185

GEORGE VI, 1937-52

■ 6d booklets
4 x 1½d (plain buff cover)
printed by Harrison, 1938   50.00
2 x 1½d, 2 x 1d, 2 x ½d (plain pink cover)
printed by Harrison, 1938   £225
4 x 1d, 4 x ½d (plain green cover)
printed by Harrison, 1940   80.00

■ 1/- booklets
4 x 1½d, 4 x 1d, 4 x ½d (in panes of two)
printed by Harrison, 1947; stamps in pale shades   15.00
4 x 1½d, 4 x 1d, 4 x ½d (in panes of four)
printed by Harrison, 1948; stamps in pale shades   £6,000
4 x 1½d, 4 x 1d, 4 x ½d (in panes of two)
printed by Harrison, 1951; stamps in changed colours   15.00
4 x 1½d, 4 x 1d, 4 x ½d (in panes of four)
printed by Harrison, 1951; stamps in changed colours   15.00

■ 2/- booklets
10 x 1½d, 6 x 1d, 6 x ½d (royal cypher on cover)
printed by Harrison, 1937   £650
10 x 1½d, 6 x 1d, 6 x ½d (GPO cypher on cover)
printed by Harrison, 1938   £650

■ 2/6 booklets
6 x 2½d, 6 x 2d, 6 x ½d (red cover)
printed by Harrison, 1940   £1,000
6 x 2½d, 6 x 2d, 6 x ½d (blue cover)
printed by Harrison, 1940   £1,000
6 x 2½d, 6 x 2d, 6 x ½d (green cover)
printed by Harrison, 1940   £750
6 x 2½d, 6 x 2d, 6 x ½d (green cover)
printed by Harrison, 1942; stamps in pale shades   £750

6 x 2½d, 6 x 2d, 6 x ½d (green cover, no advertising)
printed by Harrison, 1943; stamps in pale shades   85.00
6 x 2½d, 6 x 2d, 6 x ½d (green cover, no advertising)
printed by Harrison, 1951; stamps in changed colours   40.00
6 x 2½d, 6 x 1½d, 3 x 1d, 6 x ½d
printed by Harrison, 1952   30.00

■ 3/- booklets
18 x 1½d, 6 x 1d, 6 x ½d (royal cypher on cover)
printed by Harrison, 1937   £1,100
18 x 1½d, 6 x 1d, 6 x ½d (GPO cypher on cover)
printed by Harrison, 1938   £1,100

■ 5/- booklets
34 x 1½d, 6 x 1d, 6 x ½d (royal cypher on cover)
printed by Harrison, 1937   £1,400
34 x 1½d, 6 x 1d, 6 x ½d (GPO cypher on cover)
printed by Harrison, 1938   £1,400
18 x 2½d, 6 x 2d, 6 x ½d (GPO cypher on cover)
printed by Harrison, 1940   £1,400
18 x 2½d, 6 x 2d, 6 x ½d (GPO cypher on cover)
printed by Harrison, 1942; stamps in pale shades   £1,400
18 x 2½d, 6 x 2d, 6 x ½d (GPO cypher, no advertising)
printed by Harrison, 1944; stamps in pale shades   £100
18 x 2½d, 6 x 2d, 6 x ½d (GPO cypher, no advertising)
printed by Harrison, 1951; stamps in changed colours   50.00
18 x 2½d, 6 x 1½d, 3 x 1d, 6 x ½d
printed by Harrison, 1952   35.00
12 x 2½d, 6 x 2d, 6 x 1½d, 6 x 1d, 6 x ½d
printed by Harrison, 1953   45.00

ELIZABETH II WILDINGS, 1953-68

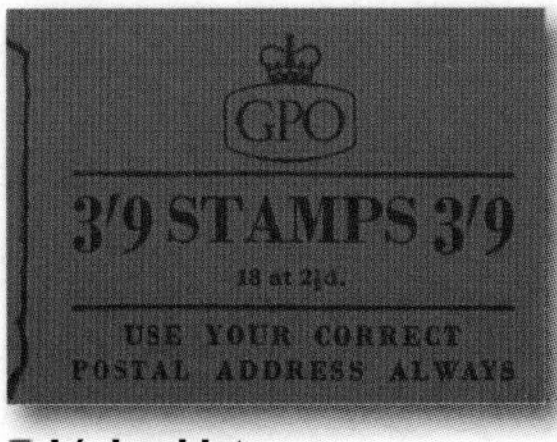

■ 1/- booklets
4 x 1½d, 4 x 1d, 4 x ½d (panes of 2). Wmk: Tudor Crown
printed by Harrison, 1953   5.00
4 x 1½d, 4 x 1d, 4 x ½d (panes of 4). Wmk: Tudor Crown
printed by Harrison, 1954   5.00
4 x 1½d, 4 x 1d, 4 x ½d (panes of 2). Wmk: St. Edward's Crown
printed by Harrison, 1957   30.00
4 x 1½d, 4 x 1d, 4 x ½d (panes of 4). Wmk: St. Edward's Crown
printed by Harrison, 1956   5.00
4 x 1½d, 4 x 1d, 4 x ½d (panes of 4). Wmk: Multiple Crowns
printed by Harrison, 1959   5.00

■ 2/- booklets
4 x 3d, 4 x 1½d, 4 x 1d, 4 x ½d. Wmk: St. Edward's Crown
printed by Harrison, 1959; pink cover   4.00
4 x 3d, 4 x 1½d, 4 x 1d, 4 x ½d. Wmk: Multiple Crowns (upright)
printed by Harrison, 1960; pink cover   6.00

4 x 3d, 4 x 1½d, 4 x 1d, 4 x ½d. Wmk: Multiple Crowns (upright)
printed by Harrison, 1961; yellow cover 6.00

4 x 3d, 4 x 1½d, 4 x 1d, 4 x ½d. Wmk: Multiple Crowns (sideways)
printed by Harrison, 1961-62; yellow cover 25.00

4 x 3d, 4 x 1½d, 4 x 1d, 4 x ½d. Wmk: Multiple Crowns (sideways)
printed by Harrison, 1961-65; yellow cover; phos bands 50.00

4 x 4d, 2 x 1d se-tenant with 2 x 3d. Wmk: Multiple Crowns
printed by Harrison, 1965-67; 3d with no phos bands 3.00

4 x 4d, 2 x 1d se-tenant with 2 x 3d. Wmk: Multiple Crowns
printed by Harrison, 1965-67; 3d with one phos band 8.00

4 x 4d, 2 x 1d se-tenant with 2 x 3d. Wmk: Multiple Crowns
printed by Harrison, 1965-67; 3d with two phos bands 2.00

8 x 2½d, 3 x ½d se-tenant with 1 x 2½d. Wmk: Multiple Crowns
printed by Harrison, 1963 3.00

8 x ½d, 8 x 2½d (se-tenant in panes). Wmk: Multiple Crowns
printed by Harrison, 1964 2.00

8 x 3d. Wmk: Multiple Crowns (sideways)
printed by Harrison, 1965 1.00

■ 2/6 booklets

6 x 2½d, 6 x 1½d (QEII), 3 x 1d, 6 x ½d (KGVI)
printed by Harrison, 1953-54 30.00

6 x 2½d, 6 x 1½d, 6 x ½d (QEII), 3 x 1d (KGVI)
printed by Harrison, 1954 £400

6 x 2½d, 6 x 1½d, 6 x 1d. Wmk: Tudor Crown
printed by Harrison, 1954-55 40.00

6 x 2½d, 6 x 1½d, 6 x 1d. Wmk: St Edward's Crown
printed by Harrison, 1955-57 25.00

6 x 2½d, 6 x 2d, 6 x ½d, Wmk: St Edward's Crown
printed by Harrison, 1957 22.00

■ 3/- booklets

6 x 3d, 6 x 1½d, 6 x 1d, 6 x ½d. Wmk: St Edward's Crown
printed by Harrison, 1958 16.00

6 x 3d, 6 x 1½d, 6 x 1d, 6 x ½d. Wmk: Multiple Crowns
printed by Harrison, 1958-59 22.00

6 x 3d, 6 x 1½d, 6 x 1d, 6 x ½d. Wmk: Multiple Crowns
printed by Harrison, 1959-60; stamps with graphite lines £180

6 x 3d, 6 x 1½d, 6 x 1d, 6 x ½d. Wmk: Multiple Crowns
printed by Harrison, 1960-65; stamps with phos bands 50.00

■ 3/9 booklets

18 x 2½d. Wmk: Tudor Crown
printed by Harrison, 1953-55 22.00

18 x 2½d. Wmk: St Edward's Crown
printed by Harrison, 1956-57 18.00

■ 4/6 booklets

18 x 3d. Wmk: St Edward's Crown
printed by Harrison, 1957-58 18.00

18 x 3d. Wmk: Multiple Crowns
printed by Harrison, 1959 20.00

18 x 3d. Wmk: Multiple Crowns
printed by Harrison, 1959-60; stamps with graphite lines 15.00

18 x 3d. Wmk: Multiple Crowns
printed by Harrison, 1960-65; stamps with phos bands 35.00

12 x 4d, 6 x 1d. Wmk: Multiple Crowns
printed by Harrison, 1965-67 18.00

12 x 4d, 6 x 1d. Wmk: Multiple Crowns
printed by Harrison, 1965-68; stamps with phos bands 7.00

■ 5/- booklets

12 x 2½d, 6 x 1½d (QEII), 6 x 2d, 6 x 1d, 6 x ½d (KGVI)
printed by Harrison, 1953-54 30.00

12 x 2½d, 6 x 1½d, 6 x ½d (QEII), 6 x 2d, 6 x 1d (KGVI)
printed by Harrison, 1954 £275

12 x 2½d, 6 x 1½d, 6 x ½d, 6 x 1d (QEII), 6 x 2d (KGVI)
printed by Harrison, 1954 £150

12 x 2½d, 6 x 1½d, 6 x ½d, 6 x 1d, 6 x 2d. Wmk: Tudor Crown
printed by Harrison, 1954-55 50.00

12 x 2½d, 6 x 1½d, 6 x ½d, 6 x 1d, 6 x 2d. Wmk: St Edward's
printed by Harrison, 1955-57 25.00

12 x 3d, 6 x 2½d, 6 x 1½d, 6 x ½d. Wmk: St Edward's Crown
printed by Harrison, 1958 18.00

12 x 3d, 6 x 2½d, 6 x 1½d, 6 x ½d. Wmk: Multiple Crowns
printed by Harrison, 1959-65 30.00

12 x 3d, 6 x 2½d, 6 x 1½d, 6 x ½d. Wmk: Multiple Crowns
printed by Harrison, 1959-60; stamps with graphite lines £100

12 x 3d, 6 x 2½d, 6 x 1½d, 6 x ½d. Wmk: Multiple Crowns
printed by Harrison, 1960-62; 2½d with two phos bands £150

12 x 3d, 6 x 2½d, 6 x 1½d, 6 x ½d. Wmk: Multiple Crowns
printed by Harrison, 1962-65; 2½d with one phos band £100

■ 6/- booklets

18 x 4d. Wmk: Multiple Crowns
printed by Harrison, 1965-67 24.00

18 x 4d. Wmk: Multiple Crowns
printed by Harrison, 1965-67; stamps with phos bands 35.00

■ 10/- booklets

30 x 3d, 6 x 2d, 6 x 1½d, 6 x 1d, 6 x ½d
printed by Harrison, 1961 £100

30 x 3d, 6 x 2½d, 6 x 1½d, 6 x 1d
printed by Harrison, 1962-64 90.00

24 x 4d, 6 x 3d, 6 x 1d
printed by Harrison, 1965-66 25.00

24 x 4d, 6 x 3d, 6 x 1d
printed by Harrison, 1967; 3d with side phos band8.00

24 x 4d, 6 x 3d, 6 x 1d
printed by Harrison, 1967-68; 3d with centre phos band 5.00

ELIZABETH II PRE-DECIMAL MACHINS, 1968-70

■ 2/- booklets

4 x 4d sepia (two phos bands), 2 x 1d se-tenant with 2 x 3d (two phos bands)
printed by Harrison, 1968; yellow cover 0.80

4 x 4d sepia (two phos bands), plus 2 x 4d sepia (centre

phos band) se-tenant with two labels
printed by Harrison, 1968-70; grey cover   0.65
4 x 4d sepia (centre phos band), plus 2 x 4d sepia (centre
phos band) se-tenant with two labels
printed by Harrison, 1968-69; grey cover   0.65
4 x 4d red (centre phos band) plus 2 x 4d red (centre
phos band) se-tenant with two labels
printed by Harrison, 1969-70; grey cover   2.00

■ 4/6 booklets. Ships series
6 x 4d sepia, 6 x 4d sepia (two phos bands), 6 x 1d
printed by Harrison, 1968; blue plain cover   6.00
6 x 4d sepia, 6 x 4d sepia (two phos bands), 6 x 1d
printed by Harrison, 1968; Cutty Sark cover   1.80
6 x 4d sepia, 6 x 4d sepia (centre phos band), 6 x 1d
printed by Harrison, 1968; Golden Hind cover   2.00
6 x 4d sepia, 6 x 4d sepia (centre phos band), 6 x 1d
printed by Harrison, 1968; Discovery cover   2.00
6 x 4d red, 6 x 4d red (centre phos band), 6 x 1d
printed by Harrison, 1969; Queen Elizabeth 2 cover   3.00
6 x 4d red, 6 x 4d red (centre phos band), 6 x 1d
printed by Harrison, 1969; Sirius cover   2.50
6 x 4d red, 6 x 4d red (centre phos band), 6 x 1d
printed by Harrison, 1969; Dreadnought cover   3.50
6 x 4d red, 6 x 4d red (centre phos band), 6 x 1d
printed by Harrison, 1969-70; Mauretania cover   4.00
6 x 4d red, 6 x 4d red (centre phos band), 6 x 1d
printed by Harrison, 1970; Victory cover   4.00
6 x 4d red, 6 x 4d red (centre phos band), 6 x 1d
printed by Harrison, 1970; Sovereign on the Seas cover   4.00

■ 5/- booklets. English Homes series
6 x 5d, 6 x 5d
printed by Harrison, 1968; Ightham Mote cover   2.00
6 x 5d, 6 x 5d
printed by Harrison, 1969; Little Moreton Hall cover   2.00
6 x 5d, 6 x 5d
printed by Harrison, 1969; Long Melford Hall cover   2.50
6 x 5d, 6 x 5d
printed by Harrison, 1969; Mompesson House cover   2.50
6 x 5d, 6 x 5d
printed by Harrison, 1970; Cumberland Terrace cover   2.50
6 x 5d, 6 x 5d
printed by Harrison, 1970; Vineyard, Saffron Walden cover   2.50
6 x 5d, 6 x 5d
printed by Harrison, 1970; Mereworth Castle cover   4.00
6 x 5d, 6 x 5d
printed by Harrison, 1970; Philympia 1970 cover   1.50

■ 6/- booklets. Birds series
6 x 4d sepia, 6 x 4d sepia, 6 x 4d sepia (phos bands), gum arabic
printed by Harrison, 1967-68; plain purple cover   28.00
6 x 4d sepia, 6 x 4d sepia, 6 x 4d sepia (phos bands), PVA gum
printed by Harrison, 1970; plain purple cover   £250
6 x 4d sepia, 6 x 4d sepia, 6 x 4d sepia (two phos bands)
printed by Harrison, 1968; Kingfisher cover   2.00
6 x 4d sepia, 6 x 4d sepia, 6 x 4d sepia (two phos bands)
printed by Harrison, 1968; Peregrine Falcon cover   1.80
6 x 4d sepia, 6 x 4d sepia, 6 x 4d sepia (centre phos band)
printed by Harrison, 1968; Peregrine Falcon cover   2.00

6 x 4d sepia, 6 x 4d sepia, 6 x 4d sepia (centre phos band)
printed by Harrison, 1968; Pied Woodpecker cover   2.00
6 x 4d sepia, 6 x 4d sepia, 6 x 4d sepia (centre phos band)
printed by Harrison, 1968; Great Crested Grebe cover   2.25
6 x 4d sepia, 6 x 4d sepia, 6 x 4d sepia (centre phos band)
printed by Harrison, 1969; Barn Owl cover   3.00
6 x 4d red, 6 x 4d red, 6 x 4d red (centre phos band)
printed by Harrison, 1969; Barn Owl cover   3.00
6 x 4d red, 6 x 4d red, 6 x 4d red (centre phos band)
printed by Harrison, 1969; Jay cover   3.00
6 x 4d red, 6 x 4d red, 6 x 4d red (centre phos band)
printed by Harrison, 1969; Puffin cover   3.00
6 x 4d red, 6 x 4d red, 6 x 4d red (centre phos band)
printed by Harrison, 1969-70; Cormorant cover   4.00
6 x 4d red, 6 x 4d red, 6 x 4d red (centre phos band)
printed by Harrison, 1970; Wren cover   4.00
6 x 4d red, 6 x 4d red, 6 x 4d red (centre phos band)
printed by Harrison, 1970; Golden Eagle cover   4.00

■ 10/- booklets. Explorers series
6 x 4d sepia, 6 x 4d sepia, 6 x 4d sepia, 6 x 4d sepia (two
phos bands), 6 x 3d, 6 x 1d
printed by Harrison, 1968; Livingstone cover   5.50
6 x 5d, 6 x 5d, 6 x 4d sepia, 6 x 4d sepia (centre phos band),
4 x 1d se-tenant with 2 x 4d sepia (one phos band)
printed by Harrison, 1968; Scott cover   4.00
6 x 5d, 6 x 5d, 6 x 4d red, 6 x 4d red (centre phos band),
4 x 1d se-tenant with 2 x 4d red (one phos band)
printed by Harrison, 1969; Kingsley cover   3.50
6 x 5d, 6 x 5d, 6 x 4d red, 6 x 4d red (centre phos band),
4 x 1d se-tenant with 2 x 4d red (one phos band)
printed by Harrison, 1969; Shackleton cover   5.00
6 x 5d, 6 x 5d, 6 x 4d red, 6 x 4d red (centre phos band),
4 x 1d se-tenant with 2 x 4d red (one phos band)
printed by Harrison, 1970; Frobisher cover   6.00
6 x 5d, 6 x 5d, 6 x 4d red, 6 x 4d red (centre phos band),
4 x 1d se-tenant with 2 x 4d red (one phos band)
printed by Harrison, 1970; Cook cover   6.00

ELIZABETH II DECIMAL MACHINS, 1971-76

■ 10p booklets. Pillar box series
2 x ½p, 2 x 1p, 2 x 1½p, 2 x 2p
printed by Harrison, 1971; London's first box 1855 cover   1.50
2 x ½p, 2 x 1p, 2 x 1½p, 2 x 2p
printed by Harrison, 1971; Pillar box 1856 cover   1.50
2 x ½p, 2 x 1p, 2 x 1½p, 2 x 2p
printed by Harrison, 1971; Urban pillar box 1857 cover   3.00

2 x ½p, 2 x 1p, 2 x 1½p, 2 x 2p
printed by Harrison, 1971-72; Penfold box 1866 cover   3.50
2 x ½p, 2 x 1p, 2 x 1½p, 2 x 2p
printed by Harrison, 1972; Double-aperture 1899 cover   2.50
2 x ½p, 2 x 1p, 2 x 1½p, 2 x 2p
printed by Harrison, 1972; Mellor type 1968 cover   2.50
2 x ½p, 2 x 1p, 2 x 1½p, 2 x 2p
printed by Harrison, 1973; KEVIII type 1936 cover   2.50
2 x ½p, 2 x 1p, 2 x 1½p, 2 x 2p
printed by Harrison, 1973; QEII type 1952 cover   3.00
2 x ½p, 2 x 1p, 2 x 1½p, 2 x 2p
printed by Harrison, 1973; Double-aperture 1973 cover   2.50
2 x ½p, 2 x 1p, 2 x 1½p, 2 x 2p
printed by Harrison, 1974; Philatelic box 1974 cover   2.00

■ 10p booklets. Postal Uniforms series
2 x ½p, 2 x 1p, 2 x 1½p, 2 x 2p
printed by Harrison, 1974; Letter carrier 1793 cover   1.50
2 x ½p, 2 x 1p, 2 x 1½p, 2 x 2p
printed by Harrison, 1974; Letter carrier 1837 cover   1.50
2 x ½p, 2 x 1p, 2 x 1½p, 2 x 2p
printed by Harrison, 1975-76; Letter carrier 1855 cover 1.00

■ 25p booklets. Veteran Transport series
5 x ½p, 9 x 2½p
printed by Harrison, 1971; Knifeboard omnibus cover   2.75
5 x ½p, 9 x 2½p
printed by Harrison, 1971; B-type Omnibus cover   4.00
5 x ½p, 9 x 2½p
printed by Harrison, 1971; Showman's Engine cover   7.00
5 x ½p, 9 x 2½p
printed by Harrison, 1972; Royal Mail Van 1913 cover   5.50
5 x ½p, 9 x 2½p
printed by Harrison, 1972; Motor Wagonette 1901 cover   4.50
5 x ½p, 9 x 2½p
printed by Harrison, 1972; London Taxi Cab 1931 cover   5.25
5 x ½p, 9 x 2½p
printed by Harrison, 1973; Electric Tramcar cover   6.25

■ 25p booklets. 80 Years of British Stamp Books
5 x ½p, 9 x 2½p
printed by Harrison, 1971; 80 Years of Stamp Books cover 3.25

■ 25p booklets. Save The Children Fund
5 x ½p, 9 x 2½p
printed by Harrison, 1973; Help Children cover   6.00

■ 30p booklets. British Birds series
10 x 3p
printed by Harrison, 1971; Curlew cover   4.00
10 x 3p
printed by Harrison, 1971; Lapwing cover   4.00
10 x 3p
printed by Harrison, 1971; Robin cover   4.00
10 x 3p
printed by Harrison, 1971-72; Pied Wagtail cover   4.50
10 x 3p
printed by Harrison, 1972; Kestrel cover   4.50
10 x 3p
printed by Harrison, 1972; Black Grouse cover   4.50

10 x 3p
printed by Harrison, 1973; Skylark cover   4.50
10 x 3p
printed by Harrison, 1973; Oystercatcher cover (purple) 5.00
10 x 3p
printed by Harrison, 1973; Oystercatcher cover (bistre) 4.50

■ 30p booklets. 80 Years of British Stamp Books
10 x 3p
printed by Harrison, 1971; 80 Years of Stamp Books cover 4.50

■ 30p booklets. Save The Children Fund
10 x 3p
printed by Harrison, 1974; Help Children cover   6.00

■ 30p booklets. Canada Life Assurance
10 x 3p
printed by Harrison, 1974; Canada Life cover   4.50

■ 35p booklets. British Coins series
10 x 3½p
printed by Harrison, 1973-74; Cuthred Penny cover   5.00
10 x 3½p
printed by Harrison, 1974; Edward I Silver Groat cover 5.00

■ 35p booklets. Canada Life Assurance
10 x 3½p
printed by Harrison, 1974; Canada Life cover   3.50

■ 45p booklets. British Coins series
10 x 4½p
printed by Harrison, 1974; Elizabeth Gold Crown cover   5.00

■ 50p booklets. British Flowers series
5 x ½p, 7 x 2½p, 10 x 3p
printed by Harrison, 1971; Large Bindweed cover   8.00
5 x ½p, 7 x 2½p, 10 x 3p
printed by Harrison, 1971; Primrose cover   8.00
5 x ½p, 7 x 2½p, 10 x 3p
printed by Harrison, 1971; Honeysuckle cover   8.00
5 x ½p, 7 x 2½p, 10 x 3p
printed by Harrison, 1971; Hop cover   8.50
5 x ½p, 7 x 2½p, 10 x 3p
printed by Harrison, 1971; Common Violet cover   8.50
5 x ½p, 7 x 2½p, 10 x 3p
printed by Harrison, 1972; Lords-and-Ladies cover   8.00
5 x ½p, 7 x 2½p, 10 x 3p
printed by Harrison, 1972; Wood Anemone cover   8.00
5 x ½p, 7 x 2½p, 10 x 3p
printed by Harrison, 1972; Deadly Nightshade cover   8.00

■ 50p booklets. Canada Life Assurance
5 x ½p, 7 x 2½p, 10 x 3p
printed by Harrison, 1973; Canada Life cover (blue-green) 7.00
5 x 3p, 10 x 3½p
printed by Harrison, 1973; Canada Life cover (deep green) 8.00

■ 85p booklets. Canada Life Assurance
5 x 3½p, 15 x 4½p
printed by Harrison, 1973; Canada Life cover   5.50

Did you miss the boat or did you take our advice?

In 1973 we recommended and sold the British definitive 1/2p (SGX842) with one phosphor band on side. We told our customers to buy them at 25p each. WE WERE RIGHT!! Today this stamp is catalogued at £55.00 each. If you had taken our advice, for an outlay of only £50 in 1973, the current catalogue value of your investment would be a staggering total of £11,000.00.

In 1999 we recommended our customers to buy the Princess Diana Welsh Language Presentation Packs. The catalogue value was only £2.50 each, but we were telling our customers to buy them for up to double catalogue value £5 each. Within only 6 years they had increased by 5,900%.

As everyone knows, investments can go down as well as up and the past is not necessarily a guide to the future. However, being selective and taking sound advice is the best way to make your hobby pay for itself.

In 2003 we recommended our customers to buy the Coronation £1 Green (SG 2380) which was catalogued by Stanley Gibbons at £1.50 per stamp. Within 1 year the catalogue value had increased to £50 per stamp, an increase of over 3,200%.

In 2004 we told our customers to buy the Fruit & Veg Presentation Pack – it was catalogued at £4.50. We said ignore the catalogue value, it's cheap at even treble the catalogue value – this pack increased in Stanley Gibbons Catalogue to £60 within two years; an increase of well over 1,200%. We hope that you took our advice in 2004. We recommended you to buy the Locomotives Miniature Sheet (SG.MS.2423). The Stanley Gibbons Catalogue value was £3.75 each. Within 1 year the Stanley Gibbons Catalogue had increased to £25 each - an increase of over 550% in only one year.

In 2005 we recommended the 2003 Rugby Presentation Pack. The 2005 Stanley Gibbons Concise Catalogue listed this at £6 and, within 3 years, the catalogue value had soared. The 2008 Concise Catalogue value for the Rugby Presentation Pack was £35 each, a truly massive increase. We hope you took our advice.

In 2008 we recommended the 2002 Bridges of London Presentation pack (number 338). At the time the catalogue value was £8 each. Within 2 years of our recommendation the catalogue value of the Presentation Pack increased to £25 each. This year the catalogue value increased once again from £25 per pack to £60 per pack.

Earlier this year we recommended our customers to buy the Nobel Prizes Presentation Pack. The catalogue value was £10 each. After our recommendation the price zoomed in the latest catalogue to a staggering £50 each. Our customers have complemented us and said once again "you were right!"

We now strongly recommend you to buy the Great Britain 1967 EFTA Presentation Pack at the best possible price

PLEASE LISTEN TO US NOW!

For our most recent up to the minute recommendations Please telephone 01273 326994

12 Prince Albert Street, Brighton,
Sussex BN1 1HE
Tel: 01273 326994
We do not have an email address so please contact us the old fashioned way, by telephone
Tel: 01273 326994

Est. 1971 dealing in stamps for over 40 years

FOLDED BOOKLETS

In this section, items are priced in mint condition only.

VENDING BOOKLETS OF MACHIN DEFINITIVES, 1976-2000

These booklets were sold from vending machines. They contain panes attached to covers by their top selvedge, so the Queen's portrait is face-down. In most cases, panes are folded along their perforations.

■ 10p booklet
2 x ½p, 3 x 1p, 1 x 6p
printed by Harrison, 1976-77; dotted '10p' cover   1.20

■ 10p booklets. Farm Buildings series
2 x ½p, 2 x 1p, 1x 7p
printed by Harrison, 1978; Kent buildings cover   0.80
2 x ½p, 2 x 1p, 1x 7p
printed by Harrison, 1978; N Ireland buildings cover   0.80
2 x ½p, 2 x 1p, 1x 7p
printed by Harrison, 1978; Yorkshire buildings cover   0.80
2 x ½p, 2 x 1p, 1x 7p
printed by Harrison, 1978; Wales buildings cover   0.80
2 x ½p, 2 x 1p, 1x 7p
printed by Harrison, 1979; Scotland buildings cover   0.80
2 x ½p, 2 x 1p, 1x 7p
printed by Harrison, 1979; Sussex buildings cover   0.80

■ 10p booklet. London 1980 Exhibition
2 x 1p, 1 x 8p
printed by Harrison, 1979-80; London 1980 cover   0.75
(* This booklet exists with differing postal rates on its inner covers.)

■ 50p booklets
2 x ½p, 2 x 1p, 2 x 6½p (phos band at left), 4 x 8½p
printed by Harrison, 1977; bold '50p' cover   2.40
2 x ½p, 2 x 1p, 2 x 6½p (phos band at right), 4 x 8½p
printed by Harrison, 1977; bold '50p' cover   2.40
2 x 1p, 3 x 7p (phos band at left), 3 x 9p
printed by Harrison, 1977; bold '50p' cover   5.00
2 x 1p, 3 x 7p (phos band at right), 3 x 9p
printed by Harrison, 1977; bold '50p' cover   4.00

■ 50p booklets. Commercial Vehicles series
2 x 1p, 3 x 7p (phos band at left), 3 x 9p
printed by Harrison, 1978; Clement Talbot Van cover   5.00
2 x 1p, 3 x 7p (phos band at right), 3 x 9p
printed by Harrison, 1978; Clement Talbot Van cover   3.00
2 x 1p, 3 x 7p (phos band at left), 3 x 9p
printed by Harrison, 1978; Austin Cape Taxi cover   5.00
2 x 1p, 3 x 7p (phos band at right), 3 x 9p
printed by Harrison, 1978; Austin Cape Taxi cover   3.00
2 x 1p, 3 x 7p (phos band at left), 3 x 9p
printed by Harrison, 1978; Morris Royal Mail Van cover   5.00
2 x 1p, 3 x 7p (phos band at right), 3 x 9p
printed by Harrison, 1978; Morris Royal Mail Van cover   3.50
2 x 1p, 3 x 7p (phos band at left), 3 x 9p
printed by Harrison, 1978; Guy Electric Dustcart cover   5.00
2 x 1p, 3 x 7p (phos band at right), 3 x 9p
printed by Harrison, 1978; Guy Electric Dustcart cover   3.50
2 x 1p, 3 x 7p (phos band at left), 3 x 9p
printed by Harrison, 1979; Albion Van cover   6.50
2 x 1p, 3 x 7p (phos band at right), 3 x 9p
printed by Harrison, 1979; Albion Van cover   5.50

2 x 1p, 3 x 7p (phos band at left), 3 x 9p
printed by Harrison, 1979; Leyland Fire Engine cover   5.00
2 x 1p, 3 x 7p (phos band at right), 3 x 9p
printed by Harrison, 1979; Leyland Fire Engine cover   3.50
2 x 2p, 2 x 8p (phos band at left or right), 3 x 10p
printed by Harrison, 1979; Leyland Fire Engine   2.00

■ 50p booklets. Veteran Cars series

2 x 2p, 2 x 8p (phos band left or right), 3 x 10p
printed by Harrison, 1979; Rolls Royce Silver Ghost cover 2.50
3 x 2p, 2 x 10p (phos band left or right), 2 x 12p
printed by Harrison, 1980; Grand Prix Austin cover   2.75
3 x 2p, 2 x 10p (phos band left or right), 2 x 12p
printed by Harrison, 1980; Vauxhall cover   2.00
3 x 2p, 2 x 10p (phos band left or right), 2 x 12p
printed by Harrison, 1980; Daimler cover   2.00
1 x ½p, 1 x 1p, 1 x 14p, 3 x 11½p (phos band left or right)
printed by Harrison, 1981; Lanchester cover   2.00
1 x ½p, 1 x 1p, 1 x 14p, 3 x 11½p (phos band left or right)
printed by Harrison, 1981; Bullnose Morris cover   2.75

■ 50p booklets. Follies series

1 x ½p, 1 x 1p, 1 x 14p, 3 x 11½p (phos band left or right)
printed by Harrison, 1981; Mugdock Castle cover   2.00
3 x 2½p, 2 x 4p, 3 x 11½p (phos band at left)
printed by Harrison, 1981; Mugdock Castle cover   3.00
3 x 2½p, 2 x 4p, 3 x 11½p (phos band at right)
printed by Harrison, 1981; Mugdock Castle cover   6.00
3 x 2½p, 2 x 4p, 3 x 11½p (phos band at left)
printed by Harrison, 1981; Mow Cop Castle cover   3.50
3 x 2½p, 2 x 4p, 3 x 11½p (phos band at right)
printed by Harrison, 1981; Mow Cop Castle cover   3.50
1 x ½p, 4 x 3p pink, 3 x 12½p (phos band left or right)
printed by Harrison, 1982; Paxton's Tower cover   2.00
1 x ½p, 4 x 3p pink, 3 x 12½p (phos band left or right)
printed by Harrison, 1982; Temple of the Winds cover   2.00
1 x ½p, 4 x 3p pink, 3 x 12½p (phos band left or right)
printed by Harrison, 1982; Temple of the Sun cover   2.00
1 x ½p, 4 x 3p pink, 3 x 12½p (phos band left or right)
printed by Harrison, 1982; Water Garden cover   2.00

■ 50p booklets. Rare Farm Animals series

1 x ½p, 4 x 3p pink, 3 x 12½p (phos band left or right)
printed by Harrison, 1983; Bagot Goat cover   3.00
2 x 1p, 3 x 3½p, 3 x 12½p (all with centre phos band)
printed by Harrison, 1983; Gloucester Old Spot Pig cover 4.00
2 x 1p, 3 x 3½p, 3 x 12½p (all with centre phos band)
printed by Harrison, 1983; Toulouse Goose cover   4.00
2 x 1p, 3 x 3½p, 3 x 12½p (all with centre phos band)
printed by Harrison, 1983; Orkney Sheep cover   4.00

■ 50p booklets. Orchids series

3 x 1p, 2 x 4p, 3 x 13p (all with centre phos band)
printed by Harrison, 1984; Dendrobium nobile cover   2.50
3 x 1p, 2 x 4p, 3 x 13p (all with centre phos band)
printed by Harrison, 1985; Cyripedium and ophrys cover   2.50
3 x 1p, 2 x 4p, 3 x 13p (all with centre phos band)
printed by Harrison, 1985; Bifienasia and Vandatricolour 2.50
3 x 1p, 2 x 4p, 3 x 13p (all with centre phos band)
printed by Harrison, 1985; Cymbidium and Arpophyllum   2.50

■ 50p booklet

3 x 17p (two phos bands, stars printed on gummed side)
printed by Harrison, 1985; Pillar box cover   2.50

■ 50p booklets. Pond Life series

3 x 17p (two phos bands, stars printed on gummed side)
printed by Harrison, 1986; Emperor Dragonfly cover   2.50
3 x 17p (two phos bands, stars printed on gummed side)
printed by Harrison, 1986; Common Frog cover   3.00
3 x 17p (two phos bands, without stars on gummed side)
printed by Harrison, 1986; Common Frog cover   2.50
1 x 1p, 2 x 5p, 3 x 13p (all with centre phos band)
printed by Harrison, 1986; Moorhen and Dabchicks cover   5.00
1 x 1p, 2 x 5p, 3 x 13p (all with centre phos band)
printed by Harrison, 1987; Giant Pond Snail cover   4.50

■ 50p booklets. Roman Britain series

2 x 1p, 4 x 12p emerald-green (all with centre phos band)
printed by Harrison, 1986; Hadrian's Wall cover   4.50
1 x 1p (right band), 1 x 13p (left band), 2 x 18p (two bands)
printed by Harrison, 1986; Roman Theatre cover   3.00
1 x 1p (right band), 1 x 13p (left band), 2 x 18p (two bands)
printed by Harrison, 1987; Portchester Castle cover   3.00

■ 50p booklets. Marylebone Cricket Club series

1 x 1p (right band), 1 x 13p (left band), 2 x 18p (two bands)
printed by Harrison, 1987; Weather Vane at Lord's cover 2.50
1 x 1p (right band), 1 x 13p (left band), 2 x 18p (two bands)
printed by Harrison, 1987; Ashes Urn cover   2.50
1 x 1p (right band), 1 x 13p (left band), 2 x 18p (two bands)
printed by Harrison, 1987; Lord's pavilion cover   2.50
1 x 1p (right band), 1 x 13p (left band), 2 x 18p (two bands)
printed by Harrison, 1988; Lord's New Stand cover   2.50

■ 50p booklets. Botanical Gardens series

1 x 1p, 2 x 5p, 3 x 13p (all with centre phos band)
printed by Harrison, 1987; Bodnant Gardens, cover   4.00
1 x 1p, 2 x 5p, 3 x 13p (all with centre phos band)
printed by Harrison, 1987; Edinburgh Gardens, cover   4.00
1 x 1p, 2 x 5p, 3 x 13p (centre phos bands, side edges imperf)
printed by Harrison, 1987; Mount Stuart cover   4.00
1 x 1p, 2 x 5p, 3 x 13p (all with centre phos band)
printed by Harrison, 1987; Mount Stewart (corrected)   3.50
1 x 1p, 2 x 5p, 3 x 13p (all with centre phos band)
printed by Harrison, 1988; Kew Gardens cover   3.00

■ 50p booklets. London Zoo series

1 x 1p, 1 x 13p, 2 x 18p
printed by Harrison, 1988; Pigs   2.50
1 x 1p, 1 x 13p, 2 x 18p
printed by Harrison, 1988; Birds   2.75
1 x 1p, 1 x 13p, 2 x 18p
printed by Harrison, 1988; Elephants   2.50

■ 50p booklets. Marine Life series

1 x 1p, 2 x 5p, 3 x 13p (all with centre phos band)
printed by Harrison, 1988; Anenome, whelk, jellyfish cover 2.50
1 x 14p, 2 x 19p
printed by Harrison, 1989; Crab, bladder wrack cover   2.50

■ 50p booklets. Gilbert and Sullivan Operas series
1 x 14p, 2 x 19p
printed by Harrison, 1988; Yeomen of the Guard cover   3.00
1 x 14p, 2 x 19p
printed by Harrison, 1989; Pirates of Penzance cover   3.50
1 x 14p, 2 x 19p
printed by Harrison, 1989; Mikado cover   3.00

■ 50p booklets. Aircraft series
2 x 15p, 1 x 20p
printed by Harrison, 1989; AW Atalanta & DH Dragon   4.00
2 x 15p, 1 x 20p (Penny Black Anniversary stamps)
printed by Harrison, 1990; AW Atalanta & DH Dragon   4.00
2 x 15p, 1 x 20p
printed by Harrison, 1990; BAC 1-11 & VC10   3.50
2 x 15p, 1 x 20p
printed by Harrison, 1991; BAe ATP, 146 & Concorde   3.75

■ 50p booklets. Archaeology series
2 x 1p, 2 x 24p
printed by Harrison, 1991; Sir Arthur Evans at Crete   2.00
2 x 1p, 2 x 24p
printed by Harrison, 1992; Howard Carter, Tutankhamun   2.00
2 x 1p, 2 x 24p
printed by Harrison, 1992; Sir Austen Layard in Assyria   2.00
2 x 1p, 2 x 24p
printed by Harrison, 1992; Sir Flinders Petrie at Giza   2.50

■ 50p booklet. Sheriff's Millennium
2 x 1p, 2 x 24p
printed by Harrison, 1992; Sheriff's millennium cover   2.00

■ 50p booklet. Postal History series
2 x 1p, 2 x 24p
printed by Harrison, 1993; Airmail markings cover   2.00
2 x 1p, 2 x 24p
printed by Harrison, 1993; Ship mail markings cover   2.00
2 x 1p, 2 x 24p
printed by Harrison, 1993; Registered mail cover   2.00
2 x 25p
printed by Harrison, 1993; 'Paid' marking cover   2.00

■ 50p booklet. Coaching Inns series
2 x 25p
printed by Harrison, 1994; Swan With Two Necks cover   2.00
2 x 25p
printed by Harrison, 1994; Bull & Mouth cover   2.00
2 x 25p
printed by Harrison, 1994; Golden Cross cover   2.00
2 x 25p
printed by Harrison, 1994; Pheasant Inn cover   2.00

■ 50p booklet. Sea Charts series
2 x 25p
printed by Harrison, 1995; John O'Groats cover   2.00
2 x 25p
printed by Harrison, 1995; Land's End cover   2.00
2 x 25p
printed by Harrison, 1995; St. David's Head cover   3.00
2 x 25p
printed by Harrison, 1995; Giant's Causeway cover   3.25

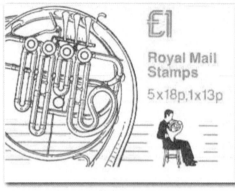

■ £1 booklets. Musical Instruments series
6 x 17p (advanced coated paper)
printed by Harrison, 1986; Violin cover   4.00
1 x 13p (phos band at right), 5 x 18p (two phos bands)
printed by Harrison, 1986; French Horn cover   4.50
1 x 13p (phos band at right), 5 x 18p (two phos bands)
printed by Harrison, 1987; Bass Clarinet cover   4.00

■ £1 booklets. Sherlock Holmes series
1 x 13p (phos band at right), 5 x 18p (two phos bands)
printed by Harrison, 1987; A Study in Scarlet cover   5.00
1 x 13p (phos band at right), 5 x 18p (two phos bands)
printed by Harrison, 1987; Hound of the Baskervilles cover   4.50
1 x 13p (band at right), 5 x 18p (two bands), edges imperf
printed by Harrison, 1987; Adventure of the Speckled Band   4.50
1 x 13p (band at right), 5 x 18p (two bands), edges imperf
printed by Harrison, 1988; The Final Problem cover   4.50

■ £1 booklet. London Zoo series
1 x 13p (phos band at right), 5 x 18p (two phos bands)
printed by Harrison, 1988; Bears   4.50

■ £1 booklets. Charles Dickens series
1 x 13p (phos band at right), 5 x 18p (two phos bands)
printed by Harrison, 1988; Oliver Twist cover   4.50
1 x 13p (phos band at right), 5 x 18p (two phos bands)
printed by Harrison, 1988; Nicholas Nickleby cover   5.00
1 x 13p (phos band at right), 5 x 18p (two phos bands)
printed by Harrison, 1989; David Copperfield cover   4.00
1 x 13p (phos band at right), 5 x 18p (two phos bands)
printed by Harrison, 1989; Great Expectations cover   4.50

■ £1 booklet. Marine Life series
1 x 13p (phos band at right), 5 x 18p (two phos bands)
printed by Harrison, 1989; Sea urchin, starfish, crab   4.00

■ £1 booklets. Mills series
5 x 20p
printed by Harrison, 1989; Wicken Fen cover (matt)   5.00
5 x 20p (Penny Black Anniversary stamps)
printed by Walsall, 1990; Wicken Fen cover (glossy)   11.00
5 x 20p (Penny Black Anniversary stamps)
printed by Harrison, 1990; Click Mill cover   4.00

2 x 17p, 3 x 22p
printed by Harrison, 1990; Jack & Jill Mills cover   3.50
2 x 17p, 3 x 22p
printed by Harrison, 1991 Howell Mill cover   3.50

■ **£1 booklets. Punch Magazine series**
2 x 2p, 4 x 24p
printed by Harrison, 1991; illustrations by Doyle, Hoffnung   3.25
2 x 2p, 4 x 24p
printed by Harrison, 1992; illustrations by Tenniel, Burgin   3.25
2 x 2p, 4 x 24p
printed by Harrison, 1992; illustrations by Tenniel, Anton   3.25
2 x 2p, 4 x 24p
printed by Harrison, 1992; illustrations by Tenniel, Hewison 3.25

■ **£1 booklet. Sheriff's Millennium**
2 x 2p, 4 x 24p
printed by Harrison, 1992; Sheriff's Millennium cover   3.25

■ **£1 booklets. Educational Institutions series**
2 x 2p, 4 x 24p
printed by Walsall, 1993; University of Wales cover   4.00
2 x 2p, 4 x 24p
printed by Walsall, 1993; St. Hilda's College, Oxford   4.00
2 x 2p, 4 x 24p
printed by Walsall, 1993; Marlborough College cover   4.00
4 x 25p
printed by Walsall, 1993; Free Church of Scotland College 5.00

■ **£1 booklets. Prime Ministers series**
4 x 25p
printed by Walsall, 1994; Herbert Asquith cover   3.00
4 x 25p
printed by Harrison, 1994; David Lloyd-George cover   3.00
4 x 25p
printed by Harrison, 1994; Winston Churchill cover   3.00
4 x 25p
printed by Harrison, 1994; Clement Attlee cover   3.00

■ **£1 booklets. Second World War series**
4 x 25p
printed by Harrison, 1995; Violette Szabo cover   3.25
4 x 25p
printed by Harrison, 1995; Dame Vera Lynn cover   3.25
4 x 25p
printed by Harrison, 1995; R. J. Mitchell cover   3.25
4 x 25p
printed by Harrison, 1995; Archibald McIndoe cover   3.25

■ **£1 booklets. Red cover series**
4 x 25p (litho)
printed by Questa, 1996; Royal Mail cruciform cover   4.00
2 x 1p, 1 x 20p, 3 x 26p (litho)
printed by Questa, 1996-97; Royal Mail cruciform cover   4.00
2 x 1p, 1 x 20p, 3 x 26p (gravure)
printed by Questa, 1998; Royal Mail cruciform cover   15.00
1 x 1p, 1 x 2p, 1 x 19p, 3 x 26p (gravure)
printed by Questa, 1999; Royal Mail cruciform cover   4.00
1 x 2nd, 3 x 1st (gravure)
printed by Questa, 2000-01; Royal Mail cruciform cover   4.50

■ **£2 booklets. Postal Vehicles series**
8 x 25p
printed by Harrison, 1993; Motorised Cycle cover   4.50
8 x 25p
printed by Harrison, 1994; Motor Mail Van cover   4.50
8 x 25p
printed by Harrison, 1994; Electric Mail Van cover   4.50

■ **£2 booklets. Sir Rowland Hill series**
8 x 25p
printed by Harrison, 1995; London & Brighton Railway   4.50
8 x 25p
printed by Harrison, 1995; Hazlewood School   4.50
8 x 25p
printed by Harrison, 1995; Secretary to the Post Office   5.00
8 x 25p
printed by Harrison, 1995; Uniform Penny Postage   5.00

■ **£2 booklets. Red cover series**
8 x 25p
printed by Questa, 1996; Royal Mail cruciform cover   5.00
1 x 20p, 7 x 26p (litho)
printed by Questa, 1996; Royal Mail cruciform cover   5.00
1 x 20p, 7 x 26p (gravure)
printed by Questa, 1998; Royal Mail cruciform cover   17.50
1 x 19p, 7 x 26p
printed by Questa, 1999; Royal Mail cruciform cover   4.00
2 x 2nd, 6 x 1st
printed by Questa, 2000; Royal Mail cruciform cover   4.50

COUNTER BOOKLETS OF MACHIN DEFINITIVES, 1976-89

These booklets were sold over post office counters. They contain panes attached to covers by their side selvedge, so the Queen's portrait appears upright. Panes can have a margin to the left or right; prices are the same for both, except where stated.

65p booklets
10 x 6½p (right margin)
printed by Harrison, 1976; bold '65p' cover — 4.50
10 x 6½p (left margin)
printed by Harrison, 1976; bold '65p' cover — 6.00

70p booklets
10 x 7p
printed by Harrison, 1977; bold '70p' cover — 4.50

70p booklets. Country Crafts series
10 x 7p (right margin)
printed by Harrison, 1978; Horse-Shoeing cover — 4.50
10 x 7p (left margin)
printed by Harrison, 1978; Horse-Shoeing cover — 20.00
10 x 7p (right margin)
printed by Harrison, 1978; Thatching cover — 4.50
10 x 7p (left margin)
printed by Harrison, 1978; Thatching cover — £180
10 x 7p (right margin)
printed by Harrison, 1978; Dry-Stone Walling cover — 4.50
10 x 7p (left margin)
printed by Harrison, 1978; Dry-Stone Walling cover — £150
10 x 7p (right margin)
printed by Harrison, 1978; Wheel-Making cover — 5.00
10 x 7p (left margin)
printed by Harrison, 1978; Wheel-Making cover — 5.00
10 x 7p (right margin)
printed by Harrison, 1979; Wattle Fence-Making cover — 5.50
10 x 7p (left margin)
printed by Harrison, 1979; Wattle Fence-Making cover — 15.00
10 x 7p (right margin)
printed by Harrison, 1979; Basket-Making cover — 5.00
10 x 7p (left margin)
printed by Harrison, 1979; Basket-Making cover — 7.00

70p booklet. Derby Letter Office series
10 x 7p
printed by Harrison, 1979; Keddlestone Hall cover — 6.00

80p booklets. Military Aircraft series
10 x 8p
printed by Harrison, 1979; Vickers Gun Bus cover — 3.25

85p booklets
10 x 8½p (right margin)
printed by Harrison, 1976; bold '85p' cover — 8.00
10 x 8½p (left margin)
printed by Harrison, 1976; bold '85p' cover — 8.00

90p booklets
10 x 9p (left margin)
printed by Harrison, 1977; bold '90p' cover — 4.50
10 x 9p (right margin)
printed by Harrison, 1977; bold '90p' cover — 5.00

90p booklets. British Canals series
10 x 9p (right margin)
printed by Harrison, 1978; Grand Union Canal cover — 5.00
10 x 9p (left margin)
printed by Harrison, 1978; Grand Union Canal cover — 23.00
10 x 9p (right margin)
printed by Harrison, 1978; Llangollen Canal cover — £300
10 x 9p (left margin)
printed by Harrison, 1978; Llangollen Canal cover — 4.00
10 x 9p (right margin)
printed by Harrison, 1978; Kennet & Avon Canal cover — 7.00
10 x 9p (left margin)
printed by Harrison, 1978; Kennet & Avon Canal cover — 11.00
10 x 9p (right margin)
printed by Harrison, 1978; Caledonian Canal cover — 6.50
10 x 9p (left margin)
printed by Harrison, 1978; Caledonian Canal cover — 5.00
10 x 9p (right margin)
printed by Harrison, 1979; Regent's Canal cover — 9.00
10 x 9p (left margin)
printed by Harrison, 1979; Regent's Canal cover — 8.00
10 x 9p
printed by Harrison, 1979; Leeds & Liverpool Canal cover — 5.00

90p booklets. Derby Letter Office series
10 x 9p
printed by Harrison, 1979; Tramway Museum, Crich, cover — 6.50

£1 booklets. Industrial Archaeology series
10 x 10p (all-over phosphor)
printed by Harrison, 1979; Ironbridge, Telford, cover — 3.75

£1 booklets. Military Aircraft series
10 x 10p (one centre phos band)
printed by Harrison, 1980; Sopwith Camel, Vickers Vimy — 4.00
10 x 10p (one centre phos band)
printed by Harrison, 1980; Hawker Fury, HP Heyford — 4.00
10 x 10p (one centre phos band)
printed by Harrison, 1980; Wellington, Hurricane — 4.00

£1.15 booklets. Military Aircraft series
10 x 11½p (one centre phos band)
printed by Harrison, 1981; Spitfire, Lancaster — 4.25
10 x 11½p (one centre phos band)
printed by Harrison, 1981; Lightning, Vulcan — 4.25

£1.15 booklets. Museums series
10 x 11½p (one centre phos band)
printed by Harrison, 1981; Natural History Museum — 4.25
10 x 11½p (one centre phos band)
printed by Harrison, 1981; National Museum of Antiquities — 4.25

■ £1.20 booklets. Industrial Archaeology series

10 x 12p yellow-green
printed by Harrison, 1980; Beetle Mill cover   4.50
10 x 12p yellow-green
printed by Harrison, 1980; Tin Mines cover   4.50
10 x 12p yellow-green
printed by Harrison, 1980; Bottle Kilns cover   4.50

■ £1.20 booklets

10 x 12p emerald-green (one centre phos band)
printed by Harrison, 1986; Pillar Box   4.50
10 x 12p emerald-green (one centre phos band)
printed by Harrison, 1986; National Gallery cover   4.25
10 x 12p emerald-green (one centre phos band)
printed by Harrison, 1986; 'Maybe' cover   4.25

■ £1.25 booklets. Museums series

10 x 12½p (one centre phos band)
printed by Harrison, 1982; Ashmolean Museum cover   4.25
10 x 12½p (one centre phos band)
printed by Harrison, 1982; National Museum of Wales   4.50
10 x 12½p (one centre phos band)
printed by Harrison, 1982; Ulster Museum, Belfast   4.50
10 x 12½p (one centre phos band)
printed by Harrison, 1982; Castle Museum, York   4.50

■ £1.25 booklets. Railway Engines series

10 x 12½p (one centre phos band)
printed by Harrison, 1983; GWR IK Brunel cover   5.00
10 x 12½p (one centre phos band)
printed by Harrison, 1983; LMS Class 4P cover   5.00
10 x 12½p (one centre phos band)
printed by Harrison, 1983; LNER Mallard cover   5.00
10 x 12½p (one centre phos band)
printed by Harrison, 1983; SR/BR Clan Line cover   5.00

■ £1.30 booklets. Postal History series

6 x 14p (two phos bands), 2 x 11½p (left phos band),
2 x 11½p (right phos band) (right margin)
printed by Harrison, 1981; Penny Black cover   5.25
6 x 14p (two phos bands), 2 x 11½p (left phos band),
2 x 11½p (right phos band) (left margin)
printed by Harrison, 1981; Penny Black cover   5.00
6 x 14p (two phos bands), 2 x 11½p (left phos band),
2 x 11½p (right phos band) (left margin)
printed by Harrison, 1981; Downey Head' cover   5.50
6 x 14p (two phos bands), 2 x 11½p (left phos band),
2 x 11½p (right phos band) (right margin)
printed by Harrison, 1981; Downey Head' cover   14.00

■ £1.30 booklets. Trams series

10 x 13p (one centre band)
printed by Harrison, 1984; Swansea Car cover   4.25
10 x 13p (one centre band)
printed by Harrison, 1985; Glasgow Car cover   4.75
10 x 13p (one centre band)
printed by Harrison, 1985; Blackpool Car cover   4.25
10 x 13p (one centre band)
printed by Harrison, 1985; London Car cover   4.25

■ £1.30 booklets. Special Offer series

10 x 13p (one centre band)
printed by Harrison, 1986; Books For Children offer   4.25
10 x 13p (one centre band)
printed by Harrison, 1987; 'Keep In Touch' pack offer   4.25
10 x 13p (one centre band)
printed by Harrison, 1987; 'Ideas For Your Garden' offer   4.25
10 x 13p (one centre band)
printed by Harrison, 1987; 'Brighter Writer' pack offer   4.25
10 x 13p (one centre band)
printed by Harrison, 1987; 'Jolly Postman' pack offer   4.25
10 x 13p (one centre band)
printed by Harrison, 1988; Natural History postcards offer   4.25
10 x 13p (one centre band)
printed by Harrison, 1988; Recipe cards offer   4.00
10 x 13p (one centre band)
printed by Harrison, 1988; Children's Party Pack offer   4.00

■ £1.40 booklets. Industrial Archaeology series

10 x 14p (phos-coated paper)
printed by Harrison, 1981; Preston Mill cover   4.50
10 x 14p (phos-coated paper)
printed by Harrison, 1981; Talyllyn Railway cover   5.75

■ £1.40 booklets. Women's Costumes series

10 x 14p (phos-coated paper)
printed by Harrison, 1981; Costumes of 1800-1815   5.00
10 x 14p (phos-coated paper)
printed by Harrison, 1981; Costumes of 1815-1830   5.00

■ £1.40 booklet. Special Offers series

10 x 14p (phos-coated paper)
printed by Harrison, 1988; Pocket Planner offer   4.50

■ £1.40 booklet. Fox Talbot Photography

10 x 14p (phos-coated paper)
printed by Harrison, 1989; photography equipment cover   4.50

■ £1.43 booklets. Postal History series

6 x 15½p (two bands), 2 x 12½p (left band), 2 x 12½p (right band)
printed by Harrison, 1982; James Chalmers cover   4.50
6 x 15½p (two bands), 2 x 12½p (left band), 2 x 12½p (right band)
printed by Harrison, 1982; Edmund Dulac cover   4.50
6 x 15½p (two bands), 2 x 12½p (left band), 2 x 12½p (right band)
printed by Harrison, 1982; Forces Postal Service cover   4.50
6 x 15½p (two bands), 2 x 12½p (left band), 2 x 12½p (right band)
printed by Harrison, 1982; £5 Orange cover   4.75
6 x 15½p (two bands), 2 x 12½p (left band), 2 x 12½p (right band)
printed by Harrison, 1983; Postmark History cover   4.75

■ £1.43 booklets. Holiday Postcard Stamp Book

6 x 15½p (two bands), 2 x 12½p (left band),
2 x 12½p (right band)
printed by Harrison, 1982; Golden Hinde cover   4.50

■ £1.45 booklet. Britain's Countryside

10 x 16p (phos-coated paper, 'D' printed on the gummed
side) printed by Harrison, 1983; Lyme Regis cover   5.50
(* Sold at a discount of 15p off face value.)

■ £1.46 booklets. Postal History series
6 x 16p (two bands), 2 x 12½p (left band), 2 x 12½p (right band)
printed by Harrison, 1983; Seahorses cover   8.50
6 x 16p (two bands), 2 x 12½p (left band), 2 x 12½p (right band)
printed by Harrison, 1983; Parcel Post cover   7.50
6 x 16p (two bands), 2 x 12½p (left band), 2 x 12½p (right band)
printed by Harrison, 1983; Regional stamps cover   7.50
(* Panes have either the four 12½p followed by one 16p on the
bottom row, or one 16p followed by four 12½p.)

■ £1.50 booklets. Special Offer series
6 x 17p (two bands), 2 x 12p (left band), 2 x 12p (right band)
printed by Harrison, 1986; 'Write Now' letter pack offer   5.00
6 x 17p (two bands), 2 x 12p (left band), 2 x 12p (right band)
printed by Harrison, 1986; National Gallery offer   4.75
6 x 17p (two bands), 2 x 12p (left band), 2 x 12p (right band)
printed by Harrison, 1986; 'No' Graphology offer   5.00
(* Panes have either the four 12p followed by one 17p on the
bottom row, or one 17p followed by four 12p.)

■ £1.54 booklets. Postal History series
6 x 17p (two bands), 2 x 13p (left band), 2 x 13p (right band)
printed by Harrison, 1984; To Pay Labels cover   4.50
6 x 17p (two bands), 2 x 13p (left band), 2 x 13p (right band)
printed by Harrison, 1985; Embossed Stamps cover   4.50
6 x 17p (two bands), 2 x 13p (left band), 2 x 13p (right band)
printed by Harrison, 1985; Surface-Printed Stamps cover   4.50
6 x 17p (two bands), 2 x 13p (left band), 2 x 13p (right band)
printed by Harrison, 1985; 350 Years of Service cover   4.50
(* Panes have either the four 13p followed by one 17p on the
bottom row, or one 17p followed by four 13p.)

■ £1.55 booklets. Women's Costumes series
10 x 15½p (phos-coated paper)
printed by Harrison, 1982; Costumes of 1830-1850   5.00
10 x 15½p (phos-coated paper)
printed by Harrison, 1982; Costumes of 1850-1860   5.00
10 x 15½p (phos-coated paper)
printed by Harrison, 1982; Costumes of 1860-1880   4.75
10 x 15½p (phos-coated paper)
printed by Harrison, 1982; Costumes of 1880-1900   4.75

■ £1.55 booklet. Social Letter Writing series
10 x 17p (phos-coated paper, 'D' printed on gummed side)
printed by Harrison, 1985; Paper Boat and Plane cover   6.00
(* Sold at a discount of 15p off face value.)

■ £1.60 booklets. Special Offers series
10 x 16p (phos-coated paper)
printed by Harrison, 1983; Birthday Box offer   6.00
10 x 16p (phos-coated paper)
printed by Harrison, 1984; 'Write It' wallet offer   5.50

■ £1.60 booklet. Britain's Countryside series
10 x 16p (phos-coated paper)
printed by Harrison, 1983; Weavers' Cottages cover   5.00

■ £1.70 booklets. Social Letter Writing series
10 x 17p (phos-coated paper)
printed by Harrison, 1984; Love Letters cover   5.50

10 x 17p (phos-coated paper)
printed by Harrison, 1984; Fan Letters cover   4.75

■ £1.70 booklets. Special Offers series
10 x 17p (phos-coated paper)
printed by Harrison, 1985; 'Write Now' pack offer   5.00
10 x 17p (phos-coated paper)
printed by Harrison, 1986; National Gallery offer   5.00
10 x 17p (phos-coated paper)
printed by Harrison, 1986; 'Yes' Graphology offer   5.00

■ £1.80 booklets. Special Offers series
10 x 18p (phos-coated paper)
printed by Harrison, 1986; Books For Children offer   6.00
10 x 18p (phos-coated paper)
printed by Harrison, 1987; 'Keep In Touch' pack offer   6.00
10 x 18p (phos-coated paper)
printed by Harrison, 1987; 'Ideas For Your Garden' offer   6.00
10 x 18p (phos-coated paper)
printed by Harrison, 1987; 'Brighter Writer' pack offer   6.00
10 x 18p (phos-coated paper)
printed by Harrison, 1987; 'Jolly Postman' pack offer   5.50
10 x 18p (phos-coated paper)
printed by Harrison, 1988; Natural History postcards offer   5.50
10 x 18p (phos-coated paper)
printed by Harrison, 1988; Recipes pack offer   5.50
10 x 18p (phos-coated paper)
printed by Harrison, 1988; Children's Party pack offer   6.00

■ £1.90 booklet. Special Offer series
10 x 19p
printed by Harrison, 1988; Pocket Planner offer   6.25

■ £1.90 booklet. Fox Talbot Photography
10 x 19p
printed by Harrison, 1989; Fox Talbot with camera cover   6.25

COUNTER BOOKLETS OF ROYAL MAIL COMMEMORATIVES, 1985

■ £1.53 booklet. 350th Anniversary of Royal Mail Service to the Public
10 x 17p 350th Anniversary stamp ('D' pattern on gummed side)
printed by Harrison, 1985; van, plane, Concorde cover   5.50
(* Sold at a discount of 17p off face value.)

Introducing the

STAMP
MAGAZINE ™

web app
for iPad, iPhone and Android

You can now access your favourite magazine
wherever you go using the new Stamp Magazine web app.

FREE to all subscribers, this app allows you to access Stamp Magazine on the iPad
and all other electronic tablets via your browser rather than from an app store.

Go to: **www.stampmagazine.co.uk/app**
on your device to check it out now!

RETAIL STAMP BOOKS

In this section, items are priced in mint condition only. These booklets were intended to be sold not only over post office counters, but also through alternative retail outlets. All have a barcode on the outside back cover.

BOOKLETS OF DEFINITIVES WITHOUT ELLIPTICAL PERFORATIONS, 1987-93

Booklets with a 'window' in the cover, through which one of the stamps can be seen, and with the panes surrounded by a white margin.

■ **4 x 13p**
August 4, 1987. Printed by Harrison   2.75

■ **10 x 13p**
August 4, 1987. Printed by Harrison   3.75

■ **4 x 14p**
August 23, 1988. Printed by Harrison   4.50
October 11, 1988. Stamps by Harrison; cover by Walsall   4.50

■ **10 x 14p**
August 23, 1988. Printed by Harrison   6.25
October 11, 1988. Printed by Questa   11.00

■ **4 x 18p**
August 4, 1987. Printed by Harrison   3.00

■ **10 x 18p**
August 4, 1987. Printed by Harrison   5.00

■ **4 x 19p**
August 23, 1988. Printed by Harrison   4.25
October 11, 1988. Stamps by Harrison; cover by Walsall   4.50

■ **10 x 19p**
August 23, 1988. Printed by Harrison   9.50

October 11, 1988. Printed by Questa   12.50

■ **4 x 26p**
August 4, 1987. Printed by Harrison   10.00

■ **4 x 27p**
August 23, 1988. Printed by Harrison   8.50

Booklets with an illustration of the contents in place of the 'window' on the cover, containing panes with no margin, and with either the top and bottom or all three edges imperforate.

■ **4 x 14p**
October 11, 1988. Printed by Harrison   4.50
January 24, 1989. Stamps by printed Harrison,
cover printed by Walsall   15.00

■ **10 x 14p**
October 11, 1988. Printed by Harrison   8.00
October 11, 1988. Printed by Questa   11.00

■ **4 x 19p**
October 11, 1988. Printed by Harrison   5.00
January 24, 1989. Stamps by printed Harrison,
cover printed by Walsalll   17.50

■ **10 x 19p**
October 11, 1988. Printed by Harrison   7.00
October 11, 1988. Printed by Questa   11.50

■ **4 x 27p**
October 11, 1988. Printed by Harrison   20.00

■ **4 x 29p**
October 2, 1989. Printed by Walsall (two phos bands)   8.50
April 17, 1990. Printed by Walsall (phos paper)   7.50

■ **4 x 31p**
September 17, 1990. Printed by Walsall   4.75

■ **4 x 33p**
September 16, 1991. Printed by Walsall   4.75
September 8, 1992. Printed by Walsall (yellow strip at
right is inscribed 'For Worldwide Postcards')   5.00

■ **2 x 39p**
July 28, 1992. Printed by Harrison   3.95

■ **4 x 39p**
September 16, 1991. Printed by Walsall   4.50

Booklets with an illustration of the contents on the cover, containing non-value indicator stamps in panes with no margin, and with either the top and bottom edges or all three edges imperforate.

■ **4 x 2nd bright blue**
August 22, 1989. Printed by Walsall   4.00
November 28, 1989. Stamps by Harrison; cover by Walsall   11.00
August 6, 1991. Printed by Walsall
Cover features Royal Mail cruciform   3.50
January 21, 1992. Printed by Walsall
Cover features logos of Olympic and Paralympic Games   3.50

■ **10 x 2nd bright blue**
August 22, 1989. Printed by Harrison   6.00
September 19, 1989. Printed by Questa   6.50
August 6, 1991. Printed by Walsall
Cover features Royal Mail cruciform   5.50
August 6, 1991. Printed by Questa
Cover features Royal Mail cruciform   5.50
January 21, 1992. Printed by Walsall
Cover features logos of Olympic and Paralympic Games   5.00
March 31, 1992. Printed by Questa
Cover features logos of Olympic and Paralympic Games   5.50
September 22, 1992. Printed by Harrison
Cover features Royal Mail cruciform   5.50

■ **4 x 2nd deep blue**
August 7, 1990. Printed by Walsall   3.75

■ **10 x 2nd deep blue**
August 7, 1990. Printed by Harrison   5.00
August 7, 1990. Printed by Questa   6.00
August 7, 1990. Printed by Walsall   5.25

■ **4 x 1st brownish-black**
August 22, 1989. Printed by Walsall   5.00
December 5, 1989. Stamps by Harrison; cover by Walsall   12.50

■ **10 x 1st brownish-black**
August 22, 1989. Printed by Harrison   7.50
September 19, 1989. Printed by Questa   9.50

■ **4 x 1st orange-red**
August 7, 1990. Printed by Walsall   4.25
August 7, 1990. Printed by Walsall. Perf: 13   7.00
January 21, 1992. Printed by Walsall
Cover features logos of Olympic and Paralympic Games   4.25

■ **10 x 1st orange-red**
August 7, 1990. Printed by Harrison   5.50
August 7, 1990. Printed by Questa   6.00
August 7, 1990. Printed by Walsall   6.00
January 21, 1992. Printed by Harrison
Cover features logos of Olympic and Paralympic Games   6.00
January 21, 1992. Printed by Walsall
Cover features logos of Olympic and Paralympic Games   6.00
February 9, 1993. Printed by Walsall
Cover features Royal Mail cruciform; back cover has advertisement for Greetings stamps   6.00

BOOKLETS OF PENNY BLACK ANNIVERSARY DEFINITIVES, 1990

Booklets with an illustration of the contents on the cover, containing denominated stamps in panes with all four edges perforated, or with either two or three edges imperforate.

■ **4 x 15p**
January 30, 1990. Printed by Walsall   4.50

■ **10 x 15p**
January 30, 1990. Printed by Harrison   5.50
April 17, 1990. Printed by Questa   11.00
June 12, 1990. Printed by Walsall   6.00

■ **4 x 20p**
January 30, 1990. Printed by Walsall   4.00
April 17, 1990. Stamps by Harrison; cover by Walsall   5.00

■ **5 x 20p**
January 30, 1990.
Cover shows Wicken Fen, printed on glossy card   10.00

January 30, 1990.
Cover shows Click Mill 4.00

■ 10 x 20p
January 30, 1990. Printed by Harrison 6.00
April 17, 1990. Printed by Questa 11.00
June 12, 1990. Printed by Walsall 7.50

■ 2 x 15p, 1 x 20p se-tenant
January 30, 1990.
Cover showing Vickers Viscount and De Havilland Comet 3.50

BOOKLETS OF DEFINITIVES WITH ELLIPTICAL PERFORATIONS, 1993-2000

Booklets of denominated stamps in panes with all four edges perforated.

■ 4 x 30p
May 5, 1998. Printed by Walsall 4.50
August 3, 1998. Printed by Walsall
Cover inscribed 'Make their post memorable' 5.00

■ 4 x 35p
November 1, 1993. Printed by Walsall
Cover illustrates a single stamp 4.25
May 16, 1995. Printed by Walsall
Cover shows a block of stamps 4.00
March 19, 1996. Printed by Walsall
Back cover features Olympic symbols 7.00

■ 4 x 37p
July 8, 1996. Printed by Walsall.
Back cover features Olympic symbols 4.50
February 4, 1997. Printed by Walsall.
No Olympic symbols 5.00
August 26, 1997. Printed by Walsall.
Cover shows street names in London 500
August 3, 1998. Printed by Walsall
Cover inscribed 'Make their post memorable' 5.00

■ 4 x 38p
April 26, 1999. Printed by Walsall 5.50

■ 4 x 40p
April 27, 2000. Printed by Walsall 6.00

■ 4 x 41p
November 1, 1993. Printed by Walsall
Cover illustrates a single stamp 4.25
May 16, 1995. Printed by Walsall
Cover shows a block of stamps 4.25
March 19, 1996. Printed by Walsall
Back cover features Olympic symbols 7.00

■ 4 x 60p
August 9, 1994. Printed by Walsall
Cover illustrates a single stamp 5.50
October 4, 1994. Printed by Walsall
Cover illustrates a single stamp but 'Worldwide
Airmail Stamps' in a scroll design 5.00
May 16, 1995. Printed by Walsall
Cover shows a block of stamps 5.00
March 19, 1996. Printed by Walsall
Back cover features Olympic symbols 7.50

■ 4 x 63p
July 8, 1996. Printed by Walsall
Back cover features Olympic symbols 5.50
February 4, 1997. Printed by Walsall
No Olympic symbols. Stamps printed in litho 6.00
August 26, 1997. Printed by Walsall
Stamps printed in gravure 6.50
May 5, 1998. Printed by Walsall
Cover shows air mail label below block of stamps 6.00

■ 4 x 64p
April 26, 1999. Printed by Walsall 6.50

■ 4 x 65p
April 27, 2000. Printed by Walsall 6.50

Booklets of non-value indicator stamps in panes with all four edges perforated.

■ 4 x 2nd bright blue
April 6, 1993. Printed by Walsall 4.25
September 7, 1993. Printed by Harrison 4.75
January 10, 1995. Printed by Harrison.
Cover has white lines through block of stamps 4.50
December 12, 1995. Printed by Walsall.
Cover shows block of stamps 4.50
February 6, 1996. Printed by Walsall.
Back cover features Olympic symbols 4.50

February 4, 1997. Printed by Walsall.
Cover has no line through block of stamps 6.00
August 26, 1997. Printed by Walsall
Stamps printed in gravure 4.75

■ 10 x 2nd bright blue
April 6, 1993. Printed by Questa 7.00
November 1, 1993. Printed by Walsall 5.25
January 10, 1995. Printed by Questa
Cover has white lines through block of stamps 7.00
December 12, 1995. Printed by Harrison
Cover shows block of stamps 5.25
February 6, 1996. Printed by Harrison.
Back cover features Olympic symbols 6.50
February 6, 1996. Printed by Questa
Back cover features Olympic symbols 7.00
August 6, 1996. Printed by Harrison
Cover has no white line through block of stamps
Back cover features Olympic symbols 7.00
August 6, 1996. Printed by Questa
Cover has no white line through block of stamps
Back cover features Olympic symbols 7.00
February 4, 1997. Printed by Harrison
Cover has no white line through block of stamps 7.00
February 4, 1997. Printed by Questa
Cover has no white line through block of stamps 7.00
May 5, 1998. Printed by De La Rue
Cover has no white line through block of stamps 7.00
December 1, 1998. Printed by Questa
Stamps printed in gravure 7.00

■ 4 x 1st orange-red
April 6, 1993. Printed by Harrison 4.50
August 17, 1993. Printed by Walsall 4.50
January 10, 1995. Printed by Walsall
Cover has white lines through block of stamps 4.50
February 6, 1996. Printed by Walsall
Back cover features Olympic symbols 4.50
February 4, 1997. Printed by Walsall
Cover has no white line through block of stamps 4.50
August 26, 1997. Printed by Walsall
Stamps printed in gravure 5.50

■ 4 x 1st orange-red with commemorative label
July 27, 1994. Printed by Questa.
Label marks 300th anniversary of Bank of England 5.00
May 16, 1995. Printed by Walsall
Label marks the centenary of birth of R. J. Mitchell 5.00
April 16, 1996. Printed by Walsall
Label marks 70th birthday of Queen Elizabeth II 5.00
February 12, 1997. Printed by Walsall
Label marks Hong Kong '97 stamp exhibition 5.00
October 21, 1997. Printed by Walsall
Label marks Commonwealth Heads of Govt Meeting 5.00
November 14, 1998. Printed by Walsall
Label marks 50th birthday of the Prince of Wales 4.50
May 12, 1999. Printed by Walsall
Label marks 50th anniversary of the Berlin Airlift 5.00
October 1, 1999. Printed by Walsall.
Label marks the Rugby World Cup 5.00

■ 4 x 1st olive-brown with commemorative label
March 21, 2000. Printed by Walsall
Label shows Postman Pat 5.00
April 4, 2000. Printed by Walsall
Label shows the National Botanic Garden of Wales 5.00

■ 8 x 1st orange-red, 2 x Millennium 26p
May 12, 1999. Printed by Walsall
Containing the Settlers' Tale 26p 8.00
September 21, 1999. Printed by Walsall
Containing the Farmers' Tale 26p 8.00

■ 8 x 1st olive-brown, 2 x Millennium 26p
May 26, 2000. Printed by Walsall
Containing the Above and Beyond 26p 8.75
September 5, 2000. Printed by Walsall
Containing the Stone and Soil 26p 8.75

■ 10 x 1st orange-red
April 6, 1993. Printed by Harrison 7.25
April 6, 1993. Printed by Walsall 7.25
November 1, 1993. Printed by Questa 7.25
November 1, 1993. Printed by Walsall
Back cover has advertisement for Greetings stamps 8.00
February 22, 1994. Printed by Walsall
With 'FREE POSTCARDS' on yellow edge at right 8.00
July 1, 1994. Printed by Walsall
With 'OPEN NOW Chance to win a kite' on yellow strip,
and 'Better luck next time' on inside back cover 8.00
July 1, 1994. Printed by Walsall
With 'OPEN NOW Chance to win a kite' on yellow strip,
and 'You've won' on inside back cover 8.00
September 20, 1994. Printed by Walsall
With 'STAMPERS' and 'DO NOT OPEN UNTIL' on cover 8.00
September 20, 1994. Printed by Walsall
With 'STAMPERS' and 'KEEP IN TOUCH' on cover 8.00
September 20, 1994. Printed by Walsall
With 'STAMPERS' and 'HAPPY BIRTHDAY' on cover 8.00
September 20, 1994. Printed by Walsall
With 'STAMPERS' and 'What's happenin' on cover 8.00
January 10, 1995. Printed by Harrison
Cover has white lines through block of stamps 8.00
January 10, 1995. Printed by Questa
Cover has white lines through block of stamps 8.00
January 10, 1995. Printed by Walsall
Cover has white lines through block of stamps 8.00
February 14, 1995. Printed by Walsall.
Cover shows Thornton's chocolates 8.00
April 4, 1995. Printed by Harrison
Stamps have two phosphor bands 8.00
April 24, 1995. Printed by Walsall
With 'W.H. Smith Special Offer' on yellow strip 8.00
June 26, 1995. Printed by Questa
With 'Sainsbury's Promotion' on yellow strip 10.00
September 4, 1995. Printed by Harrison
Cover shows Benjy Bear and Harry Hedgehog 8.00
February 6, 1996. Printed by Walsall
Back cover features Olympic symbols 8.00
February 19, 1996. Printed by Harrison
Cover showing Walt Disney World 8.00

March 19, 1996. Printed by Harrison	
Back cover features Olympic symbols	6.75
May 13, 1996. Printed by Harrison	
Cover shows lighting the Olympic flame	
Back cover shows Shot Put	8.00
May 13, 1996. Printed by Harrison	
Cover shows lighting of Olympic flame,	
Back cover shows Hurdles	8.00
May 13, 1996. Printed by Harrison	
Cover shows lighting of Olympic flame	
Back cover shows Archery	8.00
July 15, 1996. Printed by Walsall	
With 'W. H. Smith Offer Inside' on yellow strip	8.00
August 16, 1996. Printed by Harrison	
Cover has no white line through block of stamps	
Back cover features Olympic symbols	8.00
August 16, 1996. Printed by Walsall	
Cover has no white line through block of stamps	
Back cover features Olympic symbols	8.00
September 9, 1996. Printed by Walsall	
Cover shows iced cakes	8.00
October 7, 1996. Printed by Walsall.	
With 'Offer Inside' on yellow strip	8.00
February 4, 1997. Printed by Harrison	
Cover has no white line through block of stamps	8.00
February 4, 1997. Printed by Walsall	
Cover has no white line through block of stamps	8.00
November 8, 1997. Printed by Walsall	
Stamps printed in gravure	8.00
February 2, 1998. Printed by De La Rue	
With 'Win an Adventure holiday to Disney	
Animal Kingdom'	8.00
April 27, 1998. Printed by De La Rue	
Cover shows Peugeot 106. 'Stick one of these on	
your drive'	7.25
May 5, 1998. Printed by De La Rue	8.00
July 1, 1998. Printed by De La Rue	
Cover shows JVC Camcorder	7.25
August 3, 1998. Printed by De La Rue	
Cover inscribed 'Make their post memorable'	7.25
September 7, 1998. Printed by Questa	
Stamps printed in litho	8.00
December 1, 1998. Printed by Questa	
Stamps printed in gravure	8.00

■ 10 x 1st gold

April 21, 1997. Printed by Harrison	8.00
April 21, 1997. Printed by Walsall	7.00
September 15, 1997. Printed by Harrison	
Cover shows a beach, and is inscribed 'FIRST CLASS	
TRAVEL'	8.00

■ 10 x 1st olive-brown

January 6, 2000. Printed by Questa	8.00
January 6, 2000. Printed by Walsall	8.00

■ 4 x E dark blue

January 19, 1999. Printed by Walsall	
Cover shows a block of stamps and 'By Air Mail'	
label	6.25

BOOKLETS OF SELF-ADHESIVE DEFINITIVES, 1993-2010

Experimental booklet with a horizontal format.

■ 20 x 1st orange-red

October 19, 1993. Printed by Walsall	12.00

Booklets with a mainly red cover, and an illustration of the contents.

■ 6 x 2nd bright blue

January 29, 2001. Printed by Walsall	4.75

■ 10 x 2nd bright blue

January 29, 2001. Printed by Questa	6.00

■ 12 x 2nd bright blue

January 29, 2001. Printed by Questa	8.00

■ 6 x 1st orange-red and commemorative label

January 29, 2001. Printed by Walsall	
Label marks centenary of the death of Queen Victoria	6.25

■ 6 x 1st orange-red

January 29, 2001. Printed by Walsall	6.00
July 4, 2002. Printed by Questa	4.50

■ 10 x 1st orange-red

January 29, 2001. Printed by Questa	6.75

■ 12 x 1st orange-red

January 29, 2001. Printed by Questa	7.25
January 29, 2001. Printed by Walsall	7.25

Booklets in the colour of the stamps, and with one (1st class), two (2nd class) or no notches (other values) along the right hand edge.

■ **12 x 2nd bright blue**
July 4, 2002. Printed by Questa   7.00
March 27, 2003. Printed by Walsall
Inscription 'The Real Network' under Royal Mail cruciform   7.00
June 15, 2004. Printed by Walsall
No 'The Real Network' inscription   7.25
June 5, 2007. Printed by Walsall
Includes PiP information   5.25

■ **6 x 1st gold**
June 5, 2002. Printed by Questa   5.25
June 5, 2002. Printed by Walsall   5.25
March 27, 2003. Printed by Walsall
Inscription 'The Real Network' under Royal Mail cruciform   5.25
June 15, 2004. Printed by Walsall
Inscription 'Supporting London 2012'   5.25
March 22, 2005. Printed by Walsall
Advertisement for Smilers on inside front cover   5.25
June 5, 2007. Printed by Walsall
Includes PiP information   5.25
June 5, 2007. Printed by Walsall
Includes facsimile of Arnold Machin's signature   5.25
August 28, 2007. Printed by Walsall
Advertisement for Harry Potter stamps   5.25
September 29, 2007. Printed by Walsall
Improved postcode information   4.50
June 10, 2008. Printed by Walsall
Advertisement for Classic Carry On & Hammer stamps   4.50

■ **12 x 1st gold**
June 5, 2002. Printed by Walsall   8.00
March 27, 2003. Printed by Walsall
Inscription 'The Real Network' under Royal Mail cruciform   8.00
June 5, 2007. Printed by Walsall
Includes PiP information   6.25

■ **6 x E**
July 4, 2002. Printed by Walsall   10.00
May 28, 2003. Printed by Walsall
Inscription 'The Real Network' under Royal Mail cruciform   9.50

■ **6 x 42p**
July 4, 2002. Printed by Walsall   14.00

May 28, 2003. Printed by Walsall
Inscription 'The Real Network' under Royal Mail cruciform 13.00

■ **6 x 68p**
July 4, 2002. Printed by Walsall   22.00
May 28, 2003. Printed by Walsall
Inscription 'The Real Network' under Royal Mail cruciform 22.00

■ **4 x Europe up to 20g**
March 30, 2010. Printed by Walsall   5.00

■ **4 x Europe up to 40g**
March 27, 2003. Printed by Walsall
Inscription 'The Real Network' under Royal Mail cruciform   9.00
June 15, 2004. Printed by Walsall
No 'The Real Network' inscription   7.00

■ **4 x Worldwide up to 20g**
April 1, 2004. Printed by Walsall   7.00
March 30, 2010. Printed by Walsall   7.00

■ **4 x Worldwide up to 40g**
March 27, 2003. Printed by Walsall
Inscription 'The Real Network' under Royal Mail cruciform 10.00
June 15, 2004. Printed by Walsall
No 'The Real Network' inscription   8.00

BOOKLETS OF SELF-ADHESIVE DEFINITIVES & COMMEMORATIVES, 2001-2008

Booklets with a cover illustrating the special stamps inside (except Cats & Dogs).

■ **2 x 1st orange-red, 10 x 1st class Cats & Dogs**
February 13, 2001. Printed by Walsall   22.00

■ **4 x 1st orange-red, 2 x 1st class Submarines**
April 17, 2001. Printed by Questa   75.00

■ **4 x 1st orange-red, 2 x 1st class Punch & Judy**
September 4, 2001. Printed by Questa   20.00

■ **4 x 1st orange-red, 2 x 1st class Flags & Ensigns**
October 22, 2001. Printed by Questa   20.00

■ **4 x 1st orange-red, 2 x 1st class Airliners**
May 2, 2002. Printed by Questa   8.00

■ **4 x 1st orange-red, 2 x 1st class World Cup**
May 21, 2002. Printed by Questa   7.50

■ **4 x 1st gold, 2 x 1st class Bridges of London**
September 10, 2002. Printed by Questa   7.50

■ **4 x 1st gold, 2 x 1st class Hello!**
March 4, 2003. Printed by Questa   8.00

■ **4 x 1st gold, 2 x 1st class Extreme Endeavours**
April 29, 2003. Printed by De La Rue   8.00

■ **4 x 1st gold, 2 x 1st class British Journey: Scotland**
July 15, 2003. Printed by De La Rue   8.00

■ **4 x 1st gold, 2 x 1st class Toys**
September 18, 2003. Printed by De La Rue   8.00

■ **4 x 1st gold, 2 x 1st class British Journey: Northern Ireland**
March 16, 2004. Printed by De La Rue   8.00

■ **4 x 1st gold, 2 x 1st class Ocean Liners**
April 13, 2004. Printed by De La Rue   8.00

■ **4 x 1st gold, 2 x 1st class British Journey: Wales**
June 15, 2004. Printed by De La Rue   8.00

■ **4 x 1st gold, 2 x 1st class Beside The Seaside**
March 13, 2008. Printed by Walsall   5.00

BOOKLETS OF SELF-ADHESIVE SMILERS STAMPS, 2005-08

■ **6 x 1st Smilers stamps of October 4, 2005**
October 4, 2005. Printed by Walsall   5.50
July 17, 2006. Printed by Walsall. With PiP information.   5.00

■ **6 x 1st Smilers stamps of October 17, 2006**
October 17, 2006. Printed by Walsall   5.00

■ **1x 1st 'Love', 5 x 1st gold**
January 16, 2007. Printed by Walsall   7.50
January 15, 2008. Printed by Walsall   5.50

■ **6 x 1st Smilers stamps of 2005 and 2006**
February 28, 2008. Printed by Walsall   5.50

BOOKLETS OF SELF-ADHESIVE PRICING-IN-PROPORTION DEFINITIVES, 2006-07

■ **4 x 2nd Large**
August 15, 2006. Printed by Walsall   5.00

■ **4 x 1st Large**
August 15, 2006. Printed by Walsall   5.00

■ **6 x 1st gold**
September 12, 2006. Printed by Walsall   5.00
February 1, 2007. Printed by Walsall
With postcode advertisement inside front cover   5.25

■ **12 x 2nd bright blue**
September 12, 2006. Printed by Walsall   6.00

■ **12 x 1st gold**
September 12, 2006. Printed by Walsall   7.25

BOOKLETS OF SELF-ADHESIVE SECURITY DEFINITIVES, 2009 to date

■ **12 x 2nd blue**
March 31, 2009. Printed by Walsall   8.00
August 19, 2010. Printed by Walsall
Printer's name removed from outside back cover   8.00
October 25, 2011. Printed by Walsall
FSC logo added to outside back cover   8.00

■ 6 x 1st gold

March 31, 2009. Printed by Walsall
Web address on inside front cover reads 'Postcodes4free' 6.00
December 15, 2009. Printed by Walsall
Printer's name removed from outside back cover 6.00
January 26, 2010. Printed by Walsall
Web address on inside front cover reads 'postcodes4free' 6.00
March 30, 2010. Printed by Walsall
Publicity for Festival of Stamps on inside front cover 6.00
October 25, 2011. Printed by Walsall
FSC logo added to outside back cover 6.00

■ 12 x 1st gold

March 31, 2009. Printed by Walsall 9.00
December 15, 2009. Printed by Walsall
Printer's name removed from outside back cover 9.00
October 25, 2011. Printed by Walsall
FSC logo added to outside back cover 7.00

■ 4 x 2nd Large blue

March 31, 2009. Printed by Walsall 4.50
March 22, 2011. Printed by Walsall
Printer's name removed from outside back cover 4.50
October 25, 2011. Printed by Walsall
FSC logo added to outside back cover 4.50

■ 4 x 1st Large gold

March 31, 2009. Printed by Walsall 6.00
March 22, 2011. Printed by Walsall
Printer's name removed from outside back cover 6.00
October 25, 2011. Printed by Walsall
FSC logo added to outside back cover 6.00

BOOKLETS OF SELF-ADHESIVE SECURITY DEFINITIVES & COMMEMORATIVES, 2009 to date

■ 6 x 1st. Design Classics

4 x 1st gold, 1 x 1st Telephone Kiosk, 1 x 1st Routemaster
March 10, 2009. Printed by Walsall 4.50
4 x 1st gold, two x 1st Mini
April 21, 2009. Printed by Walsall 7.50
4 x 1st gold, 2 x 1st Concorde
August 18, 2009. Printed by Walsall 7.50
4 x 1st gold, 2 x 1st Mini Skirt
September 17, 2009. Printed by Walsall 7.50

4 x 1st gold, 2 x 1st Spitfire
September 15, 2010. Printed by Walsall 7.50

■ 6 x 1st. 50th anniversary of National Association of Flower Arrangment Societies

4 x 1st, gold 1 x 1st Iris latifolia, 1 x 1st Tulipa
May 21, 2009. Printed by Walsall 7.50

■ 6 x 1st. Olympic and Paralympic Games

4 x 1st gold, 1 x 1st Paralympic Archery, 1 x 1st Judo
January 7, 2010. Printed by Walsall 6.00
4 x 1st gold, 1 x 1st Track Athletics, 1 x 1st Basketball
February 25, 2010. Printed by Walsall 6.00
4 x 1st gold, 1 x 1st Paralympic Rowing, 1 x 1st Table Tennis
July 27, 2010. Printed by Walsall 6.00
4 x 1st gold, 1 x 1st Football, 1 x 1st Cycling
October 12, 2010. Printed by Walsall 6.00
4 x 1st gold, 1 x 1st Wheelchair Rugby, 1 x 1st Paralympic Sailing
July 27, 2011. Printed by Walsall 6.00
4 x 1st gold, 1 x 1st Gymnastics, 1 x 1st Fencing
September 15, 2011. Printed by Walsall 4.00

■ 6 x 1st. Mammals

4 x 1st gold, 1 x 1st Otter, 1 x 1st Hedgehog
June 15, 2010. Printed by Walsall 6.50

■ 6 x 1st. Thunderbirds

4 x 1st gold, 2 x 1st Thunderbirds
January 11, 2011. Printed by Walsall 6.50

■ 6 x 1st. Medical Breakthroughs

4 x 1st gold, 2 x 1st Beta-Blockers
February 24, 2011. Printed by Walsall 6.50

■ 6 x 1st. Thomas the Tank Engine

4 x 1st gold, 2 x 1st Goodbye Bertie
June 14, 2011. Printed by Walsall 6.00

■ 6 x 1st. Classic Locomotives of England

4 x 1st gold, 2 x 1st BR Dean Goods
August 23, 2011. Printed by Walsall 6.00

■ 6 x 1st. Diamond Jubilee

4 x 1st diamond blue, 2 x 1st Golden Jubilee 2002
May 31, 2012. Printed by Walsall 6.00

BOOKLETS OF SELF-ADHESIVE OLYMPICS DEFINITIVES, 2012

■ 6 x 1st. Olympic and Paralympic Games

3 x 1st Olympic Games logo, 3 x 1st Paralympic Games logo
Cover: Union flag. Inside front cover: quote from Lord Coe
January 5, 2012. Printed by Walsall 6.00

■ 6 x 1st. Olympic and Paralympic Games

3 x 1st Olympic Games logo, 3 x 1st Paralympic Games logo
Cover: Union flag. Inside front cover: timetable of events
January 5, 2012. Printed by Walsall 6.00
(* The arrangement of the stamps varies between the booklets.)

CHRISTMAS BOOKLETS

In this section, prices are quoted for mint condition only. These booklets contain definitive stamps and Christmas special issues.

COUNTER BOOKLETS

■ 1978, November 15
£1.60 (10 x 7p, 10 x 9p definitives).
Decoration of holly cover, 'Greetings Christmas 1978' 3.50

■ 1979, November 14
£1.80 (10 x 8p, 10 x 10p definitives).
Christmas cracker cover, 'Greetings Christmas 1979' 3.75

■ 1980, November 12
£2.20 (10 x 10p, 10 x 12p definitives).
Nativity scene, cover 'Greetings Christmas 1980' 4.00

■ 1981, November 11
£2.55 (10 x 14p, 10 x 11½p definitives).
Skating scene cover, 'Christmas Greetings 1981' 5.50

■ 1982, November 10
£2.50 (10 x 15½p, 10 x 12½p definitives).
Christmas mummers cover 6.50
(* Sold at a discount of 30p off face value; stamps have a blue star printed on the gummed side)

■ 1983, November 9
£2.20 (20 x 12½p definitives).
Pantomime scene cover 6.00
(* Sold at a discount of 30p off face value; stamps have a blue star printed on the gummed side.)

■ 1984, November 20
£2.30 (20 x 13p Christmas stamps)
Manger scene cover 6.00
(* Sold at a discount of 30p off face value; stamps have a blue star printed on the gummed side)

■ 1985, November 19
£2.40 (20 x 12p Christmas stamps).
Cinderella's slipper cover 5.50

■ 1986, December 2
£1.20 (10 x 13p definitives).
Cooking Shetland yule cakes cover 5.00
(* Sold at a discount of 10p off face value; stamps have a blue star printed on the gummed side.)

RETAIL BOOKLETS

■ 1990, November 13
20 x 17p Christmas stamps 7.00

■ 1991, November 12
20 x 18p Christmas stamps 7.00

■ 1992, November 10
20 x 18p Christmas stamps 6.50

■ 1993, November 9
20 x 19p Christmas stamps 7.00
10 x 25p Christmas stamps 5.75

1994, November 1
20 x 19p Christmas stamps 6.75
10 x 25p Christmas stamps 5.00

1995, October 30
20 x 19p Christmas stamps 7.00
10 x 25p Christmas stamps 4.50
4 x 60p Christmas stamps 4.50

1996, October 28
20 x 2nd Christmas stamps 9.00
10 x 1st Christmas stamps 6.00

1997, October 27
20 x 2nd Christmas stamps 9.00
10 x 1st Christmas stamps 6.00

1998, November 2
20 x 20p Christmas stamps 7.50
10 x 26p Christmas stamps 5.50

1999, November 2
20 x 19p The Christians' Tale stamps 7.00
10 x 26p The Christians' Tale stamps 5.00

2000, November 7
20 x 2nd Spirit and Faith stamps 9.00
10 x 1st Spirit and Faith stamps 6.00

SELF-ADHESIVE FOLDERS

2001, November 6
24 x 2nd Christmas stamps 12.00
12 x 1st Christmas stamps 7.50

2002, November 5
24 x 2nd Christmas stamps 12.00
12 x 1st Christmas stamps 7.50

2003, November 4
24 x 2nd Christmas stamps 12.00
12 x 1st Christmas stamps 7.50

2004, November 2
24 x 2nd Christmas stamps 15.00
12 x 1st Christmas stamps 9.00

2005, November 1
24 x 2nd Christmas stamps 13.00
12 x 1st Christmas stamps 7.50

SELF-ADHESIVE BOOKLETS

2006, November 7
12 x 2nd Christmas stamps 6.50
12 x 1st Christmas stamps 8.50

2007, November 6
12 x 2nd Christmas stamps 7.50
12 x 1st Christmas stamps 9.00

2008, November 4
12 x 2nd Christmas stamps.
Pane inscribed 'Oh yes it is' 7.00
12 x 2nd Christmas stamps.
Pane inscribed 'Oh no it isn't' 7.00
12 x 1st Christmas stamps.
Pane inscribed 'It's behind you' 9.00
12 x 2nd Christmas stamps.
Pane inscribed 'Abracadabra' 9.00

2009, November 3
12 x 2nd Christmas stamps 8.00
12 x 1st Christmas stamps 10.00

2010, November 2
12 x 2nd Christmas stamps 6.50
12 x 1st Christmas stamps 9.00

2011, November 8
12 x 2nd Christmas stamps 9.00
12 x 1st Christmas stamps 11.00

1d RED PLATES

Plate	m/m	Used	Plate	m/m	Used	Plate	m/m	Used	Plate	m/m	Used	Plate	m/m	Used
71	£25.00	£0.60	116	£30.00	£1.80	161	£18.75	£1.40	204	£15.00	£0.50			
72	£27.50	£0.80	117	£18.00	£0.50	162	£18.75	£1.40	205	£15.00	£0.60			
73	£27.50	£0.60	118	£20.00	£0.50	163	£18.75	£0.60	206	£15.00	£1.80			
74	£27.50	£0.50	119	£18.00	£0.50	164	£17.50	£0.60	207	£15.00	£1.80			
76	£27.50	£0.50	120	£11.50	£0.50	165	£18.75	£0.50	208	£15.00	£3.20			
78	£27.50	£0.50	121	£16.00	£1.90	166	£11.50	£1.20	209	£15.00	£1.80			
79	£18.75	£0.50	122	£11.50	£0.50	167	£11.50	£0.50	210	£19.50	£2.40			
80	£18.00	£0.50	123	£16.00	£0.50	168	£12.50	£1.40	211	£23.00	£5.75			
81	£20.00	£0.55	124	£11.50	£0.50	169	£15.00	£1.40	212	£19.50	£2.25			
82	£85.00	£0.80	125	£16.00	£0.50	170	£11.50	£0.50	213	£19.50	£2.25			
83	£95.00	£1.50	127	£22.00	£0.55	171	£11.50	£0.50	214	£19.50	£3.60			
84	£27.50	£0.55	129	£16.00	£1.60	172	£11.50	£0.50	215	£19.50	£3.60			
85	£16.00	£0.55	130	£22.00	£0.55	173	£17.50	£1.80	216	£19.50	£3.60			
86	£20.00	£0.80	131	£26.00	£3.20	174	£11.50	£0.50	217	£19.50	£1.50			
87	£13.75	£0.50	132	£95.00	£10.00	175	£15.00	£0.70	218	£19.50	£1.75			
88	£130.00	£2.00	133	£60.00	£3.00	176	£17.50	£0.55	219	£38.50	£25.00			
89	£16.00	£0.50	134	£11.50	£0.50	177	£15.00	£0.50	220	£12.50	£1.50			
90	£16.00	£0.50	135	£38.00	£5.25	178	£19.50	£0.70	221	£17.50	£4.00			
91	£22.00	£1.20	136	£36.00	£4.00	179	£15.00	£0.55	222	£23.00	£14.00			
92	£16.50	£0.50	137	£11.00	£0.55	180	£20.00	£1.00	223	£37.50	£25.00			
93	£20.00	£0.50	138	£11.50	£0.50	181	£11.50	£0.50	224	£40.00	£25.00			
94	£18.00	£1.00	139	£24.00	£3.50	182	£32.50	£1.00	225	£950.00	£250.00			
95	£16.00	£0.50	140	£11.50	£0.50	183	£19.50	£0.60						
96	£18.00	£0.50	141	£44.00	£1.80	184	£11.50	£0.50	SG48/9	½d	Plates			
97	£16.00	£0.70	142	£28.00	£4.80	185	£19.50	£0.60	1	£50.00	£13.75			
98	£20.00	£1.20	143	£18.75	£3.00	186	£15.00	£0.55	3	£35.00	£3.00			
99	£22.00	£1.00	144	£39.50	£4.00	187	£15.00	£0.50	4	£30.00	£2.25			
100	£24.00	£0.75	145	£12.00	£0.55	188	£19.50	£2.00	5	£20.00	£1.75			
101	£24.00	£1.80	146	£16.00	£1.20	189	£19.50	£1.40	6	£20.00	£1.75			
102	£16.00	£0.50	147	£20.00	£0.60	190	£15.00	£1.20	8	£50.00	£11.50			
103	£20.00	£0.70	148	£16.00	£0.60	191	£11.50	£1.40	9	£1200.00	£150.00			
104	£32.50	£1.00	149	£16.00	£1.20	192	£15.00	£0.50	10	£20.00	£1.75			
105	£37.50	£1.50	150	£11.50	£0.50	193	£12.50	£0.50	11	£20.00	£1.75			
106	£22.00	£0.50	151	£20.00	£1.80	194	£15.00	£2.00	12	£20.00	£1.75			
107	£24.00	£1.50	152	£15.00	£1.10	195	£15.00	£2.00	13	£20.00	£1.75			
108	£36.00	£0.55	153	£45.00	£2.00	196	£15.00	£1.00	14	£20.00	£1.75			
109	£35.00	£0.70	154	£15.00	£0.50	197	£20.00	£1.80	15	£20.00	£2.75			
110	£24.00	£1.80	155	£15.00	£0.55	198	£11.50	£1.20	19	£40.00	£6.00			
111	£29.00	£0.55	156	£15.00	£0.50	199	£17.50	£1.20	20	£47.50	£9.50			
112	£28.00	£0.55	157	£15.00	£0.50	200	£15.00	£0.50						
113	£20.00	£2.50	158	£15.00	£0.50	201	£11.50	£1.00	SG21/2	1½d	Plates			
114	£115.00	£2.50	159	£15.00	£0.50	202	£15.00	£1.60	1	£100.00	£6.45			
115	£36.00	£0.55	160	£17.50	£0.50	203	£11.50	£3.20	3	£85.00	£5.00			

All the above are offered on 7 days approval against cash with order subject only to remaining unsold, and are all sound good used (Mint are mounted with gum). **REFUND** is guaranteed provided stamps are returned within 7 days (21 days for overseas clients). To all orders under £50 please add 75p to help with post and packing. (Overseas customers please add £2.00 to all orders regardless of value.)

Reconstructors Wants Lists Welcomed!

GRAHAME W. MANN
Dept. BSMV13, P.O. Box 116, LUDLOW, Shropshire, SY8 3WQ
Tel: 01584 891303 Mon.-Sat. (9.00am to 5.00pm)
E mail: stampmann@stampsuk.com
For my complete stock range visit: **www.stampsuk.com**

GREETINGS BOOKLETS

In this section, prices are quoted for mint condition only. These booklets contain Greetings stamps, which are listed individually in the Queen Elizabeth II Decimal section. Normally the panes comprise one of each design, with additional greetings labels.

Greetings book, 1989

■ **1989, January 31. Greetings**
Two of each of the five 19p designs as January 31, 1989, plus 12 labels. Cover shows elements of designs   25.00

Smiles book, 1989

■ **1990, February 6. Smiles**
One each of ten 20p designs as February 6, 1990, plus 12 labels. Cover shows stamps within smiling lips   15.00

■ **1991, February 5. Good Luck**
One each of ten 1st class designs as February 5, 1991, plus 12 labels. Cover shows good luck charms   8.00

■ **1991, March 26. Smiles**
One each of ten 1st class designs as March 26, 1991, plus 12 labels. Cover shows a happy pillar box   8.00

■ **1992, January 28. Memories**
One each of ten 1st class designs as January 28, 1992, plus 12 labels. Cover shows a label and pressed flowers   7.00

■ **1993, February 2. Gift Giving**
One each of ten 1st class designs as February 2, 1993, plus 20 labels. Cover shows Rupert the Bear   7.50

■ **1994, February 1. Messages**
One each of ten 1st class designs as February 1, 1994, plus 20 labels. Cover shows Rupert and Paddington   7.00

■ **1995, March 21. Art**
One each of ten 1st class designs as March 21, 1995, plus 20 labels. Cover shows a clown
yellow strip at right with the inscription 'Pull Open'   6.50
yellow strip at right with no inscription   6.50

Cartoons book, 1996

■ **1996, February 26. Cartoons**
One each of ten 1st class designs as February 26, 1996, plus 20 labels. Cover shows More! Love design   9.00

■ **1996, November 11. Cartoons**
One each of ten 1st class designs as November 11, 1996, plus 20 labels. Cover shows More! Love design   25.00

Flower Paintings book, 1997

■ **1997, January 6. Flower Paintings**
One each of ten 1st class designs as January 6, 1997, plus 20 labels. Cover shows a flower   7.00

■ **1997, February 3. Flower Paintings**
One each of ten 1st class designs as January 6, 1997, plus 20 labels. Cover shows a flower with added inscription 'WIN A BEAUTIFUL BOUQUET INSTANTLY'   7.50

■ **1998, January 5. Flower Paintings**
One each of ten 1st class designs as January 6, 1997, plus 20 labels. Cover shows a box of chocolates.   7.50

■ **1998, August 3. Flower Paintings**
One each of ten 1st class designs as January 6, 1997, plus 20 labels. Cover inscribed 'Make their post memorable'   8.00

PRESTIGE STAMP BOOKS

In this section, prices are quoted for mint condition only.

Stamps for Cooks, 1969

■ 1969, December 1. £1 Stamps for Cooks

Pane of six 1d, three 4d, three 4d, three 5d (recipe label)	9.00
Pane of fifteen 4d (label 'Stuffed Cucumber')	2.00
Pane of fifteen 4d (label 'Method')	2.00
Pane of fifteen 5d (recipe label)	2.00
Complete book	10.00

(* A stapled version of this stitched book exists that is much more rare. Price: around £400.)

The Story of Wedgwood book, 1972

■ 1972, May 24. £1 The Story of Wedgwood

Pane of twelve 3p	3.00
Pane of six 2½p, six 3p	6.00
Pane of nine 2½p, one ½p	7.50
Pane of four ½p, two 2½p	40.00
Complete book	45.00

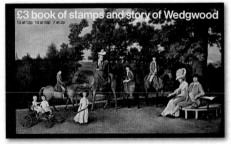

The Story of Wedgwood book, 1980

■ 1980, April 16. £3 The Story of Wedgwood

Pane of six 2p	1.00
Pane of nine 10p	2.50
Pane of nine 12p	2.50
Pane of one 2p, four 10p, four 12p	2.00
Complete book	5.00

■ 1982, May 19. £4 Story of Stanley Gibbons

Pane of six 12½p	2.25
Pane of six 15½p	2.00
Pane of nine 15½p	2.00
Pane of one 2p, one 3p, seven 12½p	3.50
Complete book	6.00

■ 1983, September 14. £4 The Story of the Royal Mint

Pane of six 12½p (label 'The Royal Mint & America')	2.00
Pane of six 12½p (label 'Maundy Money')	2.00
Pane of nine 16p	2.50
Pane of one 3p, two 3½p, six 16p	3.50
Complete book	6.00

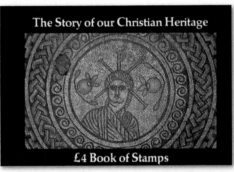

The Story of our Christian Heritage book, 1984

■ 1984, September 4. £4 The Story of Our Christian Heritage

Pane of six 17p	2.25
Pane of six 13p (label 'William Wilberforce')	2.00
Pane of six 13p (label 'Lillian Bayliss')	2.00
Pane of one 10p, one 13p, seven 17p	14.00
Complete book	16.00

■ 1985, January 8. £5 The Story of The Times

Pane of six 17p	2.50
Pane of nine 13p	2.50
Pane of nine 17p	2.75
Pane of two 4p, four 13p, two 17p, one 34p	8.50
Complete book	12.00

■ 1986, March 18. £5 The Story of British Rail

Pane of six 17p	2.75
Pane of nine 12p	3.00
Pane of nine 17p	3.00
Pane of six 12p, two 17p, one 31p	12.00
Complete book	15.00

■ 1987, March 3. £5 The Story of P&O

Pane of six 13p	2.00
Pane of nine 13p	3.00
Pane of nine 18p	3.25
Pane of one 1p, two 13p, five 18p, one 26p	9.00
Complete book	12.50

■ 1998, March 3. £5 FT100 (Financial Times)

Pane of nine 18p	4.00
Pane of six 13p	2.50
Pane of six 13p, one 18p, one 22p, one 34p	14.00
Pane of six 18p	2.50
Complete book	18.50

■ 1989, March 21. £5 The Scots Connection

Pane of nine 19p Scotland	2.75
Pane of six 14p Scotland	1.50
Pane of five 14p, two 19p, one 23p, all Scotland	11.00
Pane of six 19p Scotland	2.50
Complete book	12.00

■ 1990, March 20. £5 London Life

Pane of four 20p Alexandra Palace	2.50
Pane of six 20p Penny Black Anniversary (label 'Eros')	2.50
Pane of six 20p Penny Black Anniversary (label 'Street Signs')	2.50
Pane of one 15p, one 20p, one 29p all Penny Black Anniversary, plus one 2nd, one 1st, one 15p, one 20p, one 50p	12.00
Complete book	15.00

■ 1991, March 19. £6 Alias Agatha Christie

Pane of six 17p (label 'Styles')	2.25
Pane of six 17p (label "mousetrap')	2.25
Pane of nine 22p	4.50
Pane of six 22p, two 33p	5.50
Complete book	11.00

■ 1992, February 25. £6 Cymru Wales

Pane of four 39p Wintertime	2.50
Pane of six 18p Wales	2.00
Pane of two 18p, two 24p, all Wales, plus one 2nd, one 1st, two 33p	8.00
Pane of six 24p Wales	2.25
Complete book	11.00

Tolkien book, 1992

■ 1992, October 27. £6 Tolkien The Centenary

Pane of six 24p (label 'Runes')	2.50
Pane of six 24p (label 'Hobbit')	2.50
Pane of six 18p	2.00
Pane of one 2nd, one 1st, two 18p, two 24p, two 39p	7.50
Complete book	11.00

The Story of Beatrix Potter book, 1992

■ 1993, August 10. £5.64 The Story of Beatrix Potter

Pane of four 1st Beatrix Potter	2.50
Pane of one 24p of each of Scotland, Wales and Northern Ireland, one 18p of each of Scotland, Wales and Northern Ireland	6.50
Pane of three 1st, three 2nd	4.00
Pane of two 2nd, two 18p, two 33p, two 39p	7.00
Complete book	12.00

■ 1994, July 26. £6.04 Northern Ireland

Pane of four 30p Prince of Wales Paintings	2.50
Pane of one 6p, one 19p, four 25p	9.00
Pane of two 19p, four 25p, one 30p, one 41p, all Northern Ireland	5.00
Pane of one 19p, one 25p, one 30p, one 41p, all Northern Ireland	3.50
Complete book	14.00

■ 1995, April 25. £6 The National Trust

Pane of six 25p National Trust	2.75
Pane of two 19p, two 25p, one 10p, one 30p, one 35p, one 41p	10.00
Pane of one 19p of each of Scotland, Wales and Northern Ireland, plus one 25p of each of Scotland, Wales and Northern Ireland	5.00
Pane of six 19p	7.00
Complete book	13.00

■ 1996, May 14. £6.48 European Football Championships

Pane of four 19p Football Legends	1.75
Pane of four 25p Football Legends	2.00
Pane of two 35p, two 41p, two 60p Football Legends	5.00
Pane of two 25p, two 25p Scotland, two 25p Wales, two 25p Northern Ireland	3.50
Complete book	11.00

■ 1997, September 23. £6.15 75 Years of the BBC

Pane of one 26p, one 37p Scotland, one 26p, one 37p Wales, one 26p, one 37p Northern Ireland	6.00
Pane of four 26p gold, four 1st gold	4.00
Pane of three 20p, three 26p	3.75
Pane of four 20p Children's Television	4.50
Complete book	11.00

■ 1998, March 10. £7.49 The Wilding Definitives

Pane of nine 26p Wilding	6.00
Pane of six 20p Wilding	3.00
Pane of four 20p, two 26p, two 37p Wilding	5.50
Pane of three 26p, three 37p Wilding	5.50
Complete book	12.50

Breaking Barriers book, 1998

■ 1998, October 13. £6.16 Breaking Barriers

Pane of four 20p Land Speed Records	5.50
Pane of one 20p Scotland, one 20p Wales, one 20p Northern Ireland, three 43p	6.00
Pane of three 2nd, one 26p Scotland, one 26p Wales, one 26p Northern Ireland	5.00
Pane of three 43p, two 10p, three 2nd	6.50
Complete book	19.00

Profile on Print book, 1999

■ 1999, February 16. £7.54 Profile on Print

Pane of eight 1st orange-red	5.50
Pane of four 1st Machin large format embossed	7.00
Pane of four Machin large format intaglio	7.00
Pane of four Machin large format typographed	7.00
Pane of nine 1st orange-red	6.00
Complete book	19.00

■ 1999, September 21. £6.99 World Changers

Pane of four 20p Millennium Jenner's vaccination	2.00
Pane of four 44p Millennium Faraday's electricity	6.00
Pane of four 26p Darwin's theory	5.50
Pane of four 63p Computers in brain	7.00
Pane of four 1p, three 19p, one 26p	2.50
Complete book	16.00

Special by Design book, 2000

■ 2000, February 15. £7.50 Special by Design

Pane of eight 1st Millennium definitive	5.50
Pane of three 1st Scotland, three 1st Wales, three 1st Northern Ireland	11.00
Pane of four 19p, olive-green, two 38p	9.00
Pane of six 1st Penny Black Anniversary	5.50
Complete book	20.00

■ 2000, August 4. £7.03 HM Queen Elizabeth The Queen Mother

Pane of six 2nd Scotland, two 65p Scotland	5.00
Pane of nine 1st Millennium definitives	5.00
Queen Mother's Century miniature sheet	7.00
Pane of four 27p Queen Mother	6.00
Complete book	15.00

■ 2000, September 18. £7 A Treasury of Trees

Pane of two 65p Millennium Doire Dach forest	3.00
Pane of four 45p Millennium Sycamore seeds,	4.00
Pane of two 65p Millennium Bluebell wood	2.50
Pane of four 1st Millennium definitives, four 2nd Wales	10.00
Pane of four 2nd Millennium Roots of trees	2.50
Complete book	19.00

■ 2001, October 21. £6.76 Unseen and Unheard

Pane of two 1st, two 65p Submarines	7.00
Pane of two 2nd, two 45p Submarines	7.00
Pane of four Flags and Ensigns	5.50
Pane of four 1st Scotland, four E Scotland	5.50
Complete book	18.00

■ 2002, February 6. £7.29 A Gracious Accession

Pane of four 2nd, four E	5.50
Pane of one 2nd, one 1st, one E, one 45p Golden Jubilee	8.50
Pane of one 1st, one E, one 45p, one 65p Golden Jubilee	7.50
Pane of four 1st Wilding, five 2nd Wilding (one tilted)	8.50
Complete book	18.00

■ 2002, September 24. £6.83 Across the Universe

Pane of four 1st England, four 2nd England,	
one 1st Scotland	5.50
Pane of four 1st Millennium National Space Centre	9.50
Pane of four 1st gold, four E	6.00
Astonomy miniature sheet	4.00
Complete book	16.00

■ 2003, February 25. £6.99 Microcosmos

Pane of four 1st Northern Ireland,	
five 2nd Northern Ireland	5.00
Pane of four 1st gold, four E	6.50
Pane of two 1st and two 2nd Discovery of DNA	2.75
Pane of four E Discovery of DNA	3.00
Complete book	18.00

■ 2003, June 2. £7.46 A Perfect Coronation

Pane of four 1st gold, four 2nd	4.75
Pane of four 1st 50th Anniversary of Coronation	2.75
Pane of four (different) 1st Anniversary of Coronation	2.75
Pane of two 47p Wilding, two 68p Wilding,	
one £1 1953 Coronation	30.00
Complete book	36.00

Letters by Night book, 2004

■ 2004, March 16. £7.44 Letters by Night

Pane of three 2nd Scotland, three 68p Scotland	5.00
Pane of one 28p, one E, one 42p Classic Locomotives	4.25
Pane of four 1st Pub Signs	2.50
Pane of four 1st gold, four 37p	6.00
Complete book	15.00

■ 2004, May 25. £7.23 The Glory of the Garden

Pane of four 1st gold, two 42p, two 47p	7.00
Pane of one 2nd, one E, one 68p, one 42p RHS	5.00
Pane of one 1st Iris latifolia, two 1st Tulipa,	
one 1st Gentiana acaulis	7.50
Pane of two 1st, two 47p RHS	4.00
Complete book	21.00

■ 2005, February 24. £7.43 The Brontë Sisters

Pane of four 2nd, two 39p, two 42p	4.50
Pane of two 2nd England, two 40p England	3.00
Pane of two 1st Brontë, two 1st Bronté	2.00
Pane of one 40p, one 57p, one 68p, one £1.12 Bronté	5.50
Complete book	15.00

■ 2005, October 4. £7.26 Battle of Trafalgar

Pane of four 1st, two 50p, two 68p	7.50
Pane of three 1st White Ensign	5.50
Pane of one 1st, one 42p, one 68p first Trafalgar	3.00
Pane of one 1st, one 42p, one 68p second Trafalgar	3.00
Complete book	14.00

■ 2006, February 23. £7.40 Brunel

Pane of one 40p, one 60p, one 47p all Brunel	3.50
Pane of one 1st, one 42p, one 68p all Brunel	3.50
Pane of four 1st, two 35p, two 40p	5.50
Pane of two 68p Ocean Liners, one 47p Brunel	9.00
Complete book	14.00

Victoria Cross book, 2006

■ 2006, September 21. £7.41 Victoria Cross

Pane of first 1st, 64p and 72p Victoria Cross	3.50
Pane of second 1st, 64p and 72p Victoria Cross	3.50
Pane of four 20p Gallantry Awards	9.00
Pane of four 1st, four 50p	6.00
Complete book	14.00

■ 2007, March 1. £7.68 World of Invention

Pane of three 2nd Scotland and three 44p Wales	5.00
Pane of four 1st revised style and four 5p definitives	3.25
Pane of two 1st and two 64p World of Invention	6.00
Pane of two 1st and two 72p World of Invention	6.00
Complete book	15.00

■ 2007, June 5. £7.66 40th Anniversary of the Machin

Pane of four 2p, two 46p, two 48p definitives	3.50
Pane of two £1 ruby definitives	4.00
Pane of two 1st Arnold Machin and two 1st 4d	
deep olive-sepia definitives	4.00
Pane of one 2nd and one 1st revised style, and	
two 2nd and two 1st Large definitives	4.50
Complete book	15.00

■ 2007, September 20. £7.49 British Army Uniforms

Pane of one each of 1st definitives of England,	
Northern Ireland, Scotland and Wales	12.00
Pane of three (different) 1st British Army Uniforms	4.00
Pane of three (different) 78p British Army Uniforms	6.00
Pane of two 1p, four 46p and two 54p definitives	5.50
Complete book	16.00

Ian Fleming's James Bond book, 2008

■ 2008, January 8. £7.40 Ian Fleming's James Bond

Pane of one 1st Casino Royale, one 54p Goldfinger, one 78p For Your Eyes Only	3.75
Pane of one 1st Dr No, one 54p Diamonds Are Forever, one 78p From Russia With Love	3.75
Pane of eight 1st class gold	7.50
Pane of two 1st White Ensign and two 1st Union Jack, as of October 22, 2001	5.50
Complete book	16.00

■ 2008, September 18. £7.15 Pilot to Plane: RAF Uniforms

Pane of three (different) 1st RAF Uniforms	3.00
Pane of three (different) 81p RAF Uniforms	4.50
Pane of four 1st gold and four 2nd definitives	4.50
Pane of two 1st Air Displays design of July 17, 2008, and two 20p Spitfire design of June 10, 1997	7.00
Complete book	15.00

■ 2008, September 29. £9.72 The Regional Definitives: Heraldry and Symbol

Pane of the 1958 3d, 6d and 1s 3d designs of Northern Ireland, Scotland and Wales re-denominated as 1st	7.50
Pane of the 1958 3d, 6d and 1s 3d designs of Northern Ireland, re-denominated as 1st, and three 1st class Northern Ireland of October 14, 2003	5.00
Pane of the 1958 3d, 6d and 1s 3d designs of Scotland, re-denominated as 1st, and three 1st class Scotland of October 14, 2003	5.00
Pane of the 1958 3d, 6d and 1s 3d designs of Wales, re-denominated as 1st, and three 1st class Wales of October 14, 2003	5.00
Complete book	18.00

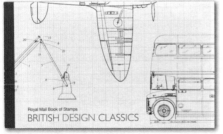

British Design Classics book, 2009

■ 2009, January 13. £7.68 British Design Classics

Pane of four 16p and four 50p definitives	4.50
Pane of one 1st Spitfire, two 1st Routemaster, one 1st Mini	3.25
Pane of one 1st London Underground Map, one 1st Telephone Kiosk, one 1st Penguin Books, one 1st Anglepoise Lamp, one 1st Polypropylene Chair, and one 1st Mini Skirt	4.50
Pane of two 1st Concorde, and two 1st Concorde design of May 2, 2002	3.25
Complete book	21.00

■ 2009, February 12. £7.75 Charles Darwin

Pane of the 48p, 50p and 56p Charles Darwin	3.00
Pane comprising the Charles Darwin miniature sheet	4.50
Pane of the 1st, 72p and 81p Charles Darwin	3.50
Pane of two 1st, two 5p, two 10p and two 48p definitives	4.00
Complete book	40.00

Treasures of the Archive book, 2009

■ 2009, August 18. £8.18 Treasures of the Archive

Pane of four 1st Penny Black Anniversary and four 20p Penny Black Anniversary	6.50
Pane of four 20p Royal Mail coach design of October 17, 1989	4.00
Pane of four (different) 1st Post Boxes	6.00
Pane of four 17p, two 22p and two 62p definitives	7.00
Complete book	15.00

■ 2009, September 17. £7.93 Royal Navy Uniforms

Pane of the three (different) 90p Naval Uniforms	3.50
Pane of the three (different) 1st Naval Uniforms	2.00
Pane of two 1st White Ensign and two 1st Jolly Roger designs of October 22, 2001	2.50
Pane of two 1p, four 17p, and two 90p definitives	4.00
Complete book	15.00

■ 2010, January 7. £8.06 Classic Album Covers

Pane of four 20p, two 54p (wrong font), two 62p definitives	5.00
Pane of six (different) 1st Classic Album Covers	6.00
Pane of four (different) 1st Classic Album Covers	4.00
Pane of two 5p (wrong font), five 10p, two 22p definitives	3.00
Complete book	28.00

▪ 2010, February 25. £7.72 The Royal Society

Pane of four (different) 1st Royal Society	3.00
Pane of four 22p, four 54p (wrong font) definitives	10.00
Pane of four (different) 1st Royal Society	3.00
Pane of four (different) 1st Royal Society	3.00
Complete book	15.00

▪ 2010, May 8. £11.15 King George V

Pane of three 1st, three £1 Centenary of Accession	7.00
Pane of two (different) £1 Seahorses	4.00
Pane of four 1st British Empire Exhibition	3.00
Pane of four 1st, two 2nd, two 50p definitives, self-adhesive	7.00
Complete book	17.50

Britain Alone book, 2010

▪ 2010, May 13. £9.76 Britain Alone

Pane of four 5p, two 10p, two 60p definitives	4.00
Pane of four (different) Britain Alone	4.00
Pane of four (different) Britain Alone	5.00
Pane of four (different) Dunkirk	5.00
Complete book	15.50

▪ 2011, March 11. £9.05 WWF

Pane of six (different) 1st WWF	4.50
Pane of four (different) 1st WWF	3.00
Pane of WWF miniature sheet	5.00
Pane of three 5p, three 10p, one 67p, one 97p definitives	7.00
Complete book	15.00

Morris and Co book, 2011

▪ 2011, May 5. £9.99 Morris and Co

Pane of two 1st, two £1.10 Morris & Co	5.00
Pane of one 1st, two 76p, one £1.10 Morris & Co	5.50
Pane of four 2nd Christmas designs of 2009	4.00
Pane of four 5p, two 10p, two 50p definitives, self-adhesive	3.50
Complete book	15.00

▪ 2011, September 9. £9.97 First UK Aerial Post

Pane of one £1.10 Aerial Post and two 1st definitives	4.00
Pane of one £1 Aerial Post and two 68p definitives	5.00
Pane of four 50p Windsor Castle designs of 2005	4.00
Pane of four 5p, two 1st, two 76p definitives	4.50
Complete book	16.00

Roald Dahl book, 2012

▪ 2012, January 10. £11.47 Roald Dahl: Master Storyteller

Pane of two 2p, two 10p and four 68p definitives	4.00
Pane of 1st, 68p and 76p Roald Dahl	3.00
Pane of 66p, £1 and £1.10 Roald Dahl	4.00
Pane of 1st, 68p, 76p, £1 from Roald Dahl miniature sheet	5.00
Complete book	16.00

Diamond Jubilee book, 2012

▪ 2012, May 31. £12.77 Diamond Jubilee

Pane of four 1st Wilding, four 1st diamond blue definitives	6.00
Pane of 1st Trooping the Colour and 77p Royal Welsh	2.50
Pane of 1st Golden Jubilee, £1.26 United Nations Address, 87p Silver Jubilee and 87p Garter Ceremony	5.50
Pane of 77p First Christmas TV Broadcast and £1.28 Commonwealth Games	3.00
Complete book	17.00

Subscribe
by Direct Debit and SAVE 15% off the shop price!

AUGUST 2012

THE WORLD'S BEST PHILATELIC MAGAZINE

STAMP
MAGAZINE ™

The elegant first issue of Canada's combined colonies

Yes, it is possible to collect Victorian covers on a budget

Olympic ideal?
Did the designs for Britain's first Games issue set a standard no others can beat?

OLYMPIC GAMES

3ᴰ 1948

1/-

1948 OLYMPIC GAMES

of P&O
om the
mpire

mps
rum

HELVETIA PRO PATRIA 1989

Pro Patria
The Swiss charity series that keeps on running

www.stampmagazine.co.uk £3.75

9 770307 667733 08

HURRY!
OFFER CLOSES 30TH AUG 2013

The Stamp Magazine Complete Package includes:

+ **12 printed issues** delivered to your door
+ **FREE** iPad, iPhone & Android access
+ **FREE** Access to the latest digital issue and online archive
+ **Plus save up to 15%** off the shop price!

FREE iPad, iPhone & Android access

Digital Only Package is also available at www.stampmagazine.co.uk/subscribe

Telephone: 08456 777 807
or go online at:
www.stampmagazine.co.uk

OFFICIAL STAMPS

During the reigns of Queen Victoria and King Edward VII stamps were overprinted for use by Government Departments. The prices in this section are quoted in two columns: mint (left) and fine used (right).

QUEEN VICTORIA, 1882-1901

■ Penny Black 'VR'
As the standard stamp but with the stars in the top corners replaced by the letters 'V' and 'R'. Not officially issued.

1d black (with gum)	£30,000	-
1d black (without gum)	£14,000	-
1d black (with trial cancellation)	-	£40,000

■ Overprinted 'I.R. OFFICIAL' for use by the Inland Revenue

½d green (1880 issue)	80.00	15.00
½d blue (1884 issue)	45.00	13.00
½d orange (1887 issue)	6.00	1.00
½d green (1900 issue)	8.00	3.50
1d lilac (1881 issue)	2.75	1.40
2½d lilac (1884 issue)	£350	50.00
2½d purple (1887 issue) (blue paper)	£100	6.00
6d grey (1881 issue)	£350	50.00
6d purple (1887 issue) (red paper)	£300	45.00
1/- green (1884 issue)	£6,000	£1,600
1/- green (1887 issue)	£900	95.00
1/- green, red (1900 issue)	£4,000	£1,100
5/- red (1884 issue)	£8,000	£2,000

10/- blue (1884 issue)	£10,000	£3,000
£1 brown (1884 issue)		
Wmk: Imperial Crowns	£50,000	£22,000
£1 brown (1888 issue)		
Wmk: Orbs	£80,000	£30,000
£1 green (1891 issue)	£10,000	£2,000

■ Overprinted 'O.W. OFFICIAL' for use by the Office of Works

½d orange (1887 issue)	£200	£100
½d green (1900 issue)	£300	£150
1d lilac (1881 issue)	£350	£100
5d purple, blue (1887 issue)	£2,700	£900
10d purple, red (1887 issue)	£4,500	£1,500

■ Overprinted 'ARMY OFFICIAL' for use by the Army

½d orange (1887 issue)	2.75	1.25
½d green (1900 issue)	3.00	5.00
1d lilac (1881 issue)	2.50	2.00
2½d purple (1887 issue) (blue paper)	25.00	10.00
6d purple (1887 issue) (red paper)	60.00	30.00

■ Overprinted 'GOVT PARCELS' for use by the Government

1d lilac (1881 issue)	70.00	10.00
1½d lilac (1884 issue)	£300	40.00
1½d purple, green (1887 issue)	£100	4.00
2d green, red (1887 issue)	£150	14.00
4½d green, red (1887 issue)	£260	£110
6d green (1884 issue)	£2,400	£900
6d purple (1887 issue) (red paper)	£200	40.00
9d green (1884 issue)	£2,000	£700
9d purple, blue (1887 issue)	£275	60.00
1/- brown (1881 issue, plate 13 or 14)	£1,200	£200
1/- green (1887 issue)	£500	£110
1/- green, red (1887 issue)	£500	£125

■ Overprinted 'BOARD OF EDUCATION'

5d purple, blue (1887 issue)	£3,000	£800
1/- green, red (1887 issue)	£8,500	£4,500

KING EDWARD VII, 1902-1904

■ Overprinted 'I.R OFFICIAL' for use by the Inland Revenue
Printed by De La Rue.

½d blue-green	20.00	2.00
1d red	15.00	1.25
2½d blue	£900	£200
6d purple	-	-
1/- green, red	£3,500	£600
5/- red	£27,000	£8,000
10/- blue	£90,000	£40,000
£1 green	£58,000	£22,000

■ Overprinted 'O.W. OFFICIAL' for use by the Office of Works
Printed by De La Rue.

½d blue-green	£400	£110
1d red	£400	£100
2d green, red	£1,500	£400
2½d blue	£2,500	£500
10d purple, red	£30,000	£6,000

■ Overprinted 'ARMY OFFICIAL' for use by the Army
Printed by De La Rue.

½d blue-green	4.00	1.25
1d red	4.00	1.25
6d purple	£130	45.00

■ Overprinted 'GOVT PARCELS' for use by the Government
Printed by De La Rue.

1d red	30.00	10.00
2d green, red	£150	25.00
6d purple	£240	20.00
9d purple, blue	£550	85.00
1/- green, red	£1,200	£250

■ Overprinted 'BOARD OF EDUCATION'
Printed by De La Rue.

½d blue-green	£150	20.00
1d red	£150	20.00
2½d blue	£4,000	£275
5d purple, blue	£26,000	£9,000
1/- green, red	£140,000	-

■ Overprinted 'R.H. OFFICIAL' for use by Royal Household
Printed by De La Rue.

½d blue-green	£300	£200
1d red	£275	£150

■ Overprinted 'ADMIRALTY OFFICIAL' for use by the Royal Navy
Printed by De La Rue.

½d blue-green	20.00	10.00
1d red	12.00	4.00
1½d purple, green	£275	70.00
2d green, red	£300	80.00
2½d blue	£425	75.00
3d purple (yellow paper)	£375	70.00

POSTAGE DUES

Up to 1936, prices are quoted in three columns: **unmounted mint (left), mounted mint (centre) and used (right)**, After 1936, they are quoted for mint (left) and fine used (right).

Except where stated, all these stamps were printed by Harrison in typography, perf 14 x 15.

½d to 1/-

2/6 to £1

■ 1914-1923

A) Wmk: Crown and script GVR (Royal Cypher), sideways; crown faces to the right when viewed from front of stamp. Printed by Harrison (all values except 1/-) or at Somerset House (½d, 1d, 5d, 1/-).

½d green	1.25	0.40	0.35
1d red	1.25	0.50	0.25
chalky paper	7.50	4.00	4.00
1½d brown	95.00	35.00	13.00
2d black	1.25	0.80	0.30
3d violet	25.00	4.00	0.60
4d green	£300	£150	40.00
5d brown	11.00	4.00	2.00
1/- blue	90.00	19.00	3.00
Set	£400	95.00	22.00

B) Wmk: inverted; crown faces to the left.

½d green	1.50	1.00	1.00
1d red	2.00	1.00	1.00
1½d brown	£120	50.00	15.00
2d black	3.00	1.00	1.00
3d violet	25.00	6.50	2.50
4d green	£110	35.00	5.00
5d brown	32.00	12.00	4.00
1/- blue	90.00	20.00	15.00

■ 1924-1931

A) Wmk: Multiple Crown and block GVR, sideways; crown faces to the left. Printed by Waterlow and (from 1934) Harrison.

½d green	1.25	0.50	0.30

1d red	1.25	0.50	0.10
1½d brown	90.00	27.00	9.00
2d black	6.00	1.25	0.20
3d violet	6.00	1.75	0.20
4d green	40.00	5.00	0.85
5d brown	110.00	35.00	17.00
1/- blue	25.00	4.00	0.25
2/6 purple (yellow paper)	190.00	50.00	0.80
Set	£450	£120	24.50

B) Wmk: inverted.

½d green	4.50	2.00	1.50
1d red	-	-	8.50
1½d brown	-	-	25.00
2d black	-	-	8.50
3d violet	50.00	15.00	15.00
4d green	£100	30.00	30.00
1/- blue	-	-	-
2/6 purple (yellow paper)	-	-	-

■ 1936-1937

Wmk: Multiple Crown and E8R (sideways).

½d green	7.00	6.50
1d red	1.00	1.50
2d black	6.00	6.00
3d violet	1.50	1.50
4d green	60.00	22.00
5d brown	40.00	18.00
1/- blue	20.00	6.50
2/6 purple (yellow paper)	£300	10.00
Set	£425	65.00

■ 1937-1938

A) Wmk: Multiple Crown and GVIR (sideways).

½d green	8.50	4.50
1d red	2.00	0.20
2d black	1.25	0.30
3d violet	7.00	0.30
4d green	60.00	7.00
5d brown	7.00	0.80
1/- blue	45.00	0.90
2/6 purple (yellow paper)	50.00	2.00
Set	£160	12.00

B) Wmk: inverted.

1d red	£150	-
2d black	£150	-
3d violet	£150	-
4d green	£300	-
5d brown	£150	-
1/- blue	£150	-

■ 1951-1952

As before but with changed colours.

½d orange	3.50	3.50
1d blue	1.25	0.50
Wmk inverted	-	-
1½d green	1.25	1.50
Wmk inverted	£110	-
4d blue	30.00	12.00

I/- brown	22.00	4.00
Wmk inverted	£2,000	-
Set	45.00	18.00

■ 1954-1955
Wmk: Tudor Crown E2R (sideways).

½d orange	8.00	8.50
Wmk inverted	75.00	
2d black	25.00	16.00
3d violet	70.00	30.00
4d blue	20.00	16.00
5d brown	15.00	10.00
2/6 purple (yellow paper)	£150	8.00
Set	£220	85.00

■ 1955-1957
A) Wmk: St Edward's Crown E2R (sideways).

½d orange	4.00	4.00
Id blue	3.00	1.25
I½d green	7.00	4.50
2d black	25.00	5.25
3d violet	3.50	1.25
4d blue	16.00	2.00
5d brown	20.00	1.75
I/- brown	40.00	2.00
2/6 purple (yellow paper)	£115	10.00
5/- red (yellow paper)	60.00	18.00
Set	£240	40.00

B) Wmk: inverted.

½d orange	50.00	-
I½d green	50.00	-
3d violet	75.00	-
4d blue	£100	-
I/- brown	-	-
2/6 purple (yellow paper)	-	-
5/- red (yellow paper)	-	£150

■ 1959-1963
A) Wmk: Multiple St Edward's Crown (sideways).

½d orange	0.15	0.25
Id blue	0.15	0.10
I½d green	1.50	2.00
2d black	1.00	0.30
3d violet	0.35	0.15
4d blue	0.35	0.15
5d brown	0.35	0.30
6d purple	0.50	0.15
I/- brown	1.00	0.15
2/6 purple (yellow paper)	1.50	0.20
5/- red (yellow paper)	4.00	0.50
10/- blue (yellow paper)	10.00	3.00
£1 black (yellow paper)	30.00	4.50
Set	45.00	9.50

B) Wmk: inverted.

½d orange	1.25	-
Id blue	75.00	-
2d black	£125	-
3d violet	50.00	-

4d blue	£200	-
5d brown	4.00	-
6d purple	£200	-
I/- brown	25.00	-
2/6 purple (yellow paper)	15.00	-
5/- red (yellow paper)	25.00	-
10/- blue (yellow paper)	40.00	-

■ 1968-1969
No watermark. Chalky paper.
i) With gum Arabic.

2d black	0.50	0.50
4d blue	0.40	0.20

ii) With PVA gum.

2d black	1.50	1.00
3d violet	0.50	0.50
5d brown	5.00	5.00
6d purple	1.00	1.25
I/- brown	3.00	2.00

■ 1968-1969
Printed in photogravure by Harrison. No watermark.
Chalky paper. PVA gum.

4d blue	4.50	5.00
8d red	0.50	1.00

½p to 7p

10p to £5

■ 1970-1975. Decimal currency
Des: J. Matthews. Printed in photogravure by Harrison. No
watermark. Chalky paper. Perf: 14 x 15.
i) PVA gum. Original coated paper.

½p turquoise	0.10	0.25
Ip purple	0.50	0.10
2p green	0.25	0.10
3p blue	0.75	0.20
4p sepia	0.25	0.10
5p violet	1.00	0.30
10p carmine	0.80	0.30
20p deep green	1.10	0.50

50p blue	2.25	1.00
£1 black	4.00	0.25

ii) PVA gum. Fluorescent coated paper.

1p purple	0.50	-
3p blue	1.75	-
5p violet	2.25	-
10p carmine	45.00	-
20p deep green	45.00	-
£5 orange, black	15.00	1.00

iii) PVAD (blue-tinged dextrin gum).

1p purple	0.10	-
2p green	0.10	-
3p blue	0.15	-
4p sepia	0.15	-
5p violet	0.15	-
7p red-brown	0.25	0.25
10p carmine	0.25	-
11p green	0.40	0.35
20p deep green	0.50	-
50p blue	1.00	-
£1 black	2.00	-
£5 orange, black	18.00	1.00
Set (one of each value)	18.00	10.00

iv) PVAD gum. Phosphor coated paper (giving a green phosphor reaction).

10p carmine	0.70	0.50
20p deep green	1.00	0.75

1p to 5p

10p to £5

■ 1982, June 9
Des: Sedley Place Design Ltd. Printed in photogravure by Harrisons. No wmk. Perf: 14 x 15.

1p crimson	0.15	0.10
2p bright blue	0.15	0.10
3p purple	0.15	0.15
4p blue	0.15	0.10

5p brown	0.15	0.10
10p light brown	0.20	0.10
20p sage green	0.40	0.30
25p blue-grey	0.60	0.60
50p charcoal	1.00	1.50
£1 red	2.00	0.50
£2 turquoise	4.00	2.50
£5 dull orange	8.50	1.25
Set	14.00	5.00
Gutter Pairs	30.00	-

1p, 2p, 5p, 10p, 20p, 25p, £1, £1.20, £5

■ 1994, February 15
Des: Sedley Place Design Ltd. Printed in lithography by House of Questa. No wmk. Perf: 14 x 15.

1p yellow, orange-red and black	0.15	0.30
2p magenta, purple and black	0.15	0.30
5p yellow, brown and black	0.20	0.30
10p yellow, green a,d black	0.30	0.40
20p violet, emerald-green and black	1.00	1.00
25p magenta, claret and black	1.50	1.50
£1 pink, violet and black	6.00	6.00
£1.20 green, blue and black	7.50	7.50
£5 green, charcoal and black	17.50	17.50
Set	27.00	28.00
First day cover		35.00

The best magazine for GB collectors

STAMP MAGAZINE — Butterflies
A kaleidoscope of endemic species from all corners of the British Isles

STAMP MAGAZINE — Jubilee celebrations
Contrasting issues marked the Queen's big anniversaries of 1977, 1992 and 2002. Which was the most glorious?

Available from newsagents, or visit www.stampmagazine.co.uk

DO YOU COLLECT GREAT BRITAIN?

• *If so you may find that our GB Price Lists would be of interest. Aimed at the more serious collector these profusely illustrated listings are extremely popular and are issued twice monthly. They contain a wide selection of better singles, rarities, proofs, colour trials, high values, multiples and much more specialised material ... seldom offered elsewhere. Please fill in the coupon below to receive the next issue FREE OF CHARGE.*

• Each list contains up to a Thousand Items, most of which are illustrated. Prices range from £4 to rarities priced in £1,000's. There are bargains galore with many items priced at WELL BELOW CURRENT MARKET LEVELS. Can YOU afford not to send for your FREE copy?

• Join the many other collectors on our WORLDWIDE MAILING LIST who collect from the comfort of their own homes using our famous price lists. Buying by mail order is safe and easy, and all stamps carry our money back guarantee if returned within 7 days.

NOW AVAILABLE IN FULL COLOUR AT www.gbstamps.co.uk

Please tick boxes of interest.

Pre Stamp/Postal History	❏	QV Line Engraved	❏
QV Surface Printed	❏	QV High Values	❏
King Edward VII	❏	King George V	❏
Essays/Proofs/Colour Trials	❏	General Great Britain	❏
Specialised Shades	❏	Cinderella	❏

ARTHUR RYAN & CO (DEPT SM), RICHMOND, SURREY TW9 1DY.

Please send me a FREE copy of your Retail List

Name. . . . .
Address . . . .
. . . .
. . . .

OR TELEPHONE: 020 8940 7777 FAX: 020 8940 7755
www.gbstamps.co.uk

287232

VENDING MACHINE STAMPS

In this section, prices are quoted in two columns: **unmounted mint** (left) and **fine used** (right). This listing is restricted to labels dispensed from self-service machines, with the value printed at point of sale and no restrictions on their date of use.

FRAMA LABELS

From May 1984 until April 1985, Frama machines were installed at four locations, printing labels to order for the 1st class rate, 2nd class rate and any value from ½p to 16p (17p from August 28, 1984).

■ 1984, May 1
Machine-printed in red on phosphor-coated white security paper with a grey-green background pattern. Gummed and imperforate.

Set (½p to 17p)	12.00	15.00
Pack (all values from ½p to 16p)	25.00	–
Pack (16½p, 17p)	4.00	–
Pack (3½p, 12½p, 16p)	4.00	–
First day cover (3½p, 12½p, 16p)	–	2.50

POST & GO STAMPS

From October 2008, Wincor Nixdorf machines located at a limited number of post offices printed stamps to order. Each bears a code to indicate the post office where the machine is sited, the machine number and the particular transaction.

It should be noted that the typeface on stamps in philatelic packs differs from that on stamps from post offices. Stamps printed in corrupted typefaces exist but are outside the scope of this publication.

■ 2008, October 8. Machin head definitive
Machine-printed in black on security paper bearing the Machin portrait and an olive-brown background pattern, printed in gravure by Walsall. Self-adhesive, with die-cut perforations. Dispensed in strips of up to five. Available for 1st class, 1st Large, Europe up to 20g, Worldwide up to 10g, Worldwide up to 20g and (after October 2011) Worldwide up to 40g services.

Strip of five (one of each value)	10.00	–
Philatelic pack (one of each value)	20.00	–

■ 2010, September. Machin head definitive
As above but with a new, smaller typeface suitable for use with pictorial designs.

Strip of five (one of each value)	7.00	–
Collector's set (all six values)	10.00	–

Blue tit
Goldfinch
House sparrow
Robin
Starling
Wood pigeon

■ 2010, September 17. Birds of Britain, series I
Des: Kate Stephens, from illustrations by Robert Gillmor. Machine-printed in black on security paper with a colour picture, printed in gravure by Walsall. Dispensed in strips of up to five. Available for 1st class, 1st Large, Europe up to 20g, Worldwide up to 10g, Worldwide up to 20g and (after October 2011) Worldwide up to 40g services.

Set of six (all 1st class)	15.00	–
Philatelic pack (all 1st class)	15.00	–
First day cover	–	15.00

Blackbird
Chaffinch
Collared dove
Greenfinch
Long-tailed tit
Magpie

■ 2011, January 24. Birds of Britain, series II
As above but new designs.

Set of six (all 1st class)	25.00	–
Philatelic pack (all 1st class)	25.00	–
First day cover	–	25.00

1st Class
up to 100g

002011 5 51840 03

Great crested grebe
Greylag goose
Kingfisher
Mallard
Moorhen
Mute swan

■ 2011, May 19. Birds of Britain, series III
As above but new designs.

Set of six (all 1st class)	7.50	–
Philatelic pack (all 1st class)	7.50	–
First day cover	–	7.50

1st Class
up to 100g

002011 9 51840 04

Arctic tern
Cormorant
Gannet
Oystercatcher
Puffin
Ringed plover

■ 2011, September 16. Birds of Britain, series IV
As above but new designs. Available for 1st class, 1st Large, Europe up to 20g, Worldwide up to 10g,, Worldwide up to 20g and Worldwide up to 40g services.

Set of six (all 1st class)	6.00	–
Collector's set (all six values)	8.00	–
Philatelic pack (all 1st class)	6.00	–
First day cover	–	6.00

1st Class
up to 100g

Dalesbred
Jacob
Leicester longwool
Soay
Suffolk
Welsh mountain badger face

■ 2012, February 24. Sheep
As above but new designs.

Set of six (all 1st class)	5.00	–
Collector's set (all six values)	7.00	–
Philatelic pack (all 1st class)	5.00	–
First day cover	–	6.00

1st Class
up to 100g

Berkshire
British saddleback
Gloucestershire old spots
Oxford sandy and black
Tamworth
Welsh

■ 2012, April 24. Pigs
As above but new designs.

Set of six (all 1st class)	5.00	–
Collector's set (all six values)	7.00	–
Philatelic pack (all 1st class)	5.00	–
First day cover	–	6.00

1st Class
up to 100g

052012 00 51840 21

Union flag

■ 2012, May 21. Union Flag
Des: Dick Davis/Royal Mail, from illustration by Anton Morris

Single stamp (lst class)	0.90	–
Philatelic pack (lst class only)	1.00	–
First day cover	–	2.00

POST & GO SPECIAL ISSUES

From September 2011, Hytech machines have been provided at Stampex exhibitions in London. These use a different typeface from Wincor Nixdorf machines, and can dispense stamps in longer strips. They have also issued stamps with commemorative inscriptions, not available from post offices.

■ Pictorial issues
Birds of Britain, series III (Autumn Stampex 2011)
Birds of Britain, series IV (Autumn Stampex 2011)
Sheep. (Spring Stampex 2012)
■ Machin-head commemorative issues
'Arnold Machin 1911-1999' (Autumn Stampex 2011)
'Diamond Jubilee 1952-2012' (Spring Stampex 2012)

SMILERS GENERIC SHEETS

Smilers sheets are personalisable, by way of having a photograph or other supplied image printed on labels alongside conventional stamps. Listed here are Royal Mail's generic sheets for each available issue, which have decorative labels instead of these photographs.

The Stamp Show, 2000

■ **2000, May 22. The Stamp Show 2000**
Sheet of 10 1st class Smiles as March 26, 1991   27.50

■ **2000, October 3. Christmas: Robin in Letterbox**
Sheet of 20 19p Robin in pillar box as October 30,
1995, inscribed copyright 'Post Office 2000'   £150

■ **2000, October 3. Christmas: Father Christmas**
Sheet of 10 1st class Father Christmas as October 27,
1997, inscribed copyright 'Post Office 2000'   £150

■ **2001, June 5. Occasions: Hallmarks**
Sheets of 20 1st class as February 6, 2001   £150

■ **2001, July 3. Smiles**
Sheet of 10 1st class Smiles as May 22, 2000,
but with revised labels and border   £200

■ **2001, October 9. Christmas: Robin in Letterbox**
Sheet of 20 19p Robin in pillar box as
October 30, 1995, inscribed copyright 'Consignia 2001'   £600

■ **2001, October 9. Christmas: Father Christmas**
Sheet of 10 1st class Father Christmas as October 27,
1997, inscribed copyright 'Consignia 2001'   £600

■ **2001, December 18. Cartoons**
Sheet of 10 1st class as February 26, 1996   35.00

■ **2002, April 23. Occasions: Pictorial Messages**
Sheet of 20 1st class as March 5, 2002   50.00

■ **2002, May 21. Football World Cup**
Sheet of 20 1st class Flag as May 21, 2002   25.00

■ **2002, October 1. Smiles**
Sheet of 10 1st class Teddy Bear and 10 1st class
Dennis the Menace as March 26, 1991   25.00

■ **2002, October 1. Christmas: Father Christmas**
Sheet of 20 1st class as October 27, 1997   30.00

■ **2003, January 21. Flowers**
Sheet of 20 1st class Flower Paintings as January 6, 1997   30.00

Occasions, 2003

■ **2003, February 4. Occasions: Multiple Choice**
Sheet of 20 1st class as February 4, 2003   25.00

■ **2003, July 29. Cartoons Crossword**
Sheet of 20 1st class as February 26, 1996   20.00

■ **2003, September 30. Christmas: Winter Robins**
Sheet of 20 1st class as November 6, 2001. Self-adhesive   20.00

■ **2003, November 4. Christmas: Ice Sculptures**
Sheet of 20 2nd class Ice Sculptures as November 4,
2003. Self-adhesive   15.00
Sheet of 20 1st class Ice Sculptures as November 4,
2003. Self-adhesive   30.00

■ **2004, January 30. Hong Kong Stamp Exhibition**
Sheet of 20 1st class Hello as March 5, 2002   15.00

■ **2004, February 3. Occasions: Entertaining Envelopes**
Sheet of 20 1st class as February 3, 2004   16.00

■ **2004, May 25. Royal Horticultural Society**
Sheet of 20 1st class as May 25, 2004   16.00

■ **2004, July 27. Rule Britannia**
Sheet of 20 1st class Union Flag as October 22, 2001   15.00

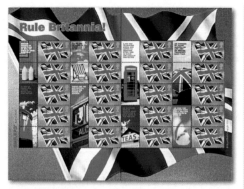

Rule Britannia, 2004

■ **2004, November 2. Christmas: Father Christmas**
Sheet of 10 1st class and 10 2nd class. Self-adhesive   15.00

■ **2005, January 11. Farm Animals**
Sheet of 20 1st class as January 11, 2005   20.00

■ **2005, March 15. Magic**
Sheet of 20 1st class as March 15, 2005   20.00

■ **2005, April 21. Pacific Explorer Stamp Exhibition**
Sheet of 20 1st class Hello as March 5, 2002   16.00

■ **2005, June 21. White Ensign**
Sheet of 20 1st class White Ensign as October 22, 2001   16.00

■ **2005, September 15. Classic ITV**
Sheet of 20 1st class as September 15, 2005   15.00

■ **2005, November 1. Christmas: Winter Robins**
Sheet of 10 1st class and 10 2nd class as November 6,
2001. Self-adhesive   15.00

■ **2006, January 10. A Bear Called Paddington**
Sheet of 20 1st class Paddington Bear as January 10,
2006. Self-adhesive   15.00

A Bear Called Paddington, 2006

■ **2006, March 7. Fun Fruit and Veg**
Sheet of 20 1st class as March 7, 2006. Self-adhesive   20.00

■ **2006, May 25. Washington Stamp Exhibition**
Sheet of 20 1st class Hello as March 5, 2002   15.00

■ **2006, June 6. World Cup Winners**
Sheets of 20 1st class as June 6, 2006   17.50

■ **2006, July 4. For Life's Special Moments**
Sheet of 20 1st class as October 4, 2005. Self-adhesive   15.00

■ **2006, October 17. For Life's Extra Special
Moments**
Sheet of 20 1st class as October 17, 2006 Self-adhesive   15.00

■ **2006, November 7. Christmas**
Sheet of 10 1st class and 10 2nd class as November 7,
2006 Self-adhesive   15.00

■ **2006, November 9. We Will Remember Them I**
Sheet of 20 1st class Poppies as November 6, 2006   15.00

■ **2006, November 14. Belgica Stamp Exhibition**
Sheet of 20 1st class Hello as March 5, 2002   12.50

Glorious Wales, 2007

■ **2007, March 1. Glorious Wales**
Sheet of 20 1st class Wales as October 14, 2003.
Self-adhesive   15.00

■ **2007, April 23. Glorious England**
Sheet of 20 1st class England as October 14, 2003.
Self-adhesive   15.00

■ **2007, May 17. Wembley Stadium**
Sheet of 20 1st class Lion & Shield of St George
as May 17, 2007   15.00

■ **2007, June 5. 40th Anniversary of the Machin
Definitive**
Sheet of 20 1st class Arnold Machin as June 5, 2007   15.00

■ **2007, July 17. Harry Potter**
Sheet of 20 1st class Crest as July 17, 2007. Self-adhesive   15.00

Christmas, 2007

2007, November 6. Christmas
Sheet of 20 2nd class, 1st class and 78p as
November 6, 2007. Self-adhesive   17.00

2007, November 8. We Will Remember Them II
Sheet of 20 1st class Poppy as November 8, 2007   15.00

2007, November 30. Glorious Scotland
Sheet of 20 1st class Scotland as October 14, 2003.
Self-adhesive   15.00

2008, January 15. I Wrote To Say ...
Sheet of 20 1st class as October 4, 2005, with
circular labels. Self-adhesive   16.00

2008, March 11. Glorious Northern Ireland
Sheet of 20 1st class Northern Ireland as October
14, 2003. Self-adhesive   14.00

2008, July 17. 100 Years of Aviation
Sheet of 20 1st class as July 17, 2008   15.00

2008, August 5. Beijing 2008 Olympic Expo
Sheet of 20 1st class Hello as March 5, 2002   15.00

Glorious United Kingdom, 2008

2008, September 29. Glorious United Kingdom
Sheet of 20 1st class England, Northern Ireland, Scotland
and Wales as as October 14, 2003. Self-adhesive   15.00

2008, November 4. Christmas
Sheet of 20 2nd class, 1st class and 81p as
November 4, 2008. Self-adhesive   15.00

2008, November 6. We Will Remember Them III
Sheet of 20 1st class Poppy as November 6, 2008   15.00

2009, January 13. The Mini
Sheet of 20 1st class Mini as January 13, 2009   15.00

2009, March 2. Concorde
Sheet of 20 1st class Concorde as January 13, 2009   14.00

2009, March 17. Castles of Northern Ireland
Sheet of 20 1st class Northern Ireland as
October 14, 2003. Self-adhesive   14.00

2009, April 23. Castles of England
Sheet of 20 1st class English flag as April 23, 2007.
Self-adhesive   14.00

2009, August 3. Thaipex 2009 (Bangkok) Expo
Sheet of 20 1st class Hello as March 5, 2002   14.00
(* Panes of 10 were sold separately at the exhibition.)

Post Boxes, 2009

2009, August 18. Post Boxes
Sheet of 20 1st class as August 18, 2009   14.00

2009, October 21. Italia 2009 Stamp Exhibition
Sheet of 20 1st class Hello as March 5, 2002   14.00

2009, November 3. Christmas
Sheet of 20 2nd class, 1st class, 56p and 90p
as November 3, 2009. Self-adhesive   15.00

2009, November 30. Castles of Scotland
Sheet of 20 1st class Scotland as October 14, 2003.
Self-adhesive   14.00

2009, December 4. MonacoPhil 2009 Exhibition
Sheet of 20 1st class Hello as March 5, 2002   14.00

■ 2010, January 26. For All Occasions
Sheet of 20 1st class, Europe and Worldwide
as January 26, 2010. Self-adhesive — 30.00

■ 2010, March 1. Castles of Wales
Sheet of 20 1st class Wales as October 14, 2003.
Self-adhesive — 15.00

■ 2010, May 8. 10th anniversary of Smilers
Sheet of 20 1st class, Europe and Worldwide
as January 26, 2010. Self-adhesive — 30.00

■ 2010, May 8. London 2010 Stamp Exhibition
Sheet of 20 1st class Hello as October 4, 2005.
Self-adhesive — 15.00

■ 2010, September 15. Battle of Britain
Sheet of 20 1st class Spitfire as January 13, 2009 — 15.00

■ 2010, November 2. Christmas
Sheet of 20 2nd class, 1st class, 60p and 97p
as November 2, 2010. Self-adhesive — 18.00

Indipex, 2011

■ 2011, February 12. Indipex 2011 Exhibition
Sheet of 20 1st class Union Flag as October 4, 2005 — 12.50

■ 2011, July 28. Philanippon 2011 Exhibition
Sheet of 20 1st class Union Flag as October 4, 2005 — 15.00

■ 2011, September 15. 350 Years of Postmarks
Sheet of 20 1st class Seal as January 26, 2010 — 15.00

■ 2011, November 8. Christmas
Sheet of 20 1st class, 2nd class, 68p, £1.10 as
November 8, 2011. Self-adhesive — 20.00

■ 2012, January 20. Year of the Dragon
Sheet of 20 1st class Firework as October 17, 2006 — 20.00

■ 2012, June 18. Indonesia 2012 Exhibition
Sheet of 20 1st class Hello as October 4, 2005 — 20.00

■ 2012, June 27. Olympic and Paralympic Games Venues
Sheet of 20 1st class and Worldwide Olympic Games
and Paralympic Games as January 5, 2012 — 25.00

Peter Rabbit, 2008

SMILERS FOR KIDS

■ 2008, October 28. Mr Happy
Sheet of 20 1st class Balloons — 14.00
Sheet of 10 1st class Balloons, and writing pack — 14.00

■ 2008, October 28. Almond Blossom
Sheet of 20 1st class Flower — 14.00
Sheet of 10 1st class Flower, and writing pack — 14.00

■ 2008, October 28. Peter Rabbit
Sheet of 20 1st class New Baby — 14.00
Sheet of 10 1st class New Baby, and writing pack — 14.00

■ 2008, October 28. Noddy
Sheets of 20 1st class Balloons — 14.00
Sheets of 10 1st class Balloons, and writing pack — 14.00

■ 2009, April 30. Little Miss Sunshine
Sheet of 20 1st class Balloons — 14.00
Sheet of 10 1st class Balloons, and writing pack — 14.00

■ 2009, April 30. Wild Cherry
Sheet of 20 1st class Flower — 14.00
Sheet of 10 1st class Flower, and writing pack — 14.00

■ 2009, April 30. Jeremy Fisher
Sheet of 20 1st class Hello — 14.00
Sheet of 10 1st class Hello, and writing pack — 14.00

■ 2009, April 30. Big Ears
Sheets of 20 1st class Balloons — 14.00
Sheets of 10 1st class Balloons, and writing pack — 14.00

COMMEMORATIVE SHEETS

Commemorative sheets are an evolution of Smilers sheets, which are not personalisable but are customised as a souvenir product by Royal Mail.

Centenary of the Territorial Army, 2008

2008, April 1. Centenary of the Territorial Army
Sheet of 10 1st class Union Flag as October 22, 2001   20.00

2008, July 24. London 1908 Olympic Games
Sheet of 10 1st class Union Flag as October 22, 2001   20.00

2008, November 14. 60th birthday of Prince Charles
Sheet of 10 1st class Wales   20.00

2009, July 21. 40th anniversary of the first Moon Landing
Sheet of 10 1st class Union Flag as October 4, 2005   20.00

2009, September 18. 150th anniversary of Big Ben
Sheet of 10 1st class Union Flag as October 4, 2005   20.00

2009, October 7. 800th anniversary of the University of Cambridge
Sheet of 10 1st class Firework as October 17, 2006   20.00

2009, October 22. Olympic and Paralympic Games
Sheet of 10 1st class as October 22, 2009   20.00

2010, May 18. Halley's Comet
Sheet of 10 1st class Union Flag as October 4, 2005   20.00

2010, July 8. British World Champion Grand Prix Drivers
Sheet of 10 1st class Union Flag as October 4, 2005   20.00

2010, July 27. Olympic and Paralympic Games
Sheet of 10 1st class as July 27, 2010   20.00

2010, August 10. 10th anniversary of the London Eye
Sheet of 10 1st class Union Flag as October 4, 2005   20.00

2010, October 28. National Memorial Arboretum
Sheet of 10 1st class Poppies   20.00

2011, March 30. 50th anniversary of the Jaguar E-Type
Sheet of 10 1st class Union Flag as October 4, 2005   20.00

2011, June 10. 90th birthday of Prince Philip, Duke of Edinburgh
Sheet of 10 1st class Union Flag as October 4, 2005   20.00

2011, July 27. Olympic and Paralympic Games
Sheet of 10 1st class as July 27, 2011   20.00

2012, April 10. RMS Titanic
Sheet of 20 1st class Seal as January 26, 2010   20.00

2012, May 1. James Bond
Sheet of 20 1st class Union Flag as October 4, 2005   20.00

Olympic and Paralympic Games, 2010

Do you collect GB? Then join

GB PS

THE GREAT BRITAIN PHILATELIC SOCIETY

For further details contact:

13 ST HUBERTS CLOSE,

GERRARDS CROSS, BUCKS, SL9 7EN

email: petertannerhs13@talktalk.net

PRESENTATION PACKS

In this section, prices are quoted for packs in mint condition only.

Many collectors regard the first GB presentation packs as those sold in 1960 to mark the international stamp exhibition in London (also marketed in the USA and therefore additionally found priced in US dollars).

In 1964 the Post Office introduced the presentation pack to accompany the Shakespeare Festival special issue, and since then they have regularly been issued for GB special stamps, as well as for new definitives.

Some have been issued in foreign language and other special versions.

'FORERUNNERS'

Wilding definitives 'forerunner' pack, 1960

■ 1960

Wilding definitives (priced in Sterling)	£175
Wilding definitives (priced in Dollars)	£275
Phosphor-graphite definitives (priced in Sterling)	£175
Phosphor-graphite definitives (priced in Dollars)	£275
Regional definitives (priced in Sterling)	£175
Regional definitives (priced in Dollars)	£275
Castle high values (priced in Sterling)	£1,100
Castle high values (priced in Dollars)	£1,600

SPECIAL ISSUES

Shakespeare Festival pack, 1964

■ 1964

Shakespeare Festival	15.00
Geographical Congress	£100
Botanical Congress	£125
Forth Road Bridge	£400

■ 1965

Churchill Commemoration	50.00
Parliament	60.00
Battle of Britain	50.00
Post Office Tower	8.00

World Cup pack, 1966

■ 1966

Robert Burns	50.00
Westminster Abbey	40.00
World Cup	11.00
Birds	9.00
Technology	8.00
Battle of Hastings	6.00
Christmas	6.00

■ 1967

EFTA	7.00
British Flowers	7.50
British Paintings	5.00
Discovery and Invention	5.50

■ 1968

British Bridges	5.00
Anniversaries	5.00
Paintings	5.00
Paintings (German version)	7.50
Christmas	2.00
Christmas (German version)	5.00

■ 1969

British Ships	5.50
British Ships (German version)	20.00
British Ships (Cunard version)	20.00
Concorde	6.50
Concorde (German version)	25.00
Anniversaries	4.50
Anniversaries (German version)	40.00
Cathedrals	5.00
Cathedrals (German version)	18.00

Prince of Wales Investiture	3.50
Prince of Wales (German version)	18.00
Prince of Wales (Welsh version)	27.50
Post Office Technology	4.00
Christmas	4.00

Inigo Jones	1.85
Parliamentary Conference	1.85
Royal Wedding	1.50
Christmas	2.00

PRESENTATION PACKS

General Anniversaries pack, 1970

Horse Chestnut pack, 1974

■ 1970
Cottages	4.50
General Anniversaries	4.00
Literary Anniversaries	5.00
Commonwealth Games	5.00
Philympia	5.00
Christmas	5.00

■ 1971
Ulster Paintings	3.50
Literary Anniversaries	3.50
Anniversaries	3.50
Universities	4.50
Christmas	3.00
Christmas (Heinz version*)	25.00

(* A Heinz soup promotion allowed the labels from eight
different Heinz soups to be exchanged for six 2½d Christmas
stamps that were sent in a presentation pack format.)

■ 1972
Explorers	4.00
Anniversaries	3.00
Churches	4.50
Churches (Belgica pack)	5.00
BBC	3.50
BBC (staff version*)	15.00
Christmas	2.50
Royal Silver Wedding	2.00
Royal Silver Wedding (Japanese version)	5.00

(* To mark the 50th anniversary of the BBC a special
version of the BBC pack was sent to all staff.)

■ 1973
EEC	1.50
The Oak	1.50
Explorers	2.25
Cricket	5.00
Paintings	1.85

■ 1974
Horse Chestnut	1.50
Fire Service	2.50
UPU	2.50
Great Britons	2.00
Winston Churchill	2.00
Christmas	2.00

■ 1975
Turner	2.00
Architecture	2.00
Sailing	1.50
Railways	3.50
Inter-Parliamentary Union	1.00
Jane Austen	2.25
Christmas	2.00

Bicentennial of American Independence pack, 1976

■ 1976
Telephones	2.00
Social Pioneers	2.00
Bicentennial of American Independence	1.00
Cultural Traditions	2.00
Roses	2.00
Printing	2.00
Christmas	2.00

1977

Racket Sports	2.00
Chemistry	2.00
Silver Jubilee	2.00
Heads of Government	0.75
Wildlife	2.00
Christmas	2.00

Energy pack, 1978

1978

Energy	2.00
Historic Buildings	2.00
25th anniversary of Coronation	2.00
Horses	2.00
Cycling	2.00
Christmas	2.00

1979

Dogs	2.00
Spring Flowers	2.00
Elections to European Assembly	2.00
Horse Racing	2.00
Year of the Child	2.00
Rowland Hill	1.75
Metropolitan Police	1.75
Christmas	1.75

1980

Birds	1.75
Liverpool & Manchester Railway	2.00
London 1980 Exhibition	1.25
Landmarks	1.50
Authoresses	1.25
Conductors	1.50
Sports Centenaries	1.50
Christmas	1.50

1981

Folklore	1.50
Year of the Disabled	1.50
Butterflies	1.50
National Trust	1.75
Royal Wedding	2.00
Royal Wedding (Japanese version)	4.50
Duke of Edinburgh Awards	1.50
Fishing	2.00
Christmas	1.75

Charles Darwin pack, 1982

1982

Darwin	1.75
Youth Organisations	1.75
Theatre	1.75
Maritime Heritage	2.50
Textiles	1.75
Information Technology	1.00
Cars	2.50
Christmas	1.75

1983

Fish	1.75
Commonwealth Day	1.75
Engineering Achievements	1.25
British Army	2.75
Gardens	1.60
Fairs and Shows	1.60
Christmas	2.00

1984

College of Arms	1.75
Cattle	2.00
Urban Renewal	1.60
Europa	1.50
Greenwich Meridian	1.75
Mail Coaches	1.75
British Council	1.75
Christmas	2.00

1985

Famous Trains	3.50
Insects	2.25
Composers	2.00
Safety at Sea	1.75
350th Anniversary of Royal Mail	1.75
Arthurian Legend	1.75
British Film Year	2.75
Christmas	2.00

1986

Industry	2.00
Halley's Comet	2.00
The Queen's 60th Birthday	2.50
Nature Conservation	2.00

Medieval Life	2.00
Commonwealth Games	3.50
Royal Wedding	1.75
RAF	2.50
Christmas	2.25

■ 1987

Flowers	2.00
Sir Isaac Newton	2.00
Architects	2.00
St John Ambulance	2.00
Order of the Thistle	2.00
Victorian Life	2.00
Pottery	2.00
Christmas	2.50

■ 1988

Linnean Society	2.25
Welsh Bible	2.25
Sports Organisations	2.25
Transport and Mail Services	2.25
Australian Bicentennary	2.00
Spanish Armada	2.00
Edward Lear	2.25
Christmas	2.50

Industrial Archaeology pack, 1989

■ 1989

RSPB	3.00
Food and Farming Year	2.25
Anniversaries and Events	2.25
Toys and Games	2.25
Industrial Archaeology	2.25
Royal Microscopical Society	2.25
Lord Mayor's Show	2.00
Christmas	2.25

■ 1990

Penny Black Anniversary	4.00
RSPCA	3.50
Europa and Glasgow	2.25
Queen's Awards	2.25
Kew Gardens	2.25
Thomas Hardy	1.00
Queen Mother	3.00

Gallantry Awards	2.25
Astronomy	2.25
Christmas	2.50

■ 1991

Dog Paintings	3.75
Scientific Achievements	2.25
Europe in Space	2.25
World Student Games	2.25
Roses	3.75
Dinosaurs	3.75
Ordnance Survey	2.40
Christmas	2.40

Wintertime pack, 1992

■ 1992

Wintertime	2.40
40th Anniversary of Accession	2.50
Alfred, Lord Tennyson	2.50
International Events	2.75
Civil War	2.40
Gilbert and Sullivan	2.50
Protection of the Environment	2.40
Single European Market	1.25
Christmas	2.50

■ 1993

Abbotsbury Swannery	3.50
John Harrison	2.50
Orchids	2.50
Contemporary Art	2.50
Roman Britain	2.40
Inland Waterways	2.40
Autumn	2.75
Sherlock Holmes	3.25
Christmas	2.50

■ 1994

Steam Locomotives	3.50
Prince of Wales	2.50
Picture Postcards	2.50
Channel Tunnel	2.25
D-Day	2.50
Scottish Golf Courses	2.60
Summertime	2.50
Medical Discoveries	2.25
Christmas	2.50

Cats pack, 1995

1995

Cats	3.50
Springtime	2.50
National Trust	2.50
Peace and Freedom	2.50
Novels of H. G. Wells	3.50
Shakespeare' Globe Theatre	3.75
Pioneers of Communications	2.60
Rugby League	3.50
Christmas	3.00

1996

Robert Burns	2.50
Wildfowl Trust	2.50
Cinema	2.50
Football Legends	3.00
Olympic Games	2.40
Famous Women	2.75
Children's Television	2.75
Classic Cars	4.50
Christmas	4.00

1997

King Henry VIII	5.00
Religious Anniversaries	2.75
Tales of Horror	2.50
British Aircraft Designers	3.25
All The Queen's Horses	3.50
Sub Post Offices	2.75
Enid Blyton	3.25
Christmas	4.00
Royal Golden Wedding Anniversary	2.75

Diana, Princess of Wales pack, 1998 (Welsh version)

1998

Endangered Species	3.75
Diana, Princess of Wales	5.00
Diana, Princess of Wales (Welsh version)	45.00
The Queen's Beasts	2.50
Lighthouses	3.50
Comedians	4.25
National Health Service	3.00
Fantasy Novels	3.25
Notting Hill Carnival	3.00
Land Speed Records	3.25
Christmas	3.25

(* The Princess of Wales pack's limited edition Welsh language version was available only at post offices in Wales.)

Inventors' Tale pack, 1999

1999

Inventors' Tale	3.00
Travellers' Tale	3.00
Patients' Tale	3.00
Settlers' Tale	3.00
Workers' Tale	3.00
Entertainers' Tale	3.00
Royal Wedding	2.00
Citizens' Tale	3.00
Scientists' Tale	3.00
Farmers' Tale	3.00
Soldiers' Tale	3.00
Christians' Tale	3.00
Artists' Tale	3.00
Millennium Timekeeper	12.00

2000

Above and Beyond	3.00
Fire and Light	3.00
Water and Coast	3.00
Life and Earth	3.25
Art and Craft	3.25
Her Majesty's Stamps	30.00
People and Places	3.25
Stone and Soil	3.25
Tree and Leaf	3.25
Queen Mother's 100th birthday	15.00
Mind and Matter	3.25
Body and Bone	3.25
Spirit and Faith	3.25
Sound and Vision	3.25

(* Her Majesty's Stamps was produced for Stamp Show 2000.)

Punch and Judy pack, 2001

■ 2003

Birds of Prey	9.00
Occasions	5.50
Discovery of DNA	5.50
Fruit and Veg	15.00
Extreme Endeavours	5.50
Wilding Definitives II	6.00
50th Anniversary of the Coronation	11.00
Prince William	8.00
British Journey: Scotland	5.50
Pub Signs	4.25
Toys	7.00
British Museum	5.00
Christmas	5.50
Rugby World Cup	10.00

■ 2001

Looking to the Future	3.75
Occasions	4.25
Cats and Dogs	8.00
The Weather	5.00
Submarines	11.00
Double-deck buses	7.00
Hats	6.00
Pond Life	4.00
Punch and Judy	4.00
Nobel Prizes	20.00
Flags and Ensigns	15.00
Christmas	4.00

Classic Locomotives pack, 2004

■ 2002

Just So Stories	8.00
Golden Jubilee	4.00
Occasions	3.25
Coastlines	4.50
Circus	4.75
Queen Mother Memorial	3.75
Airliners	7.00
Football World Cup	6.00
Commonwealth Games	5.00
Peter Pan	5.00
London Bridges	20.00
Astronomy	9.00
Pillar Boxes	4.75
Wilding Definitives I	25.00
Christmas	4.75

■ 2004

Classic Locomotives	11.00
Occasions	4.50
Lord of the Rings	9.00
British Journey: Northern Ireland	5.00
Entente Cordiale	8.00
Ocean Liners	5.50
Royal Horticultural Society	5.50
British Journey: Wales	4.50
Royal Society of Arts	5.50
Woodland Animals	9.00
Crimean War	5.75
Christmas	5.75

■ 2005

Farm Animals	9.00
British Journey: South-West England	5.00
Jane Eyre	5.75
Magic	5.00
Royal Wedding	5.50
World Heritage Sites	6.50
Trooping the Colour	6.00
Motorcycles	6.75
London 2012	5.50
Changing Tastes	5.00
Classic ITV	5.00
The Ashes	5.50
Battle of Trafalgar	5.25
Christmas	5.50

Rugby World Cup pack, 2003

Modern Architecture pack, 2006

2006

Animal Tales	6.50
British Journey: England	9.00
Brunel	5.00
Ice Age Animals	5.00
The Queen's 80th birthday	6.50
World Cup Winners	6.00
Modern Architecture	5.50
National Portrait Gallery	9.00
Victoria Cross	6.00
Sounds of Britain	5.25
Smilers	8.00
Christmas	7.00
Lest We Forget I	6.00
Celebrating Scotland	4.25

Beside The Seaside pack, 2007

2007

The Beatles	13.00
Sea Life	8.50
The Sky at Night	5.50
World of Invention	6.00
Abolition of Slavery	5.50
Celebrating England	4.50
Beside the Seaside	5.75
40th Anniversary of the Machin	4.75
Grand Prix	6.50
Harry Potter	11.00
Scouts	8.00
Endangered Birds	9.00
Army Uniforms	5.75
Diamond Wedding	9.00
Christmas	8.00
Lest We Forget II	5.75

2008

Ian Fleming	8.50
Working Dogs	7.50
Houses of Lancaster and York	9.50
Celebrating Northern Ireland	5.00
Rescue at Sea	5.75
Endangered Insects	9.00
Cathedrals	11.00
Classic Carry On & Hammer Films	5.50
Air Displays	5.50
Olympic Handover	5.50
RAF Uniforms	6.00
50th Anniversary of Country Definitives	6.00
Women of Distinction	6.00
Christmas	5.25
Lest We Forget III	6.00

Olympic and Paralympic Games pack, 2009

2009

Design Classics	11.00
Robert Burns	5.50
Charles Darwin	10.00
Celebrating Wales	4.50
Industrial Revolution	7.50
House of Tudor	10.00
Endangered Plants	13.00
Mythical Creatures	6.00
Post Boxes	4.50
Fire and Rescue	9.00
Navy Uniforms	7.00
Eminent Britons	8.50
Olympic and Paralympic Games, series I	8.50
Christmas	7.50

2010

Classic Album Covers	10.00
Business Customised and Smilers Stamps	10.00
Girlguiding	7.00
The Royal Society	9.50
Battersea Dogs & Cats Home	9.00
House of Stewart	11.00
Endangered Mammals	9.00
London 2010 (George V and King's Stamps miniature sheets)	10.00
Britain Alone	13.00
House of Stuart	12.00
Olympic and Paralympic Games, series II	9.00
Great British Railways	7.00

Great British Railways pack, 2010

Medical Breakthroughs	5.50
Winnie-the-Pooh	12.00
Christmas	9.00

■ 2011

FAB. The Genius of Gerry Anderson	13.00
Classic Locomotives of England	5.50
Musicals	9.50
Magical Realms	8.00
WWF	13.00
Royal Shakespeare Company	12.00
Royal Wedding	8.50
Morris & Co	7.50
Thomas the Tank Engine	11.50
Olympic and Paralympic Games, series III	8.50
Crown Jewels	8.50
First UK Aerial Post	5.50
House of Hanover	12.50
UK A-Z, part I	11.00
Christmas	10.00

■ 2012

Roald Dahl	12.50
House of Windsor	11.00
Diamond Jubilee miniature sheet	6.00
Britons of Distinction	8.00
Classic Locomotives of Scotland	5.50
Comics	8.00
UK A-Z, part 2	12.00
Great British Fashion	8.00
Diamond Jubilee	10.00
Charles Dickens	11.00

LOW-VALUE DEFINITIVES

Scandinavia Tour pack, 1971

1967	½d to 1/9	3.25
1967	(German version)	85.00
1971	½p to 9p	3.50
1971	Scandinavia Tour	15.00
1971	NABA stamp exhibition	85.00
1971	½p to 10p	27.00
1977	To 50p	2.75
1981	To 75p (pack no. 129a)	12.50
1983	To 75p (pack no. 1)	26.00
1984	½p to 75p	21.00
1987	1p to 75p	27.00
1988	14p to 35p	6.25
1989	15p to 37p	5.00
1990	Penny Black Anniversary	3.50
1990	10p to 33p	5.00
1991	1p to 75p	27.00
1991	6p to 39p	5.00
1993	Self-adhesive booklet	17.00
1993	19p to 41p	4.50
1995	1p to £1	30.00
1996	20p to 63p	6.00
1997	2nd and 1st	4.50
1997	26p and 1st	4.00
1998	2nd, 1st, 1p to £1	15.00
1999	7p to 64p	7.50
2000	Millennium 1st	3.00
2000	Jeffery Matthews Palette	80.00
2000	8p to 65p	7.00
2002	2nd, 1st, 1p to £1	14.00
2002	37p to 68p	4.25
2002	Wildings (part 1)	25.00
2002	Definitives Collection folder, containing the low value definitive pack (2002), high values pack (2002), Country stamps packs (2001-02)	32.00
2003	Worldwide and Europe	4.50
2003	Wildings (part 2)	6.00
2004	1st, Worldwide Postcard, 7p to 43p	12.00
2005	Re-issued Wilding Castle definitives	5.00
2005	1p, 2p, 5p, 9p, 10p, 20p, 35p, 40p, 42p, 46p, 47p, 50p, 68p, £1, plus self-adhesive 2nd, 1st, Europe, Worldwide and postcard	42.00
2005	Definitives Collection folder, containing the low value definitive pack (2005), high values pack (2003), Country stamps packs (2003), Country 42p stamps pack (2005)	32.00

2006	37p to 72p	9.50
2006	Pricing in Proportion	5.00
2007	16p to 78p	6.00
2007	1d to £1 ruby	17.50
2008	15p to 81p	4.00
2009	2nd to £1 with security features	5.50
2009	17p to 90p	3.50
2009	Post & Go labels	20.00
2010	Definitives Collection folder, containing 1p to £1.46, plus Europe, Worldwide, Worldwide Postcard and 'Recorded Signed For'	23.00
2010	Low values in current use	12.50
2010	Special Delivery	15.00
2011	1p to £1.65	7.50
2012	Olympic and Paralympic Games definitives	6.00
2012	Diamond Jubilee 1st, 1st Large, 87p, £1.28, £1.90	7.50

HIGH-VALUE DEFINITIVES

£10 definitive pack, 1993

1969	2/6 to £1	8.50
1969	2/6 to £1 (German version)	50.00
1970	10p to 50p	6.50
1971	20p to £1	9.50
1977	£1 to £5 (pack no. 91)	13.50
1987	£1 to £5 (pack no. 13)	£145
1987	£1.60	20.00
1988	Castles £1 to £5	16.00
1992	Castles £1 to £5	20.00
1993	£10	22.00
1995	£3	14.00
1997	Castles £1.50 to £5	70.00
1999	£1.50 to £5 (Enschedé)	35.00
1999	£1.50 to £5 (De La Rue)	27.50
1999	£1.50 to £5 (gravure)	17.50
2009	£1.50 to £5 with security features	17.50

COUNTRY DEFINITIVES

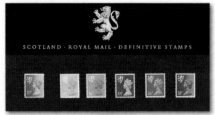

Scotland definitives pack, 1983

■ England

| 2001 | 2nd, 1st, E, 65p | 4.00 |
| 2003 | 2nd, 1st, E, 68p | 6.00 |

■ Northern Ireland

1970	3d, 4d sepia, 4d red, 5d, 9d, 1/3, 1/6	2.00
1971	2½p, 3p, 5p, 7½p	1.75
1974	3p, 3½p, 5½p, 8p	2.00
1974	3p, 3½p, 4½p, 5½p, 8p	2.00
1976	6½p, 8½p, 10p, 11p	1.40
1981	7p, 9p, 10½p, 11½p, 12p, 13½p, 14p, 15p, 18p, 22p	5.00
1983	10p, 12½p, 16p, 20½p, 26p, 28p	12.50
1984	10p, 13p, 16p, 17p, 22p, 26p, 28p, 31p	10.00
1987	12p, 13p, 17p, 18p, 22p, 26p, 28p, 31p	13.00
1999	19p, 25p, 30p, 41p	9.50
2000	1st, 40p, 65p	12.50
2001	2nd, 1st, E, 65p	4.50
2003	2nd, 1st, E, 68p	6.00

■ Scotland

1970	3d, 4d sepia, 4d red, 5d, 6d, 9d, 1/3, 1/6	4.00
1971	2½p, 3p, 5p, 7½p	1.75
1974	3p, 3½p, 5½p, 8p	1.40
1974	3p, 3½p, 4½p, 5½p, 8p	1.65
1976	6½p, 8½p, 10p, 11p	1.40
1981	7p, 9p, 10½p, 11½p, 12p, 13½p, 14p, 15p, 18p, 22p	5.50
1983	10p, 12½p, 16p, 20½p, 26p, 28p	12.50
1984	10p, 13p, 16p, 17p, 22p, 26p, 28p, 31p	9.00
1987	12p, 13p, 17p, 18p, 22p, 26p, 28p, 31p	13.00
1999	2nd, 1st, E, 64p	7.50
2000	65p	8.00
2002	2nd, 1st, E, 65p	13.00
2003	2nd, 1st, E, 68p	6.00

■ Wales

1970	3d, 4d sepia, 4d red, 5d, 9d, 1/6	2.50
1971	2½p, 3p, 5p, 7½p	1.75
1974	3p, 3½p, 5½p, 8p	1.40
1974	3p, 3½p, 4½p, 5½p, 8p	1.65
1976	6½p, 8½p, 10p, 11p	1.40
1981	7p, 9p, 10½p, 11½p, 12p, 13½p, 14p, 15p, 18p, 22p	5.50
1983	10p, 12½p, 16p, 20½p, 26p, 28p	12.50
1984	10p, 13p, 16p, 17p, 22p, 26p, 28p, 31p	10.00
1987	12p, 13p, 17p, 18p, 22p, 26p, 28p, 31p	13.00
1997	20p, 26p, 37p, 63p	10.50
1999	2nd, 1st, E, 64p	7.50
2000	65p	8.50
2002	2nd, 1st, E, 65p	13.00
2003	2nd, 1st, E, 68p	6.00

■ All Countries
(containing the stamps of Northern Ireland, Scotland and Wales up to 1998, and additionally England from 2002)

1988	14p, 19p, 23p, 32p (x 3 countries)	9.50
1989	15p, 20p, 24p, 34p (x 3 countries)	9.50
1990	17p, 22p, 26p, 37p (x 3 countries)	9.50
1991	18p, 24p, 28p, 39p (x 3 countries)	9.50
1993	19p, 25p, 30p, 41p (x 3 countries)	9.50
1996	20p, 26p, 37p, 63p (x 3 countries)	9.50

1998	20p (centre band), 26p, 37p, 63p (x 3 countries)	15.00
2002	68p (x 4 countries)	5.00
2004	40p (x 4 countries)	8.00
2005	42p (x 4 countries)	7.50
2006	44p, 72p (x 4 countries)	8.00
2007	48p, 78p (x 4 countries)	8.50
2008	50p, 81p (x 4 countries)	8.50
2008	2nd, 1st, 50p, 81p (x 4 countries)	12.50
2008	50th anniversary of country definitives	6.00
2009	56p, 90p (x 4 countries)	9.00
2010	60p, 97p (x 4 countries)	9.50
2011	68p, £1.10 (x 4 countries)	11.00
2012	87p, £1.28 (x 4 countries)	12.00

■ Isle of Man

1971	2½p, 3p, 5p, 7½p	1.00

POSTAGE DUES

Postage Dues pack, 1971

1971	½p to 5p, 10p, 20p, 50p, £1	15.00
1977	½p to £1	8.50
1982	1p to £5	25.00
1994	1p to £5	35.00

GREETINGS STAMPS

Memories pack, 1992

1992	Memories	8.00
1993	Gift giving	8.50
1994	Messages	8.50
1995	Art	8.50
1996	Cartoons	9.00
1997	Flowers	9.00

SOUVENIR PACKS

British Film Year souvenir pack, 1985

1972	Royal Silver Wedding	1.50
1973	Cricket	3.50
1973	Parliament	3.50
1974	Winston Churchill	2.25
1975	Railways	2.25
1977	Silver Jubilee	1.25
1978	25th Anniversary of Coronation	1.50
1981	Royal Wedding	1.50
1984	Mail Coaches	3.75
1985	British Film Year	5.00
1986	The Queen's birthday	4.00
1988	Australian Bicentennary	7.00
1990	Penny Black Anniversary	10.50
1997	Golden Wedding	25.00

SPECIAL PACKS

Penny Black Reproduction special pack, 2000

1971	Decimal low values (½p to 9p)	5.00
1994	Channel Tunnel	37.00
1995	National Trust	12.50
2000	Stamp Show 2000 (Penny Black reproduction)	55.00
2000	Stamp Show 2000 (three prestige stamp books)	90.00
2001	Occasions: Hallmarks (five blocks of 10)	£100
2003	Across The Universe and Microcosmos (two prestige stamp books)	40.00
2005	Miniature sheet collection	75.00
2006	Miniature sheet collection	70.00
2007	Miniature sheet collection	55.00
2008	Lest We Forget miniature sheet collection	40.00
2008	Miniature sheet collection	40.00
2009	Miniature sheet collection	37.00
2010	London 2010 (1929 PUC £1 reproduction)	8.50
2010	London 2010 (Accession of King George V 1st class pairs and blocks)	£100
2010	Miniature sheet collection	47.00
2011	Penny Red (1841 1d reproduction)	8.50
2011	Miniature sheet collection	45.00
2011	Heroes and Villains (Harry Potter)	10.00

YEAR BOOKS & PACKS

In this section, prices are quoted for packs in mint condition only.

YEAR PACKS

1967	3.50
1968 (blue cover)	3.50
1968 (red cover)	2.50
1968 (German version)	25.00
1969	10.00
1970	15.00
1971	22.00
1972	17.50
1973	12.50
1974	7.50
1975	7.50
1976	7.50
1977	4.00
1978	4.25
1979	5.00
1980	7.00
1981	8.50
1982	12.50
1983	12.50
1984	15.00
1985	15.00
1986	15.00
1987	15.00
1988	15.00
1989	15.00
1990	15.00
1991	17.00
1992	17.00
1993	18.00
1994	23.00
1995	25.00
1996	27.00
1997	30.00
1998	35.00

Year Pack, 2009

1999	45.00
2000	55.00
2001	55.00
2002	60.00
2003	60.00
2004	60.00
2005	65.00
2006	70.00
2007	90.00
2008	85.00
2009	£110
2010	£120
2011	£130

YEAR BOOKS

1984	45.00
1985	30.00
1986	27.00

Year Book, 2009

1987	17.50
1988	17.50
1989	18.50
1990	18.50
1991	18.50
1992	21.00
1993	23.00
1994	19.00
1995	19.00
1996	23.00
1997	30.00
1998	40.00
1999	50.00
2000	50.00
2001	50.00
2002	60.00
2003	75.00
2004	60.00
2005	60.00
2006	70.00
2007	95.00
2008	85.00
2009	£100
2010	£120
2011	£125

Year Pack, 1998

Year Book, 2000

ALL RISKS COVER
for ALL COLLECTABLES

Stamps, Postcards, Coins, Diecast Models

Dolls Houses etc

£6,250 Cover from £25pa * for stamps & Postcards
£5,000 Cover from £30pa * for all other collectables

*plus Insurance Premium Tax

PUBLIC LIABILITY COVER FOR SOCIETIES

DEALERS POLICY AVAILABLE

STAMP INSURANCE SERVICES

Dept 03SV C G I Services Limited

29 Bowhay Lane, Exeter EX4 1PE

tel: 01392 433 949 fax: 01392 427 632

www.stampinsurance.co.uk

Authorised and Registered by the Financial Services Authority

Use these pages to compile a 'wants' list or make any notes

....

....

....

....

....

....

....

....

....

....

....

....

....

....

....

....

....

....

....

....

....

....

NOTES

KEY CONTACTS

To help you find your way around the hobby, here are contact details for the major players in the world of British stamps

ROYAL MAIL

Philatelic Bureau
Tallents House, 21 South Gyle Crescent,
Edinburgh EH12 9PB.
Tel: 08457 641641 (orders)
www.royalmail.com/stamps

London Special Handstamp Centre
Mount Pleasant, Farringdon Road,
London EC1A 1BB.

Midlands Special Handstamp Centre
Birmingham Mail Centre, St Stephen's Street,
Birmingham B6 4AA.

**Northern England Special
Handstamp Centre**
South Shields DO, Keppell Street,
South Shields, Tyne & Wear NE33 1AA.

**Scotland & Northern Ireland Special
Handstamp Centre**
Rutherglen DO, Duchess Place,
Rutherglen, Glasgow G73 1BT.

**Wales & The West Special
Handstamp Centre**
220-228 Penarth Road,
Cardiff CF11 8TA.

FAMOUS COLLECTIONS

British Library
96 Euston Road, London
NW1 2DB.
Tel: 020 7412 7635
www.collectbritain.co.uk

British Postal Museum & Archive
Freeling House, Phoenix Place,
London WC1X 0DL.
Tel: 020 7239 2570
www.postalheritage.org.uk

Royal Philatelic Collection
www.royal.gov.uk

SOCIETIES

Royal Philatelic Society London
41 Devonshire Place, London W1N 1PE.
Tel: 020 7486 1044
www.rpsl.org.uk

National Philatelic Society
www.ukphilately.org.uk/nps

British Philatelic Trust
Suite 101, Business Design Centre,
52 Upper Street, London N1 0QH.
Tel: 020 7688 8423
www.ukphilately.org.uk/bpt

**Association of British
Philatelic Societies**
www.ukphilately.org.uk/abps

Modern British Philatelic Circle
www.mbp-circle.co.uk

**Association of Great Britain
First Day Cover Collectors**
www.gbfdc.co.uk

Machin Collectors Club
www.machins.org

British Thematic Association
www.brit-thematic-assoc.com

Philatelic Traders Society
PO Box 139, Brighton, West Sussex BN41 9DH.
Tel: 01273 594110
www.philatelic-traders-society.co.uk

STAMP SHOWS

Stampex
www.stampex.ltd.uk

STAMP MAGAZINE

On sale at all major newsagents on the
second Thursday of every month
www.stampmagazine.co.uk

From Britain's Largest Provincial Stamp Shop
GB COLLECTIONS FOR SALE

GB MACHIN COLLECTION

X841-X1058
213 stamps including ½p side band and all band variations.

The Collection
Unmounted mint   £161.00
Fine Used   £149.00

* SPECIAL

Unmounted mint 1953 Coronation complete to 1970 Christmas
£42.50
Do fine used
£42.95

QV Victoria Collection 1840-1902

100 different stamps including a decent One Penny Black. A good representative collection with some plate variations all good used and some officials. With values to include 10/-. Arranged on stock cards. Stamps of Queen Victoria only. A fine collection. £330.00

Larger collections include 1840 2d. £1 value and other scarcer types. £635.00

GB YEAR COLLECTION

		U/m Mint	Fine used
2011	12 sets+11m/s	160.00	165.00
2010	16 sets+10 m/s	160.00	165.00
2009	12 sets+11 m/s	93.00	95.00
2008	(13+7ms)	85.00	81.00
2007	(14+7ms)	102.50	102.50
2006	(11+6ms)	85.00	85.00
2005	(11+9ms)	77.00	77.00
2004	(12+4ms)	73.00	73.00
2003	(12+5ms)	62.00	62.00
2002	(12+3ms)	50.50	50.50
2001	(11+3ms)	44.00	44.50
2000	(13 +1ms)	41.00	41.50
1999	(12 +2ms)	46.00	46.00
1998	(10 sets)	22.00	22.00
1997	(10 sets)	20.00	21.00
1996	(9 sets)	19.00	20.50
1995	(9 sets)	17.00	18.00
1994	(10 sets)	17.00	17.50
1993	(9 sets)	16.50	17.50
1992	(9 sets)	15.50	15.50
1991	(9 sets)	14.00	14.20
1990	(10+MS)	18.00	18.00
1989	(8+MS)	14.50	14.50
1988	(8+MS)	14.20	14.50
1987	(9 sets)	11.90	13.00
1986	(10 sets)	14.00	14.00
1985	(8 sets)	12.00	12.50
1984	(9 sets)	10.30	10.85
1983	(7 sets)	8.00	8.25
1982	(8 sets)	8.70	8.50
1981	(8 sets)	6.75	7.00
1980	(9+MS)	5.55	6.70
1979	(8+MS)	4.60	5.15
1978	(6+MS)	3.40	3.60
1977	(6 sets)	2.80	3.40
1976	(7 sets)	2.95	3.50
1975	(8 sets)	2.75	3.50
1974	(6 sets)	2.25	3.15
1973	(9 sets)	3.95	6.00
1972	(5 sets)	2.25	2.90
1971	(5 sets)	1.70	3.00

BIG COLLECTIONS - small prices
1971-2008 XMAS   unmounted £900
                     very fine used £920
1924-2008 XMAS includes phosphors
(excludes £1 PUC) unmounted mint £1240
                     very fine used £1230

NB: Our year set prices exclude greeting booklets and include Miniature sheets.

FREE!
Book of GB Stamps Write or phone Now!

This is our GB Book. We sell any G.B. stamp individually or by set 1840-2012. Postage appreciated.

THE PHOSPHOR COLLECTION

Special Price 1962 NPY - 1967 Flowers all 30 sets.
Mint unmounted £129
VFU £100

1924-51 Commemoratives (inc. PUC to 2½) (12 sets)
Unmounted Mint   £89.00
Fine Used   £57.00

UK orders for stamps are post free!
Minimum order £10.00

GB YEAR BOOKS
The Complete Collection 1994-2004.
Lovely bound books containing all sets.
20 books £495

Visit our Website
www.worldstamps.co.uk

EUROCARD
MasterCard

DAUWALDERS of Salisbury

VISA

42 Fisherton Street, Salisbury, Wiltshire, SP2 7RB
Tel: 01722 412100 Fax: 01722 410074 Email: sales@worldstamps.co.uk

From Britain's Largest Provincial Stamp Shop
Our Air-conditioned Shop is Open 6 Full Days each Week
MORE COLLECTIONS - MORE PLEASURE

500 DIFFERENT

GREAT BRITAIN
QV to Date
includes Q.Victoria
2d blue and many
scarcer items.
500 stamps
A fine lot of used **£16.50**

1000 DIFFERENT

Over 40% of all GB stamps
issued many higher values
includes 2/6d KGV Seahorse
1000 different used at only
2 1/2p per stamp! **£27.50**

1500 different

A massive GREAT BRITAIN
collection which includes
number of Victorian &
Edwardian types to 1/-. All
stamps are used. Comes with
a large stockbook to house
them. £75 inc post.

50 DIFFERENT GB
FIRST DAY COVERS

1967-1990 All illustrated envelopes in
fine condition.
50 different covers	**£25**
100 different covers	**£48**
150 different covers	**£80**

GB 1841-1935

40 different Victoria
& Edward only.
Includes 1902 set
1/2 d - 1/-.
All collectable.
Early items. £34.00

SELLING YOUR COLLECTION?

We are keen to buy good
collections of Great Britain
stamps.
Why not call us today
Tel: 01722 412100

PRE STAMP COVER

Own a 170 year old cover.
Pre-Victoria. Before postage
stamps were issued. With
manuscript address.
Each £5.50   3 different £15.00

High Value Commemoratives only

Absolutely no 1st or
2nd class values. 100
different good used
higher values
1948-1997 £12.70
200 different £27.00

SPECIAL ITEMS

1944 German propaganda
forgery of Silver Jubilee
stamp. Produced by
concentration camp
workers. Each £69.50

1858 1d red plate
numbers. 50
different numbers.
Good used £35.
100 different.
Good used
£80.00

1847
Embossed. 6d,
10d and 1/-.
Cut to shape
and used.
3 stamps.
Special offer
£52.50

Visit our Website
www.worldstamps.co.uk

SERVICE AND ADVICE
Since 1958 we have provided an
excellent mail order service for
stamp collectors.

Prices on this page include
postage. (inland) Overseas
enquiries welcomed

DAUWALDERS *of Salisbury*

42 Fisherton Street, Salisbury, Wiltshire, SP2 7RB

ADVERTISING INDEX

AF Brock ....Pg 6

Andrew G Lajer.. Pg 44

Arrowfile .... Pg 63

Arthur Ryan ....Pg 191 & 247

BB Stamps ....Pg IFC

Corbitt Stamps .... Pg 35

Court Philatelics .... Pg 20

Dauwalders of Sailsbury...Pg 272 & 273

Duncannon Partnership .... Pg 22

Embassy Philiatelics... Pg 43

Enfield Stamps ....Pg 192

Eric Paul.. Pg 27

G Barrington Smith... Pg 20

G Sharples.. Pg 20

Grahame Mann...Pg 232

Great Britain Philatelics ....Pg 255

H W Wood .... Pg 42

John Auld .... Pg 21

John Curtin .... Pg 20

K&C Philatelics... Pg 22

M&C Stamps .... Pg 22

Mark Bloxham Stamps... Pg OBC

Northern Stamps .... Pg 22

Omniphil.. Pg 41

Packs and Cards.. Pg 42

Philangles..Pg 193

Prinz Publications .... Pg 42

Rushstamps ....Pg 8

Sandafayre .... Pg 19

Stamp Insurance Company...Pg 267

Stampex... Pg 4

The Machin Collectors Club .... Pg 65

Tony Lester Stamps .... Pg 33

Warwick and Warwick...Pg IBC